still red

still red

georgina sam and david wang

Published by
Asian Outreach International Limited
GPO Box 3448, Hong Kong

Copyright © 2007 by Asian Outreach International Limited

Cover design by Forest Au

ISBN-13: 978-962-216-000-2
ISBN-10: 962-216-000-X

Printed in Hong Kong

To my faithful and fruitful China ministry team
D. W.

To my grandmother, LOUIE SHEE WONG.
In loving memory
G. S.

CHINA

XINJIANG

GANSU

QINGHAI

TIBET

SICHUAN

YUNNAN

N

A Note from the Authors

If success is 10% inspiration and 90% perspiration, as Thomas Edison famously said, then I must admit that at best, I was only the 10% in *Still Red*. My colleague and spiritual daughter, Georgina Sam, was definitely the 90%.

For two years Georgina traveled extensively to China, meeting with the three individuals featured in the book, their family and co-workers. She has poured over hours and hours of recorded interviews, and checked and re-checked the details of their stories. She has researched tirelessly the background of China, since the Second World War to the present day. And she has written Mingyen's, Saimen's and Lili's accounts faithfully. I can attest to that, for I've known all three and have cooperated with them hand-in-hand for more than 20 years.

D. W.

* * *

I am deeply grateful to David Wang for daring to believe that I could write a book, and for having the courage to entrust this project to me.

Mingyen, Saimen and Lili are truly incredible people. They are living proof that the extraordinary things one reads about in the Bible can and do still happen today. It was an honor and privilege to meet them, to have, as it were, "spent time at their feet", and to have learned from their experiences.

Still Red is an account of their true life stories, as personally relayed to both David and myself. To protect identities, some dates and names of people and places have been changed.

G. S.

<u>CONTENTS</u>

CHRONOLOGY

	China	Mingyen Chen	Saimen Liang	Lili Tang
1925 / 1933	Death of Sun Yat Sen, reputed Father of Modern China	Born in Shanghai (1933)		
1934-35	Communist Long March			
1937-48	Japan invades China. Japan surrenders. Civil war in China begins	Chen family moves to Hong Kong. Mother dies		
1949-50	Liberation. Mao Zedong comes to power	Becomes a Christian		
1951-54	Suppress Counter-revolutionaries and Three Antis campaigns	Chen family moves back to Shanghai. Becomes full time church worker. Arrested; imprisoned 1 month	Born in Henan (1951)	
1955-56	Uncover Hidden Counterrevolutionaries and Hundred Flowers Bloom campaigns	Gets married. Son is born. Arrested; imprisoned 2 months	Becomes a beggar	
1957-60	Anti-Rightist and Great Leap Forward campaigns	Arrested; sentenced 10 years in city jail	Father dies	
1961-64		Moves from city jail to labor camp	Stops schooling. Becomes a goatherd and a Christian	Born in Shanxi (1961)
1966-67	Cultural Revolution begins		Becomes a Red Guard	
1970-71		10 year sentence expires but is not released. Wife files for divorce	Becomes a Communist party member and part-time church worker	
1972-74	U.S. President Nixon visits China		Gets married. Son is born. Arrested; sentenced 6 years to labor camp	Becomes a Christian and part-time church worker
1976	Mao Zedong dies. Cultural Revolution ends			Finishes school. Works full time on farm and continues part-time for church
1978-80	Deng Xiaoping becomes paramount leader	Released from labor camp. Ex-wife dies	Released from labor camp. Becomes full time church worker	
1981-82		Receives full rehabilitation and exoneration from central government. Moves to Hong Kong		Becomes full time church worker
1983	Anti-Spiritual Pollution campaign			On shoot to kill list

Year				
1989	Student demonstrations in Tiananmen Square			Arrested; sentenced 3 years to labor camp
1990-93			Arrested; imprisoned 14 months	Released from labor camp. Gets married
1994-95		Most Honorary Citizen award in Anhui	Arrested; detained 14 days	Daughter is born
1997-99	Deng Xiaoping dies. Britain returns Hong Kong to Chinese sovereignty	Most Honorary Citizen award in Hubei	Arrested; imprisoned 6 months	Arrested; imprisoned 3 months
2002		Good Overseas Chinese award in Yunnan	Promotes unified missions movement among underground churches	Trains missionaries

Still Red

If these walls could speak . . .

In the heart of China there stands a village house. It is an unassuming structure, rustic in appearance, backward by most standards. If truth be told, it really doesn't look like much at all. The original shell had been constructed of rammed earth, but over the years it had been and was still being reinforced with gray brick and mortar. This had the effect of solidifying the structure but only marginally improving the slight lopsidedness of the walls. (They were not professionally trained hands that had laid the brick.) The kitchen, a little nook which doubled as entry hall to the house and through which one passed to access the main room, was blackened by repeated use of the low, single burner coal stove. There were no other appliances and there was hardly what one would deem sufficient counter space.

A damp earthy smell prevailed in the entire place, undoubtedly not improved by the presence of a chicken coop immediately to the left of the opening to the main room. The wooden furniture, consisting of a table, several chairs, a sideboard and an extended bench with a back which sufficed as a sofa, was spartan but functional, as was its layout. In vogue this sitting-cum-dining room was not.

There was a lone attempt at decoration: A photographic collage featured on the long wall that abutted the table. Of an eclectic nature it nevertheless revealed some clues as to the history of the house—that is, of its inhabitants past and present; of where they came from, where they were and where they were going. Perhaps in keeping with the utilitarian theme in the home, its presence served as a record and a reminder of yesterday, today and tomorrow.

It was, to say the least, a curious cluster of photos. The motley assortment of sizes, shades, hues and eras portrayed in the pictures only seemed to emphasize the unevenness of the crudely constructed wall on which they were taped. There was, seemingly, no order to the arrangement. Beside the comparatively large, fading sepia of great-grandmother attired in her Manchu-inspired qipao (complete with hand-embroidered shoes for bound feet, no less), was a full color, standard wallet-sized school portrait of the fifth generation son born in America. Next to this was second cousin beaming away in Mao cap and jacket in a three by five black and white. Above this sat a square still of grandson and wife when they first disembarked in Hong Kong. And so the hodgepodge display continued.

It was easy enough to understand the presence of snapshots of the current generation—who doesn't enjoy seeing the faces of loved ones around them? But why put up or keep up pictures of people one has never even seen before? Odd. Yet moving. For it becomes obvious that the residents here must have some kind of deep-rooted love and respect for their relatives near and far. It has often been said that life is a journey, and that every step taken is like adding one more brick to a wall being built. Could it be, just maybe, that each individual represented here, and any subsequent prints which might be added in the future, is contributing to the completion of a figurative building, the entirety of which will be evident one day? A work still in progress, so it would seem, just like the house itself.

Back outside, the timber doorframe of the house is adorned with paper banners, running along the top and down the sides. In blazing red they are the traditional color of celebration, of victory, a symbol of something good that has happened, is happening, will happen. It is the evidence that here lies a household which looks beyond human strength and ability for its protection, success and prosperity. Naïve superstitious folklore? Or could it possibly mean something else? Something more? Red, after all, is also the color of blood. And, in another time and tradition, it was blood painted over the doorframe of a home that marked it for preservation, for safety. This too led to an overcoming, a triumph.

If only these walls could speak.

MINGYEN CHEN

2003. It was the Year of the Goat. Conceivably then, one might presume the two objects dotting the wall of the Hengduan Mountains were species of the mountain variety. That is, of course, if one were to view the scene through the eye of a traditional Chinese landscape painter. But they weren't. They were people.

The panorama featured the conventional plethora of towering peaks which seemed to extend endlessly into the background. Yet with the range situated as it was in northern Yunnan province, these possessed an appearance more similar to that of the snowcapped Himalayas than to the famed rolling limestone hills of Guilin. The smoothness of the tree line was interrupted, giving the picture less lush greenery than would be expected—the forests here, in part, having been cleared. Open patches on the slopes revealed a smattering of shrubs and bushes, but wildlife tended to shun these areas. As a home it was generally too steep, too uncomfortable, and the supply of food was not abundant and therefore not as enticing. But the mountains, to the artist, were not just a physical barrier to be overcome; they symbolized the fact that life itself is much larger than any one person. And therein lay the challenge for these two people on a mission: Though small when considered in relation to the whole universe, they were determined to pass through to the other side, come what may.

Beads of perspiration were visibly trickling down the two faces, the first being that of an elderly male. His face was framed with a pair of large, square metal-rimmed glasses and hair that had been dyed to retain its blackness. The second belonged to an urban young female adult. Of foremost concern to her was the need to concentrate intently on her footing. In the back of her mind, however, the young woman worried that she would have hat hair by the time they arrived at their destination. Her smart, new short hair cut would be flattened and she wouldn't be able to remove her copy DKNY cap in company.

"Give me your hand."

"No. I'm okay."

"Are you sure?"

"Yeah. I said I'm okay." It was a short-tempered reply. If you can do this old man, the young woman thought to herself, I can too. Winnie doggedly continued on unassisted, yet she did so in a grumpy mood. You pretty well need to be a mountain goat to get around up here! she exclaimed in her head. The independent city girl was out of her element but she hated to admit it.

She paused to contemplate the current path. "Path" was probably being generous. A trail could just be made out meandering its way up the ancient mountain, barely wide enough at its best, to walk single file. Further aggravating the journey up were the loose pebbles which hardly allowed one to get a good foothold, and the fact that she didn't dare look to her right—a sheer drop of more than ninety craggy meters. "Oh, the walk in the alpine meadows is beautiful! Especially this time of year!" Pushing her feet on, Winnie's mind sarcastically mimicked the friendly-intended words of her colleague Kathy. But it's freezing! she yelled inside in response. It's supposed to be spring! Where are the azaleas, the poppies and other flowers in bloom? Where's the warm sunshine? She looked up at the clouds and realized, with some disdain, that the province was aptly named.[1] A gust of wind swept wildly around the corner and she slipped on a rock. Struggling to keep her weight forward, she fell to her hands and knees.

"Are you all right? Are you all right?"

"Yes. Yes. I'm okay." Shaken, a weary Winnie rose and dusted herself off of loose dirt. But she was humbled. "All right. Can you help me?"

She continued the trek upwards supported by the elderly man's hand. The air was thinner up here, causing the Hong Kong native to labor in her breathing, and it made the near two-hour hike feel like an eternity. As her legs were feeling a bit like jelly, she thought of the picture she and the old man must make: How embarrassing! A seventy-year-old gentleman helping a perfectly able young woman up the mountain; a senior citizen slowing down and readjusting his pace so she, the healthy one in the prime of life, could keep up. It should be the other way around! Frustration reasserted itself in her mind: "Oh, what's the point?"

"Hmm?"

"What's the point? Everything's so backward up here!" She stopped walking momentarily, forcing the elderly man to pause in turn, and flapped her arms helplessly, raising his supporting hand in the process. Visualizing again the photos that Kathy had shown her of the place, she spat out her discontentment. "The houses—if you can call them that—have dirt floors, the curtains are made out of newspapers, and people hang raw slabs of meat in their bedrooms!" She resumed her stride, at first almost bumping into her help, continuing to gesture with her free hand as if the said items were right before her eyes. "Who could even *think* of sleeping with half a dead pig dangling

---

[1] In Chinese characters the word "Yunnan" is translated as "south of the cloud".

upside down beside them?! That's so disgusting!" She slipped again but managed, with a firm grip from her companion, to brace herself with her free hand on a boulder. She brushed the filthy powdery dirt from her hand against the side of her jeans. "The government can't help. Neither can aid organizations. As if *we* can." Winnie grudgingly trudged on, her feet as heavy as her feelings.

"*We*? You mean our organization?"

She looked up in surprise. "Well, yeah, Pastor. Who else?"

The old pastor sighed. "You know, Winnie," he began patiently, "with or without organizations, that is not the point. We, people like you and me, we do this kind of work regardless, because it's what we're called to do." He stopped walking here and turned to face his young protégé, still holding her by the hand. Pastor Chen was a man of medium height and build, compared to other Chinese, but, as she looked up at him, the wisdom and experience of his many years caused him to loom even greater in the young lady's eyes.

"Well, couldn't you pick an easier place?" She couldn't help the pout or the slight sneer that tinged her question.

Pastor Chen tactfully chose not to notice them. He resumed his explanation in that deliberately slow way of speaking that was his: "The poverty up here is appalling, yes, but the people give me much favor. I do not know why, but the fact is, they do." He paused to see if he still had Winnie's attention. You could never just assume these days with the younger generation. "This is an open door!" he said flinging his arms out wide. "Don't you see? I am getting old, but if I don't work now, what could I say to our Lord?"

Mingyen Chen was an experienced walker. He'd been doing it for more than half his life. When he first began his journeys back in 1953, there weren't too many options to choose from, if people wanted to get around rural China. Some might have had the luxury of a water buffalo-drawn cart. An even smaller number, a very elite few, could indulge in the privilege of traveling by car, but paved roads in the countryside were sparse, poor in quality and, in most places, non-existent. So the masses, including Mingyen, walked. It could be as far as forty kilometers to the next village, but still he kept on trekking. Maybe six hours one day, more than twelve the next—no matter; it was all in a day's work. It was a journey that had to be undertaken. There was no escaping the fact. Otherwise, how else would he fulfill his goal of being a traveling evangelist?

But now look at the nation: China, in the twenty-first century, has an ample supply of modern freeways connecting metropolises. More miles of expressway, in fact, have been paved in the People's Republic than in any other nation in the world, except the United States. Too bad it's an engineer's worst nightmare to plan cost effective roads up here, thought Mingyen to himself, as he surveyed the awkward terrain he was traversing. Even a donkey has a hard time getting up and down this place.

Nevertheless, he had to admit, the Mainland was making serious gains in its drive to catch up with the industrialized world. Urbanization was progressing at a furious pace in some areas, so much so that numerous villages had been swallowed up by the ever-developing cities and suburbs. They now live in the shadows of a different kind of forest, he thought, somewhat chagrinned, the gleaming new skyscrapers, several of which are among the world's tallest. Mingyen sighed as he remembered Winnie's disparaging comments about the "houses" they would see at the end of this trail. Why is it that some peasants today are experienced users of cellular phones while others aren't even able to access electricity for their homes?

Such huge disparities between the rich and poor, Mingyen reflected. Today the proletariat line up for Starbucks Coffee in Shanghai, while in the country many folks are just happy to have running water. It was hard to imagine these days that queuing people were once satisfied if they could simply get their hands on enough rice or salt. And now there is demand for gourmet beverages! How times have changed.

Mingyen began to muse over the value of salt. How carelessly liberal were most people nowadays in tossing the seasoning on to their food, and yet, he remembered, how utterly precious the mineral once was to some villagers. Scavenging daily from the remains of the ebb tide, these people were so desperate for a livelihood that they "farmed" salt from seawater. Mingyen shook his head and silently chuckled to himself as the memories of toiling in Zhejiang province came back to mind—and just so he could have an opportunity to share the Gospel!

Back then in the early 1950s, it was gruelingly tiring work, from sun up to sun down, but Mingyen was glad to join in. Born and bred a city boy, he found, at first, it was an excruciatingly difficult challenge to adjust to the rigors of such crude, physical working conditions. How many backbreaking hours had he travailed under a blazing sun, with only a stringy straw hat to shield his virtually naked body? They were too many to count. However he persevered, and gradually, like the locals, he learned how to spot the precious white particles as they dried on top of the sand. He mastered the technique of gently scraping them off and heaping them into piles which would be rinsed through with salt water, then spread out on pans to dry in the open air. He derived the utmost satisfaction from his and the villagers' labors, as they harvested their two measly "crops" on a sunny day. And he felt the utter heartbreak of overcast skies—for it meant there was *nothing* that day.

He was constantly parched from his exertions, and the subsequent ache at the back of his throat became a familiar sensation. A relieving cool drink, however, was not easy to come by. Despite the salt-farming communities' proximity to the East China Sea, drinking water was scarce. It had to be collected when it rained, carried in pails from other villages or purchased from peddlers. In those days, Mingyen never took a bath. When he washed his hands, he was careful not to throw the water away because it would be used again and again. He could never figure out though, how the women got enough water to wash and cook the rice. It was probably better not to know! Mingyen chuckled to himself again.

"That wasn't meant to be funny." Winnie's voice abruptly broke into his consciousness, dispelling his memories of a younger time and place.

"Hmm?"

"I said my question wasn't meant to be funny."

"What question?"

"Haven't you heard anything I've just been saying?" There was a hint of impatience in the young woman's tone.

"I'm sorry, Winnie. I was thinking of something else." Mingyen realized his mind had wandered momentarily. Again. It had been doing so more of late. He was aware his body was aging and he didn't like the fact. He refocused on the present. "What was your question again?"

The young lady exhaled, reminding herself in the

process that, after all, Pastor Chen was probably preoccupied with all the meetings and teaching he was going to be doing in the villages they would tour on this trip. He couldn't always just be thinking about her needs. "I was just wondering why you're always going up to the villages. Why don't you make them come down into town for the meetings? We've come all the way from Hong Kong; the least they could do is meet us part way."

Mingyen understood where the question was coming from. He had once thought like that, when he was younger and less knowledgeable about things. "This is not about us, Winnie," he began to answer her patiently. "It's about *them*—the people who live up here." He took a few more steps as he contemplated how best to put it for the younger mind. "Think how hard it is for whole villages to come to town. It's very difficult, you know. They are very poor. They hardly scrape together enough to live on as it is, let alone afford the time to travel." He paused to let her consider the logistics. "If our mission is to serve, then we should do whatever is easier for them." The delivery of the explanation sounded a lot easier and smoother than he felt. Every time he had to answer this question though, Mingyen secretly cringed inside because it reminded him of how ignorant he had once been.

He, like Winnie, had once held that same expectation: Villagers should come to him. He was already going to great lengths and undertaking multifarious risks to meet them, traveling as he was—who knew, for example, when the authorities might discover that the purpose of his visits was to distribute Bibles and teach the Bible, and then blacklist him, never to let him return to the land of his birth? Or, he could be arrested a fourth time and sent back to a labor camp. The pressures were tremendous each time he came;

so much needed to be accomplished in so little time. It was just much more efficient and economical this way—for him, that is.

Then he saw how it was for Old Mother Fang. For several years in the early 1980s, the middle-aged widow had been his trusty "personal assistant" when he went to Henan province. She arranged his accommodation, cooked his meals and ensured he was not inconvenienced in any way when he visited. She made his bed, reminded him of the timetable, did his laundry, sourced his band-aids and so on. Mingyen informed her when he was coming, for how long, where he wanted to speak, how often, and she would make all the arrangements.

But one blistering cold winter Old Mother Fang wasn't there when he arrived. He was surprised at first, but not too concerned. Then things didn't run as smoothly or as comfortably as he was accustomed to. There were a lot more unnecessary delays, mishaps and obstructions. Finally he couldn't take it anymore. He demanded to know where Old Mother Fang was. Her substitute, A-Yi, was some fifteen years her junior. She bowed her head, dejected. She had tried her best to be as good as her predecessor. She really had. "I'm sorry, Pastor Chen. Old Mother Fang is, too. We are very, very sorry. She just couldn't come, though."

"She couldn't come?" asked Mingyen again. He was incredulous. "Why on earth not?"

A-Yi hummed and hawed for a bit. She twisted one of her waist-long braids around her index finger. She rolled her eyes to an invisible point on the wall behind Mingyen. Finally she said in a small voice, "Her cotton padded trousers are too old, too worn out. They have too many holes." She wet her lips here, all the while mustering the courage to finish her explanation. "She's too ashamed to wear them to come and see you. You see," she went on, her voice barely above a whisper, "when it's freezing like this, she can't come out of her house in the mountains. She doesn't have enough warm clothes."

Mingyen was glad Winnie couldn't see his face. He felt the heat of his blush rise from the bottom of his face to the top again. It was as if that initial shock was hitting him once more, his mortification at first learning the reason, and he was embarrassed all over again. The woman didn't have proper winter clothes! How vain he was! How blind! What an absolute fool he had been not to realize her hardship, not to fathom the depth of Mother Fang's poverty. And yet he had come to "serve the poor", and scores of people in China lived in similar circumstances.

"Well?" asked Winnie impatiently.

Mingyen was jolted out of his thoughts again. Darn, he thought, it happened again. "Well, what?"

Is the old man losing his hearing? Winnie was getting exasperated again. "No one else seems to come up here."

He was puzzled at her statement. "No one else?"

"Yeah."

Temporarily at a loss, Mingyen managed to pick up on the thought trail of his protégé. "Oh, you mean other missionaries and aid organizations."

"Yeah."

Why is she always so direct? he wondered. What happened to the genteel ways and manners we used to instill in our children? Kicking aside a large pebble, he tried next to figure out how long it would take her to understand, how to help her understand. "China is a large place," he began, deciding she probably preferred a shorter, pragmatic answer, as her attention seemed to be temporarily ensnared by a scampering pika. "Even with so many organizations working here these days, they are really only concentrated in a few areas. And so many people in need still do not receive help. We have the opportunity to diversify, to break new ground in places others cannot. Why not take it? This way more people can be reached." Mingyen paused to consider his next words. "And you know, it's not just anyone who can work up here." He looked up through the trees, behind some moving clouds, and spotted the peak of the mountain they were climbing. Was it really attainable? "The minorities don't welcome just anyone. In fact, some of them *hate* the Han Chinese."

Astonished at both the bluntness of his statement and its implication, Winnie's mind quickly returned to the conversation and she raised an eyebrow. She and Pastor Chen were ethnically Han, as were well over 90% of the people in the country.

"It's true," said Mingyen, who happened to glance back at her at the moment. "Because they have different ways, different language, for so long they've been looked down on in society, pushed out to the fringe, literally. They didn't always live so high up these mountains, you know." He stepped down on a dead protruding branch with his right foot so that he and Winnie could climb over easily. "And with the Han population having grown so large, the difficulties of integrating into city life have become more complicated by discrimination." The experienced hiker stopped for a minute to re-check the route they should take. He scanned the prospective path, up and down. Then he resumed. "They've been deeply wounded and many of them have not forgiven or forgotten. Yet they welcome me and trust me." He took a few steps in silence. Then, "Do you know what they say to me?"

"What?"

"What *kind* of work do you want to do? Imagine that! They would let me do *anything*."

Winnie contemplated what "anything" meant so far. She knew Pastor Chen had been active among the tribal peoples since 1985 and, to date, at least half the population in the areas he worked were believers. In some places it was significantly more. Understandably then, his uppermost concern these days was the availability of good, sound Bible teaching to the local Christian leaders. He had taught in, organized and enabled the building of theological seminaries in the province over the ensuing years, as the means and times had permitted, tailoring the curriculum to suit long or short terms. This was in addition to his continuous evangelizing and preaching in churches. He had also raised funds to make possible the construction of church buildings. Moreover he had opened channels for the printing and distribution of Bibles in the Miao, Wa and Lahu languages. A Lisu Bible was going to be added soon too.

But Pastor Chen did much more than this. He facilitated the construction of elementary schools and hospitals for the tribal people too. He had even had a bridge built for them. He really worked to help the community as a whole progress.

"Then how do you decide?" she asked her mentor.

"Hmm?"

"How do you decide what to do?"

"Well, it depends," he replied. "There's no formula. Basically, we consider the needs, then respond in the best way we can. Ultimately though, the goal is to bring people closer to Jesus."

"But the trend is to specialize these days. They say it isn't efficient to be a generalist. Either do the social programs or the church ones. How come you do both?"

"You know, Winnie, efficiency isn't everything. Watch out you don't limit yourself with that kind of thinking." To his shame, he couldn't help thinking of Old Mother Fang again as he pushed aside a branch with his hand. "You have to consider the people too. Some folks are so poor, for example, they can't see beyond their stomachs. When I see that, my heart cries. It aches. How can I ignore what I see? So feed them rice first." He lunged over a series of small boulders, then helped Winnie through the section before he went on. "You know, a few years ago in Henan, a man came up to me. He must have been at least eighty. He wanted to say thank you because I helped their village drill a well and install a water pump. Until that point in his life, he and everyone else in the village had to walk five kilometers for their daily supply of water—for cooking, cleaning, drinking. This didn't even include what they needed to irrigate their farms. They carried it back to their homes in buckets. This man had such a badly bent back! Everyday they had to do this—imagine!—in 1999!" He noticed that Winnie was panting quite hard. "Here. Have some water." He passed her his bottle as he knew she had drunk her own supply up a long time ago. Then, after seeing how thirstily she gulped it down, he decided to set down his backpack and sit on a rock to rest.

Winnie was grateful for the break. She quickly joined him.

"Anyway," Mingyen went on with his story, "he was very grateful. They all were, and they tried to give me gifts of sweet corn, peanuts—I tell you, there were bags of all their crops. But they have so little; I couldn't take it." Leaning slightly forward with his hands braced on his knees, Mingyen took a moment to collect himself, as if he were overwhelmed by their gratitude all over again. "But it wasn't just the villagers who were grateful. The local Communist officials were too. They had tried for years to get something done themselves but, for whatever reason, were unsuccessful."

Winnie handed the bottle back to Pastor Chen, who replaced it in the side pocket of his pack.

"The villagers tell me that because they know the pump was installed by a Christian, the cadres have been more lenient about their house church gatherings than in the past. They gather with no fear of raids or arrests these days." Mingyen stood up in preparation to resume walking. "So you tell me: How do you decide?"

SAIMEN LIANG

"I've had four professions in my life: First I was a beggar. Next, a goatherd. After that I was a Red Guard. Then I became an evangelist."

So began the thirty-year-old Saimen's talk on a crisp, clear wintry afternoon. It was the month of February, the year 1980. The temperature hovered at around six degrees Celsius as a crowd of about 800 people amassed outside in the village square of Lingan, northeast Henan. It was an unauthorized meeting but the anticipation with which they listened was, to them, so great it was worth risking the displeasure of the authorities.

"I grew up in a family that worshipped idols. My father was the oldest son, so he got given all the ancestor plaques and statues from his family's previous generations—we had more than thirty in our shrine! As a little boy I liked to play with all those wooden dolls and Father said, 'Don't ever let the neighbors see you doing that 'cause they won't like it—they're supposed to be your ancestors.'"

For many of the believers here, it was the first glimpse they had of Saimen, the brother they had undertaken to care for in the past six years, the preacher who had been incarcerated some 500 kilometers away from his home and family. During that time, the term of his prison sentence, they had been a kind of surrogate family to Saimen, unselfishly sharing with him their friendship, food and blankets from what meager stores they themselves had. His own wife could barely afford to make her annual visit to him.

"In 1956 there was a famine in our area and my family was so poor we had to go out and beg. I was five years old. We had no money to buy anything, so Mother shaved her head to sell her hair. Then one day Father decided the idols weren't helping us and said we should get rid of them. So we dug a hole and buried them in the ground. Soon after that I found out about Je—"

Saimen stopped in mid sentence. His attention was arrested by something across the way: He spied a small band of PSB[2] officers and a dozen or so specially selected, well-built thugs advancing on the square with knives and clubs in hand. The leader of the PSB looked straight ahead and, it appeared to Saimen, his eyes were piercing into him, the lone man on the makeshift stage of a couple of wooden tables pushed together. A few people in the crowd noticed the preacher's pause. They turned to see what he was staring so intently at. A raid! Panic flashed through Saimen's mind: What should I do? Run! Why isn't anybody running? What's going on? What are they waiting for? Run!

But a strange thing was happening. The crowd of believers was beginning to encircle Saimen, closing in tighter and tighter as if to protect him from what they felt was sure to be an onslaught by the police and their gang.

"Clear the way! Coming through!" shouted Tong, the first of the PSB officers to come face to face with the outer rim of the circle.

The human shield didn't budge.

"Clear the way! Do you hear me?! We're coming through!"

The shield was determined to stand its ground.

---

[2] Public Security Bureau. The PSB is the political and ideological police force in China, operating at national, provincial and local levels.

"Look folks, this is an illegal gathering! Let's not make this hard. Let us get the leader on the stage and you can all be on your way. Let me through now!" Tong commanded.

The crowd was unmoved.

"And then I met Jesus," Saimen decided to resume, "and He changed my life . . ."

"Are you deaf?! Let me through! I'm the Chief of the PSB! I order you to let me through!" Tong's face was beginning to turn red. He was outraged! Didn't they realize he was being lenient with them? How dare they ignore him!

Utterly amazed at the fact there was no carnage, Saimen's confidence was renewed and he kept on talking.

The afternoon dragged on—for Chief Tong. To his indignation, he found his orders being repeatedly ignored, drowned out by the preaching. Such a public gathering—that is to say, for religious purposes—was beyond his experience in Lingan. It had never happened before, and he was unsure now how to deal with it. The great wall of people continued to protect the speaker, even as it was absolutely determined to hear everything Saimen had to say.

As the shadows of night began to creep in, Saimen closed out his talk. He hopped down from the stage and immediately the wall closed in even tighter around him. Incredible! Where he walked, the wall walked; when he turned, the wall turned. And Chief Tong and his gang still couldn't get near him.

This is infuriating! thought the Chief. Visibility, he couldn't help noticing, was fading with the daylight and a sense of futility began to overshadow him. How are we going to spot him now in that mass?

As if in answer to that thought, the crowd suddenly dispersed. The believers ran off in a myriad of directions and it was impossible for Chief Tong to get his hands on

Saimen.

Saimen scurried to keep pace with Shu and Ying under the trees. As the crowd ran off, the two of them had pulled Saimen along in their direction and he knew he better follow them if he didn't want to wind up in prison again. Their childhood romping ground, both Shu and Ying knew these woods like the backs of their hands. Expertly hopping from stone to stone, avoiding protruding roots here and there, the two navigated their way to a nearby stream. Huffing and puffing a little way behind, Saimen eventually caught up to them.

"Just follow the stream about five kilometers that way," Shu pointed, "and you'll come to a bridge. Cross it. Follow the road north to the next village. When you get to the village, go straight through and out a few more kilometers. Further on you'll see a farm on the right hand side, just off the main road. That's Grandma Chan's. Tell her we sent you. She'll know what to do. Go now, and God be with you." Shu quickly rejoined Ying at the edge of the woods. As Saimen turned for a last look at his friends, he saw they were already gone.

Chief Tong was steaming. Two days had gone by and *everyone* in Lingan was still laughing at how "all those Christians got away". When he walked down the street, he could see the grandparents, the working men and young mothers all bending over, hands over their mouths, snickering to one other, "Look, it's the Chief! He couldn't catch any of those Christians!" It was humiliating. To add insult to injury, even the children were in on the joke and had written a silly rhyme:

The believers of God are wise indeed!
They've made Chief Tong go batty!
The believers of God are wise indeed!
They've made Chief Tong go batty!

Over and over they sang it, the girls chanting the first line and the boys replying with the second. Young people are supposed to respect their elders! And this! Must he tolerate such indignities?

"What is it, Comrade? I've never seen you so upset before."

Tong was sitting in the Mingshui district PSB headquarters. Lingan was a part of Mingshui district, and across the desk in front of him sat his superior, Secretary Wei.

"Comrade Wei, it's terrible! I can't work in that village anymore! No one respects me!" Wringing his hands, Tong relayed the events of the past few days. "Never in my life have I been so rudely treated! I won't go back there!"

"Now, Tong, calm down. Nothing's as bad as it seems." Wei was genuinely disturbed. First of all, Tong was a "star" among his village-level chiefs. He'd never had any major problems before and easily handled problematic counterrevolutionaries. Secondly, who would have thought so many people would gather to hear a religious message? Was it even possible that there existed so many believers in the area? He could have sworn the policies since Liberation, particularly the Cultural Revolution, had eradicated any traces of religious faith that still lingered in the country. And finally, who was that guy who spoke? What kind of power did he wield over the people? His officers were unable to do anything! "Tell you what," the superior said, "why don't you just stay here for a few days, eh? I'll send a team to investigate."

"Now, don't try to deny it—we know you were there. We have witnesses. They said you were the one who introduced the speaker." Secretary Wei had decided to head the investigation himself. He stood glaring down at Ying, who had been shoved onto a chair by his two accompanying officers. "Tell me, who was the man who spoke in the square?"

"I don't know."

"Don't lie to me. What's his name?"

"I'm telling you, I don't know. I don't even know where he came from."

"Then how could you introduce him? *How* did you introduce him?"

"Look, I don't know his name. I just said he was 'the servant of God.'"

Wei signaled the guard on the left, who promptly slapped Ying around the head a few times while his partner duly twisted and pulled back his arms. The pain was torturous. Ying thought his arms would come out of their sockets.

"I told you not to lie. Isn't that what you Christians teach? Who was he? Our witnesses told us you said he *suffered* for God. So what's this *servant* crap?" Wei was thinking if it was someone who had suffered, he could narrow down his list of suspects to one.

"I swear, I don't know. They must have misheard me. I know I said he was the *servant* of God."

"So what do you mean by 'servant of God' then?"

"Uh, I don't know—he told me he was the servant of God, so I introduced him as the servant of God."

"So who's the servant of God?"

"Everyone. Everyone who serves the Lord is the servant of God."

This was meaningless. After a few more cycles of slaps and questions, Wei knew he wasn't going to get anything else from the guy. We'll go check this Shu out instead, he decided. "Let him go."

"So, who was that man who spoke in the square?"

"I don't know."

Wei sighed. Here we go again. He and his cohorts were now at Shu's farm and he was not going to leave without answers this time. The secretary, not one to be trifled with— he knew he was good at his job and took great pride in the fact—decided to try another tact. He strolled over and leaned casually back on the fence enclosing the pigs, settling in beside Shu. "You know, Shu," he began in an amiable voice, "my grandmother was a Christian, like you. She was devoted and good, a good person. Really kind too. I don't remember ever seeing her angry, not even once. How did you come to believe?"

Shu looked over at Wei. He sounded like he sincerely wanted to know. There was a friendly smile on the handsome secretary's face too, but the farmer hadn't quite yet made up his mind as to whether it was meant to be genuine or deceptive. "My—my mother told me."

"Ah! My grandmother told me too." Wei tipped his hat back further on his head, exposing some of his rich, thick slicked-back black hair. With eyes half closed and his forehead angled skyward, it seemed as if all he wanted was to better catch a few more rays of the sun. "You know, she was even baptized, in the river." He turned his head and opened his eyes to face Shu again. "Have you been baptized?"

"Uh, baptized? What's that?" Shu decided he wasn't going for the nice guy act.

"You know, uh, you know—baptized—like, uh, like when two people, you know, they push you into the water." Wei stood back up off the fence, and made pushing motions with his arms to reinforce his description.

"Oh," said Shu naively, "but, but isn't that drowning?"

"Look, you dumb farmer! I'm trying to be nice to you!" Wei's patience was beginning to run thin. Two days of these moronic answers was enough! He signaled the two guards and they pushed Shu into the house and started kicking him. Shu curled up in a ball on the floor to defend himself but the kicks continued unabated. Wei bent over and pulled Shu's head up by the hair. "Tell me who the speaker was!"

"I-, I-, I-, I don't know! I don't know!"

The kicking resumed. Shu covered his head with his hands. When would it end?

"What's his name?" Wei demanded again.

"I don't know! They-, they said he was the servant of God—that's all. That's all! I don't know anymore!"

What could the secretary do? That's all anyone knew. "He's just a stinkin' dog's fart. Let's go."

This is insane. How hard could it be to find one guy? Tong really screwed up on this one, and so much time's been lost now. Secretary Wei was back in his office. Mulling over the case, he took a long drag on his cigarette, file and notes open before him. The investigation had gone on for days but he'd found nothing to confirm his suspicion further. He'd drawn up a list of possible suspects—those he knew to be in the area at the right time and those he knew to be followers of this religion. There was only one possibility: Liang. It's *got* to be Saimen Liang. *He'd* qualify as someone who suffered (that Ying had to be lying!). Just out of prison (witnesses confirmed that), his dossier labels him a Christian, exactly the type of person who'd speak at one of those things. Who else could it be? He called in his two associates.

"Feng. Huang. Go find this Saimen Liang. Here's his picture. Bring him in for questioning."

"Crap."

"What?"

"I hate these assignments."

"What do you mean?"

"You know, looking for them, the Christians."

Feng and Huang stood on the edge of the street and waited for some motorcycles and a donkey cart to pass before they crossed. Huang, who had posed the question, was squat, rather challenged for height (which was aggravated by the fact that he had no visible neck), and he veered on the rotund side. Feng, in comparison, soared a good head and a half above his partner, was lanky like a string bean, gangly, even gawky looking. He tended to walk with sagging shoulders. Viewed from behind, the duo was a bit of a comic sight, perhaps reminding one of Old Master Q and Big Potato[3].

---

[3] Old Master Q or *Lao Fu Zi* is a popular classic comic book series that originated in Hong Kong in the 1960s. Big Potato is Old Master Q's short fat friend.

"What do you mean?" asked Huang again. "We always have to look for people. What's the difference if they're Christians?"

"They're spooks! That's what! Weird things happen with them."

"Weird things? You *can't* be serious." Huang pulled out a cigarette as he said this, pointed the pack to Feng, who took one, as was his custom anytime anyone offered. They began walking through the Mingshui market, in quest of their man, as they lit up.

"I heard," said Feng in between puffs, "over in No. 9 Prison, they once handcuffed this Christian girl to her bunk all night. She was trying to convert other prisoners, right? Anyway, they made her stand all night. There's no way she could get up to her bed—*no way*—and she couldn't sit either because the cuffs were too high up." Feng swerved mid stride to avoid a cage of live chickens. "Well, in the morning, the guards found her sleeping in her bed! The cuffs were off—and no one had the key but the warden! How'd she get them off?"

Huang looked unimpressed. He ducked his head in time to avoid some flying fish scales from the fishmonger stall.

"Okay," continued Feng, as he passed a squawking goose, "Another time, same place, they were interrogating another girl. They tried to make her tell them her foreign connections but she wouldn't talk. So they pulled out the electric baton, but guess what? It wouldn't work on her! They tested it and sparks flew everywhere, but every time they put it against her body it wouldn't work! Spooks, man! I tell you, they're spooks! They can do magic."

"You're crazy! They're just stories! Why do you believe them?" Huang sidestepped an aggressive fruit seller as he said this. "There's no magic! And what's your obsession with No. 9 anyway? How do you know what goes on in there?"

"My cousin works there. He was there when they tested the electric baton. He said if he didn't see it, he wouldn't believe it!"

"Well, it's just one prison. And besides, we're not going to a prison, so don't worry."

"Oh yeah? Well, what do you think of this then? Out in Wulong there was a Christian meeting—just like in Lingan—they met in the village square."

"So?"

"So these three women were speaking and the police came to break it up. Well, what do you think happened? Huh? What do you think?"

"How the heck should I know?" There was a mixed look of scorn and incredulousness on Huang's face as he asked this. He'd never seen his partner get so wound up about a few peasants before.

"When the village PSB chief got out of his car, he pointed at them and said, 'Stop them!' and then he couldn't get his arm back down! It was stuck! It was like suddenly the whole right side of his body was paralyzed!" Feng's arms and eyes were opened wide in amazement as he said this. "They had such a hard time trying to get him back in the car! It was like trying to get one of those dummies in the shop windows into the car whole—and they don't bend! Half of him couldn't move! Now tell me they can't do magic!"

"They can't." Huang took a couple more quick puffs and littered his cigarette butt on the ground. "So, go on. What happened after that? Is he still stuck?"

"After that, it gets even worse. They say he *begged* the

women to come to his office. Can you *imagine*? You might as well kowtow in front of the whole village! That's the worst loss of face." He discovered a couple of fish scales on his shirt and flicked them away. "*I* couldn't do that! Anyway, he gave them dinner to appease them, hoping they'd agree to make him normal again. Can you believe that?"

"So what happened?"

"They prayed for him."

"Did it work?"

"*Yeeaah*!"

"You mean they actually prayed and he got unstuck?"

"*Yeeaah!*"

"Interesting."

"Interesting? That's all you have to say? It's *creepy*! What if there really *is* a God?"

"There he is."

"Crap. Are you sure? Let me see the picture."

"It's him!" Huang insisted. "You don't need to see!" The two officers peered at their subject, unseen, from behind a maple tree. The shade of the branches, however, was diminishing the quality of light with which to compare the still to the original—at least as far as Feng was concerned. The two officers jostled at each other, one trying to grab the picture from the other, pushing and shoving themselves further and further around the tree until they unwittingly worked themselves out from under its leaves. They were completely exposed. Huang resigned himself to yielding the photo to Feng. "Go tell him the chief wants to talk to him."

"No way!" exclaimed Feng. "I'm not gonna tell him!

You tell him! You're the one who says there's no magic!"

As they stood there arguing, Saimen crossed the street and made his way up to them. "What do you want with me?"

Spooks! How did he know they wanted him? Even Huang was beginning to feel the jitters.

"What's the matter with you two? Why are you shaking?"

Feng and Huang stood there mute, their knees in a slight tremor. Their eyes looked to the skies and froze in place. They didn't dare to meet Saimen's gaze. An inexplicable dread had descended on them, and it was as if they feared fire could fall from the heavens at any moment and consume them.

"Stop shaking! Look, I'm here. What do you want?" Saimen reiterated his question.

"Uh-, uh-, th-, th-, th-, the chief, uh, he-, he wants you t-, t-, to come-, to come and, and see him." Huang somehow stammered the words out. With his cigarette dangling from his lip, Feng nodded dumbly in agreement.

"Okay," said Saimen rather easily. "Let's go."

Secretary Wei strode across the interrogation room. He had a solid, firm step, one that exuded confidence and self-assertion. The air about him suggested there was no fussing, no messing around with him; it was all business. There was no disputing either: He was the man in charge; he would have his way. Physically, he was an impressive bloke, attractive, with a face that boasted mellow brown eyes and full lips. He was of perfect height and well-built with a broad set of shoulders. Wei wore his uniform well, and one had the notion looking at him that here was a man who was polished, truly someone who has "got it all together". He appeared the complete antithesis of the person he had come to question.

Saimen, on the other hand, with his tousled hair (it wasn't a priority with him to think of using a comb), ill-fitting patched trousers and an obvious hand-me-down cotton padded jacket, looked as if he had just trotted in from the wheat field. With a smear of dirt on his brow and underneath his fingernails, he hardly looked like a menacing criminal suspect.

Wei took his pistol out of its holster and placed it purposefully on the table before him. Still standing, he braced his arms on opposite ends of the table, the firearm centered in between, as if to highlight its reality. He leaned forward and stared hard at Saimen.

What's the big deal? thought Saimen. I've seen guns before—big guns, small guns, long guns and short guns.

The secretary sat down, his eyes never leaving the face of his suspect. "So, Liang, I see you're a recent release from No. 4, less than two months, in fact. Where've you been?"

"Nowhere," answered Saimen innocently. He was seated upright in his chair, hand over hand in his lap. "I've just been around here."

"What?" The interrogator feigned a look of astonishment. "What about your family? Don't you want to see them?"

"Of course, but they're on the other side of the province. I don't have enough money to go home yet." Despite his unconcerned demeanor, Saimen was fully cognizant of the significance of this "chat". The PSB officer was trying to intimidate him. Saimen knew he must not give the authority any sign of fear or reason to be suspicious of him.

"Must be tough. You working then?"

"Just some odd jobs."

"Like what?"

"Oh, this and that. It's not harvest time, you know. Not many extra jobs around at the moment. Besides, it's hard for ex-convicts to get work."

"Ah. Well, that's your own fault, you know. I've been reading your dossier—fascinating—you were once a promising party cadre, even district leader of the Red Guards. But why? *Why* would you ever give up your Communist Party membership to follow some religious nonsense? Look around you—" Wei waved his arm, "it's not God who gives the people their food and jobs! You gotta admit that wasn't very smart, Liang. Don't you know God's just superstition?"

"That's what you think. But I know otherwise."

"You seem very sure of yourself. Been to Lingan lately?" Wei caught Saimen's eyes again. They locked on and time seemed to suspend for a few seconds. Dare you lie now, Criminal Liang?

Saimen didn't flinch. "Lingan? Where's that? Other than No. 4, I'm not really familiar with this part of the province. I'm not from here, you know."

"So where've you been staying then, lately?"

"Grandma Chan's. Her farm's about ten kilometers from here."

"Grandma Chan's a Christian."

"Yeah, I know," said Saimen with a smile, "Very kind too. She knows I have nothing but she gave me a bed and food in exchange for some help with her pigs and chickens."

"And you're an expert in pigs, I see," said Wei, peering down at Saimen's file.

"Oh, I wouldn't say 'expert'. But I guess I know a little bit about them. They were my responsibility at No. 4, you know, for a number of years. The chickens are a bit trickier, I admit—I have less experience with them—" Saimen leaned forward in his chair here, apparently keen in his contemplation on the challenge of tending the birds, "but it seems if you feed them regularly, they're pretty happy. If you ask me though, goats are the best to take care of. I was a goatherd, you know, when I was a boy. I'll never forget those days, walking over the hills, sitting by the stream—"

"Okay, enough about the animals! I mean, that's, that's not what I wanted to talk about."

"Oh," said Saimen. "Then why'd you ask me if I knew how to take care of pigs?" He sat back in his chair.

"Look, let's just forget about that, okay?" Wei was getting a bit tired of this case. All these nonsensical answers! It was more than he was used to. He studied Saimen's face: It was open, and his cheeks possessed a cherubic quality. He seems honest, the secretary couldn't help thinking. And he didn't give Feng and Huang any trouble coming here. Maybe he isn't the one. Wei decided to try another angle. "Do you know Farmer Shu?"

Saimen tilted his head to one side as if to consider the question. "Shu . . . Oh, I think . . . I think I've heard of him! Isn't he supposed to have some of the best pigs around here? You know, one of Grandma Chan's pigs is sick. Do you think he could help?"

"Do I look like a peasant? How am I supposed to know?" This was exasperating! Wei took a deep breath to calm himself down. "Forget the pigs, okay? Do you think you can do that?" He reached into his pocket for his pack of cigarettes and saw he was down to the last one. Shoot, he thought, I must remember to pick up some more of these next time I'm in Beijing. "By the way," he said as he lit up, "how'd you meet Grandma Chan?"

"Grandma Chan? Oh, a friend told me about her."

"Thought you said you didn't know anyone around here."

"I met some people when I was in prison." Saimen said this quite simply.

"So where's your friend now?"

"Which one?"

Wei tried not to show his irritation. "The one who told you about Grandma Chan."

"Oh, I don't know."

"Is he still in prison?"

"I don't know. I can't remember how long everyone's sentence is."

"What's his name?"

"Wong."

"Wong what?"

"Don't know. I just knew him as Old Wong."

There must be ten thousand Wongs in *each* prison in China! "And you never bothered to find out what your friend's first name was?"

"When we met he just said, 'Call me Old Wong,' so I did."

Is this guy a simpleton? Wei felt hunger pains gnawing inside, telling him he needed food. He looked at his watch—two hours already and all I've got are idiotic responses. There's nothing on this guy. "Okay. We're done for now. You can go."

LILI TANG

"Seven *jiao*, eight, nine . . . and that makes seventy *yuan*. There you go."

"That hardly leaves anything for the rest of you."

"This is more important. You know that."

"Yeah. But still, I feel bad."

"Don't. We'll get by. We always do. Just be careful and don't get caught."

It was 1986. This meeting in a sleepy backwater of Shanxi province had been arranged over two weeks ago. Kuan and Lili now stood over a rickety camphor table in a farmhouse as they counted out the money. Through the window one could see the corn stalks in the near distance, swaying gently in the breeze, and the mildness of the setting and day did nothing to justify the province's notorious label as the 'coal warehouse of China'. Nevertheless neither Kuan nor Lili seemed to perceive the idyllic weather or situation. They were too engrossed in the matter at hand. Kuan was thirty-six, a dozen years Lili's senior, and he tended to view her with the protectiveness of an older brother.

"I've been doing it for almost five years—you don't need to remind me of that."

"Can't help it. That's a precious cargo you carry. Lives depend on it."

"I know."

"And the amount you're shipping now—my goodness! We're not talking about two sacks like when you started! Hundreds and hundreds of boxes! Do you know what would happen if the authorities found out?" Kuan's forehead furrowed as he asked this. Secretly though, he was proud of Lili's ability to regularly move such huge volumes throughout the country. Imagine what she could do if she ventured into business!

"How can we just ignore the needs of the other brothers and sisters though? Besides, what's the difference if it's five boxes or 500? I'm down there already anyway. Might as well just put a few more on to the train."

"You're right. We can't ignore them. But if I didn't know you better, I'd say you were crazy to be taking on all this extra stress."

Lili laughed. "You always say that!"

"Yeah, well, you always manage to make so much more work for us!" It wasn't the first time Lili had taken on a seemingly straightforward task and expanded it by prodigious proportions. Kuan's first encounter with her genius (or was it madness?) was several summers ago, when he, Lili and two other team members were traveling from village to village to teach the believers about Jesus. Bikes were their mode of transportation, and with only two, they had to double up. Lili, it turned out, was quite an inspirational speaker on this tour, and many parents urged and pushed their teenaged sons and daughters to tag along and learn from her. Soon their gang of four became a band of twenty! Kuan had scolded her, "Stop recruiting so many people! We only have two bicycles!" Ever the logistics expert, Lili had coolly replied, "So make them walk!" Her insistence in support of the teens ended up benefiting them. Most of her new recruits were currently leading branch churches throughout the province.

And now it was the Bibles. It was so simple at first. She would go south to pick up a few for their church. She began by carrying two bags back with her on the train. In a matter of a couple of months that became ten checked pieces of luggage. Then, in less than a year after her Bible runs had begun, that had exploded into six hundred boxes per trip! At thirty-two kilograms a box, that translated into 48,000 Bibles being transported per run!

"Just be careful," Kuan repeated.

The two of them became aware of the sound of running feet outside. Both looked at each other, immediately on the alert. A head popped in the door. "Oh good, you're still here!" Relief! It was Sheng, a fellow co-leader with Kuan and Lili in their church. "I wanted to give you this before you left." Sheng, a plump, middle-aged, hearty-looking mother of two, handed Lili a plastic bag. Inside there was a bundle of dragon eye fruit, two plums, a steamed glutinous taro tart and a few fried pork buns. "Sister Pan sends her apologies, but she couldn't come herself because her baby's sick."

Lili was grateful. "Tell her thank you."

"How long will you be gone?" asked Sheng.

"If all goes well, should be the usual—six days for buses and trains, and a day and a half or so in Guangzhou packing and loading. I'll leave a message at the usual place when I get back to Shanxi."

"Okay. Let's pray before you go," said Kuan. The three knelt and bowed their heads.

Night had descended on the city of Guangzhou. In an outer suburb the odd notes could be heard drifting out of the karaoke bars, most of which were drunken and not that pleasant to the ear. But they weren't noticed in a particular apartment on Revolution Street. There the activity was buzzing with businesslike focus.

"What time is it?"

"Nearly midnight. Five to."

"Four more hours. Come on, guys, we've got to get a move on. There are too many Bibles still sitting around. Pass me more boxes, Mo."

Mo responded by tossing a few empty cartons across the room, one after the other. Lili caught the first two, but the third went astray and slammed against the wall, falling to the floor, flattening a tower of books in the process.

"Shh!" said Han in a loud whisper. "Careful, Mo! We don't want the neighbors to hear!"

"Sorry."

"Are you sure Brother Zhang will be on time, Han?" asked Lili.

Han sighed. "Yes." Lili was always so meticulous about everything.

"But we've never used him before."

"Mrs. Jiang is very reliable. She assures me her son-in-law's trustworthy. She says everything's arranged and I trust her. Anyway, you don't want to go back to the headache of using multiple taxis, do you? They always rip you off and charge you more than you negotiated for."

A grim expression came over Lili's face. He was right.

"And the truck drivers we hired are just as bad," Han was encouraged by her silent agreement, "complaining so loud in the streets—it's a wonder the whole city doesn't wake up! And then they refuse to drive down this street 'cause they think it's too narrow. We won't have to worry about that with Zhang. He'll come right to the door with his truck."

"You know the train leaves in nine hours."

"I know."

"We'll have to make several trips, and then we'll need a couple of hours to weigh the stuff, fill in the paper work and load the boxes onto the train."

"Yes."

"'Cause a lot of people are waiting at the other end."

"Lil, everything's arranged. I know people are counting on you and the Bibles making it. But please, please try not to worry so much."

Lili sighed. "All right. I'll try."

The clock struck 4 a.m. The last few boxes were being packed by Han and Mo. Lili glanced out into the street. Nothing was stirring. Where is he? . . . Calm down, girl. He'll be here. Give him a chance.

Han and Mo were taping up the last cartons. Lili paced the floor. Probably three trips at the most, she re-calculated, judging from Han's description of the vehicle and viewing the boxes piled up ready for transport. At the train station it will probably take about fifteen minutes to unload. That's with Mr. Kong's help . . . Good old Mr. Kong. Lili thought with some fondness of the benevolent stationmaster. Without his help we'd never be able to ship so many in one go.

She remembered the day she met him. It proved to be the end of the "check in luggage" phase, about nine months after she had first begun making the Bible runs. Lili's habit had been to borrow money from Han to purchase extra train tickets so she could check in greater numbers of boxes. The tickets themselves, however, were unused and unmarked, so Lili would then get refunds after the journey and return the money to Han. But a new problem had arisen: The clerk who handled the refunds for unused passenger tickets had begun to recognize her and became suspicious. Why is it you come so often for a refund? Can't you figure out the right number of tickets that you need?

This method is a ticking time bomb waiting to blow up in my face, Lili thought. We can't afford to actually pay for all these tickets, so I don't dare check them in this way anymore. What should I do instead though? She pondered her dilemma as she stood by her dozen boxes at the train station one trip.

A drop of water fell on her head. Two. Three. Then heavier, the rain began to pour. Oh, no! she thought. The Bibles! Don't let them get wet! Lili spotted cover a short distance away and carried the boxes over one by one. Thank goodness! she thought with relief as she finished, they're safe.

She stood there for a few moments, half leaning over the boxes, to recover from the exertion of moving them. Meanwhile a PSB officer lumbered over in her direction. From within his large heavy frame, which included several folds of fat in the midriff due to his extensive enjoyment of beer at the karaoke bars, came a booming, bellowing voice: "What's this? What's in all these boxes?"

Lili assumed a look of innocence, head bowed slightly with a touch of meekness yet eyes directed upwards, wide and wondering. She didn't seem to be the sort of girl who could lie.

"Young lady, did you hear me? What's in all these boxes?" The big officer had a clumsy habit of spitting when he talked. His saliva output, unfortunately, was profuse and it sprayed ungracefully in a trajectory that went far and wide. Some even landed on Lili's blouse.

She hid her revulsion and only just managed not to shrink back. "Oh," she answered in a quiet, gentle manner, "it's nothing special, Officer. You know, just some books."

"What kind of books?" He peered closer at Lili as he asked this.

The heavy smell of garlic filled her nose and the disgusting sight of unbrushed, tea stained teeth was almost more than she could bear. But she scrambled in her mind for an answer to his question. "They're medicine books, Officer."

"Medicine books? What kind of medicine?"

"Old and new medicine. The books talk about the old kind of medicine and the new kind."

Huh? he thought, drawing back. "I want to see it. Open it up." He tapped on the box with his baton as he said this.

Oh God, help! Lili was mortified. She opened the box, grabbed a book and opened it to the title page. "See, Officer? This is the 'Old Medicine' [4] and here is the 'New Medicine' section," she said, flipping to the latter title page.

The PSB officer scrutinized the two pages suspiciously. "Where'd you get these books from?" His eyes narrowed as he asked this.

"Well, they . . ."

"What's going on here, Officer? What seems to be the problem?" Both Lili and the PSB officer looked up in surprise at the interruption. Before them stood a wizened little man with graying hair and black rimmed glasses. It was the stationmaster, and he had been drawn by the loud voice of the PSB officer.

"This young woman here—" the big officer spat out, "look!—she has so many books! Medicine books!"

"Really?" The stationmaster looked over from the officer to Lili. "May I see one, Comrade?" he asked her with

---

[4] In Chinese characters the words "Old Testament" and "New Testament" are translated as "Old Covenant" and "New Covenant" respectively. The character for "covenant" reads similar to "medicine", and the two are sometimes confused.

hand outstretched.

Lili thought she would rather die. But she had no choice. She passed the book she was holding to the stationmaster. He adjusted his glasses lower on the bridge of his nose to peruse the title on the hard cover, but finding there was none he quickly flipped through the first few pages of the book until he found the contents. Lili, standing there as virtuously as she could, was a jumble of nerves inside while he was doing this. She felt sure this was the end!

"Oh!" the stationmaster said rather suddenly. "This is a good book! This is a very good book! Such a nice Comrade you are!" He smiled at the young lady in a friendly manner as he handed her back the volume.

"Oh, she's all right, then?" the PSB officer asked, backing off from his initial aggressiveness. He was mildly surprised at how well-disposed the stationmaster appeared to be towards the young lady. Maybe he was being hasty, and it would only make sense that the stationmaster should know what kind of stuff comes through here all the time.

"Oh, yes! There's no problem here!" said the little man.

"Well, all right, if you say so." Pacified, the PSB officer continued on his way.

"What denomination are you?" As soon as the PSB officer was out of hearing range, the stationmaster asked Lili the question.

"What?"

"What denomination are you?"

"Wh-, what do you mean?"

"Are you Baptist? Lutheran? Or . . . what are you?"

Lili was astonished. This man must be a Christian, she

thought, otherwise how would he know about denominations? She decided to go out on a limb. "Uh, are you a Christian, sir?"

"My name is Kong," he began. "My parents were Christians, but they were both killed during the Cultural Revolution. I, I know about Christianity but I-, I've not been faithful. I-, I couldn't after that." Kong said this last sentence almost distantly, like he was still reconciling the matter in his mind. Then, as if forgetting Lili was there, he practically mumbled the next couple of sentences. "I'd have been blacklisted. I wouldn't have been able to get a job . . . I was too scared to believe." He felt ashamed and his eyes began to water as the memories came back to him.

Lili was filled with compassion for the man. "Mr. Kong, I'm not from any denomination. I'm just a Christian. Me and my church, we believe in Jesus."

The gentleness in her voice struck a chord in Mr. Kong, and the tears began to stream from his eyes. For so many years his emotions had been suppressed. He hesitated in his mind at first, but then, "Ca-, can you please give me a Bible?"

"Sure," said Lili gladly, handing him the one in her hand.

That wasn't so hard after all. "And, and do you have any hymnals or songbooks?"

"Not here, but I can get you one. I'll bring it next time I come."

Mr. Kong's face brightened. "You come often? I can help you, you know. You just let me know when you are coming and I'll get everything on the train for you no problem." And Lili found her solution to the problem of the refund clerk!

"Han, it's five o'clock. Where is he?" Lili tried not to let the edge in her voice show too much. "You said he'd be here."

"You've asked me that ten times already, Lil. I-, I'm sorry. I don't know where he is."

Lili knew there was no point in grilling the man. But the truth was, she was worried sick! Her mind spun into a whirl. I've already booked the train tickets. I've already made arrangements with Mr. Kong. There are at least sixty brothers and sisters traveling from other provinces to Shanxi to meet my train so they can pick up their share of the Bibles. Everything's on such a tight schedule and now we're an hour off. What am I going to do, God?

"Where does he live?" asked Lili. "I'll go over and see what's happened."

Han scribbled the address down on a piece of paper. Lili ripped it out of his hand. It was no longer worry alone that she was feeling; anger too, at the situation, mounted within her. She ran out to the street to hail a cab.

In the taxi she let go the screams inside her head. Wake him up, God! How can you let this happen? Don't you know the schedule's hard enough to meet without this? There's already enough pressure as it is! I do *not* need this! Lili paused to wipe the tears that had trickled down her face. She took a deep breath. Calm set in somewhat.

Have I ever let you down? Have I ever been late?

That only served to set the storm within her raging again. Yeah, but look now—we're going on an hour and a half behind! What do you call that?!

The taxi arrived at Brother Zhang's house. Lili ran up and pounded on the front door. Mrs. Zhang answered. "Oh, I'm so sorry! He overslept but he's already on the way. He'll be there soon."

Lili flagged down another cab. The internal tirade

resumed on the return trip. We are late, God. There's no changing that! How can we make up the lost time? Everything's so messed up! If we get to the station late, the day shift workers will be starting which means more unwanted bodies milling around, and they could see our stuff which could make them suspicious. They'll probably want to check every box!

When Lili arrived back at Revolution Street Han, Mo and Brother Zhang were already loading the truck for the first trip to the train station. Lili didn't say a word to any of them as she joined them. She was still seething. You know, God, the fact is we're still late. So I don't care if you say you've never been late before. How could a miracle possibly make this work? We are *so* off schedule.

At 6:15 a.m. the truck drove in to the train station with the first lot. As Brother Zhang was parking in the usual unloading area, Mr. Kong ran out of his office. "Oh, don't stop here," he said. "Take it straight to the platform. We'll load them on to the train directly."

"Ho-, how can this be?" a bewildered Lili asked. "We still have to weigh them."

"It's okay," Mr. Kong replied. "We'll just take one box and weigh it. The boxes are all pretty much the same weight, right?"

"Uh, yeah, more or less."

"Then just take them to the platform."

Lili was absolutely stunned. She couldn't believe it. Her miracle had happened. Bypassing the weighing of every single box meant that the train station formalities were cut by more than half the time they usually took. Every single carton made it to the train on time.

Lili sat in the hard seat carriage, her arms and legs crossed, the final beads of sweat drying on her forehead. Okay, God, she said inside, you got me out of that one. All is forgiven. But why did you have to put me through all that stress in the first place? She closed her eyes and tried to be thankful that everything was back on schedule.

An old man beside her opened up a round tiered lunch box. It was not unlike a set of stacked stainless steel dimsum dishes, except each adjoining compartment had a pair of slots to facilitate a flexible handle for portability. The smell of steamed chicken feet, mushrooms, baby kale and steamed white rice wafted into the air. How can you think of eating at a time like this? Lili asked under her breath. A new anxiety arose, churning her stomach into knots: Despite the extrication from near catastrophe this morning, she was only half way through this delivery run. Who knew what else could happen en route between Guangzhou and Shanxi?

She got up and went for a walk down the aisle, sidestepping packs, bundles and feet here and there. She prayed that nothing else would go wrong on this trip. As she made the turn for the return journey up the aisle, she noticed a tall, husky PSB officer entering the car on the opposite end.

A feeling of apprehensiveness crept into her. Stay calm, she said to herself. Act normal. She walked in a composed manner back to her seat. Meanwhile, the PSB officer, who obviously took great pride in the power his uniform gave him, slowly swaggered his way through the train. He took a few steps, kicked at a bundle that interrupted his stride and verbally abused the idiot who left it there. He passed a few rows of seats, then checked in on a mahjong card game between some factory workers and enjoyed a raunchy joke with them. Continuing on his way, he nearly hit his head on a protruding bag in the overhead rack.

Huh? he thought. Why's this bag so big? He tugged at it to bring it down. The big bulk hardly budged. "Hey!" he yelled out in the car. "Whose bag is this?" Everyone in the car looked up. Recognizing the item in question, Lili shrank in her seat.

"Whose bag is this?" he repeated even louder and more adamantly. "Come and bring it down!"

Lili took a deep breath. God, please give me the wisdom to know what to say. Then she got up from her seat.

The officer spotted an attractive girl coming down the aisle. She had long, flowing hair that swayed behind her in one silky mass from side to side, in step with her stride. A lascivious grin momentarily crept on to the officer's face; his preference was for girls with long hair. He remembered his uniform though, and quickly checked himself. He immediately drew himself up to full height, chest out. He was, after all, the one in control here. "Is this bag yours?" he drilled Lili as soon as she stopped in front of him.

"Yes, Officer," she answered demurely.

The inquisitor couldn't help being softened somewhat by her feminine manner. "What do you have in there? Why's it so heavy?"

"They're just books, Officer."

The girl before him looked so wonderfully submissive standing there, hands meekly behind her back. "Books, eh? What kind of books?" He eyed her questioningly, his alter ego all the while telling him to keep a grip on himself.

"They're books on how to build a house, Officer. My commune is studying how to build houses." On tiptoe Lili reached up and endeavored to inch the huge canvas bag back and forth along the overhead rack, trying to work it down without a crash.

How pathetic, the officer thought, watching this pretty, lithe girl so feebly struggle with a few books. "Uh, it's all right," he said. "Don't bother. But maybe next time you should use a smaller bag."

"Yes, Officer." Lili kept her head down to hide her smile and tears of relief as she returned to her seat.

Their hands barely touched as they passed each other at the arrival gates of Taiyuan city train station, covertly relaying the cargo claim papers. "Same date, next month, I'll be here," Lili said under her breath, eyes focused on the newspaper stall across the way.

Her contact, from Heilongjiang province, tipped his head subtly, acknowledging receipt of the message. He continued his way to the warehouse, to meet the others who had Bibles to collect.

MINGYEN CHEN

2003.

"Grandpa!"

"Grandpa Chen is here! Grandpa Chen is here!"

"Grandpa Chen!"

The sound of happy shouts was like a rejuvenating tonic to Mingyen and Winnie after their trek. At 3,000 meters above sea level they had finally made it to the outskirts of the Lisu village. The faces of exuberant children were popping out from behind trees, houses, rocks and bushes, and they ran to form a receiving line for the man they had been taught to revere yet endearingly considered a part of the family. As the two visitors stepped onto the main street, the children sang a cheerful song of welcome, waving colorful ribbons and brightly painted paper fans. Mingyen laughed with delight as he passed each child, pausing here and there to pat one on the head. Their song at an end, he called out, "Meimei, you have grown so tall! Jian, you too! Yanze, have you been studying hard?" And they all blurted out their responses simultaneously, creating a joyful cacophony of noise.

"Pastor Chen! Welcome, welcome back!"

"Elder Song! It is good to see you again!"

The two men embraced and shook hands warmly at the end of the receiving line. A little girl, about seven years old, shyly walked up to Mingyen and presented him with a cherry red 'necklace' made out of cotton ribbon. Mingyen carefully held it up for all to see and smiled his appreciation and acceptance of the gift.

"Let me help you," said Elder Song, taking the necklace from Mingyen's fingers. Gently he placed it around Mingyen's neck. The puffy, flower-like 'pendant' came to rest across half of Mingyen's chest and looked as if it would be the most perfect bow to top a very large birthday present. The two men smiled at each other and shook hands again. "And Sister Winnie!" continued the elder, as he turned to face her. "We are so glad to see you too. Thank you for coming up to our home!" He reached over to shake her hand too.

Mingyen and Winnie were led by Elder Song to another, shorter line, a few steps away. This was comprised of the remaining village elders and officials. Upon completing the niceties of greeting and shaking each one by the hand, Winnie discreetly headed off to play with the children and chat with the women.

"So, how have things been around here, Yuman?" asked Mingyen, referring to his friend by his given name. The two men were shown to a table and chairs set up in the front room of the village hall. Along with the other elders and officials, they were served cups of tea.

"Oh, Mingyen!" he began excitedly, "Two families from across the valley made commitments to the Lord in the last few weeks! And Grandpa Shou—remember him? You prayed for him last time you were here. He is better now." Yuman slapped his thigh in jubilation here. "He has no more cough, and he said he has given up smoking because you told him it wasn't good for his lungs! He's even given me his pipe as proof!" And so he continued updating his guest on the community news, with one or two others adding details here and there.

"That is good news indeed," Mingyen replied. He

always marveled at the remarkable memories the tribal peoples had. They could recall every little thing he prayed for them, shared with them, even if he himself couldn't. But it wasn't just that they remembered. They were appreciative. They were truly thankful that you thought of them.

"And the new Bible school is nearly done!" Yuman went on eagerly. "Come! I will take you there to see it!" He jumped out of his chair and began walking energetically out of the hall and down the road. Yuman was a little, sprightly man whose ears protruded from under his grey hair, and it was hard to resist his enthusiasm.

Mingyen rose to follow him with a smile on his face and a silent chuckle. Winnie followed too, leaving a group of mothers with promises to return, as did a couple other village leaders.

As the two men and their entourage strolled through the village, Mingyen smiled greetings at small groups of old women along the way. They were squatting in pairs and trios outside huts or at the base of spruce trees, minding the new grandchild or inspecting some recently collected wild mushrooms. All dressed in their traditional Lisu clothing, and Mingyen thought with some sadness how the cultural diversity of the country was being eroded with the drive to modernize. These women were almost the last of their kind.

The village church was next up the road. As they passed what looked like a dilapidated stable, Mingyen was dismayed. The structure had been purpose-built as a place of worship, yet it was of such poor construction. There were visible gaps in the wooden planked walls, and the roof, consisting mostly of straw, wasn't fully completed because the locals hadn't been able to source anymore of the covering material. When it rained or snowed, therefore, it did so in the church as well! Mingyen was often petitioned by churches in the comparatively wealthy and better-connected coastal cities to raise funds to help them build newer, more modern assembly facilities. Yet how could he possibly put such requests ahead of the people here, who couldn't even finish covering their little shack? He shook his head to himself as he thought of this.

"The folks can hardly wait for your preaching tonight and tomorrow all day!" Yuman piped over his shoulder. "They've even prepared most of the meals already. The cooks don't want to miss a minute more than they have to!"

Mingyen recollected the last time he spoke inside the stable, nearly nine months ago. It wasn't much prettier than the exterior. There were no pews or chairs of any kind for the congregation. There was, however, a 'carpet' of pine needles to sit on. Everyone sat jam-packed on the ground, and he could very well imagine how uncomfortable it was—especially for the elderly. Three hours was the shortest service they ever had, and you would be cramped up all that time with no room to readjust your position. Aiyah! What if you had arthritis? Mingyen felt the aches in his own bones.

"Well, what do you think?" asked an extremely pleased Yuman. He raised his arms to present the Bible school. Indisputably it was of sounder construction than the church they had just passed. There were no gaps between the evenly cut timber boards. The doors and windows had not yet been installed though. They would be made of wood too, shutters to cover the square openings cut out of the wall.

"It's really coming together, isn't it?" answered a smiling Mingyen as he drew closer to the building. He fingered the outer wall, then looked through the window to the interior.

"Come inside," said Yuman as he stepped through the door.

Mingyen stepped into the dim corridor. The smell of timber permeated the place and the pungency was particularly noticeable with a deep intake of breath. He didn't mind, however, as it was always preferable to him to inhale the fragrance of nature than the pollution discharged from some forms of technology. Then, spying several stacked tables in the first room, he made his way over to inspect them. He knocked on the first table top, checking its solidity and sound. As he finished he saw his friend looking at him expectantly. "It's good."

The elder beamed. "The benches are being made now."

Mingyen continued to walk around inside, touching the walls here and there, feeling the coarse grain of the timber. It was coated with the perennial dust of construction, and he rubbed his hands together to loosen it off. As he inspected the hall and remaining classrooms, there was a feeling of immense satisfaction within him at seeing a project come to fruition. At the same time though, there was also a slight feeling of melancholy, for the inspiration of this particular project was the tragic death of his friend, Li. A former co-worker with Mingyen, Li was a teacher and evangelist of Lisu ethnicity. He used to live across the valley on the other side, a five day journey on foot to the very place Mingyen now stood. The snowfalls that winter were heavy, like any other year, but Li was determined that nothing should hinder the training of Christian leaders, especially when there was so much need for them. He set out on the fateful trip. He may or may not have slipped on the icy trails before he froze to death, but regardless, it was a lamentable discovery for his family who found his body in the subsequent spring.

It was an unnecessary way to die, thought Mingyen. The man only wanted to teach the Bible. If there had been a seminary here already, he wouldn't have had to come. The teacher would be resident.

"You're thinking of Li, aren't you?" asked Yuman softly. He had walked over to stand by his friend.

Mingyen nodded his head.

"We miss him too."

"How are his father and brother? Have you seen them lately?"

"Elder Li is well. I saw him last month. His son is still preaching too."

Mingyen nodded again and proceeded to make his way back outside. Li's death had impacted him tremendously; his resolve to serve God had intensified despite his own advancing years. The need was too great up in these mountains. He would keep working to help these minorities have what they needed to live life to the fullest.

The sun emerged from behind a cloud. Mingyen lifted his face upwards to feel the rays of its warmth. As he turned to address Yuman, he noticed a shrunken man tottering up to them with the aid of a stick. He must be at least ninety, Mingyen figured. "Old Uncle!" he called out warmly in greeting. "How are you?"

"Very well, Pastor Chen. Very well." Old Uncle took off his cap to wipe his forehead, the activity of his longer-than-usual walk having winded him somewhat.

"Here," said Mingyen, "sit down." He moved to help Old Uncle settle himself on a nearby rock. Yuman offered an arm of support too.

"Thank you. Thank you."

"Don't mention it," said Mingyen.

Old Uncle replaced his cap and let out a long breath, as if he had recovered himself.

Mingyen crouched down to talk to Old Uncle face to

face. "Now, what do you mean by coming all this way?" he asked merrily.

"To see you!"

"Me? Why didn't you just wait until tonight? Or tomorrow? You know I'm here for a couple of days."

"I didn't want to forget," replied Old Uncle.

"Forget what?" Mingyen's curiosity was aroused now. But he maintained his happy manner with the long-lived fellow.

"Aiyah! My memory is not so good now," Old Uncle began. "I got to do things while I can."

Mingyen and Yuman smiled at each other, bemused.

"I want to ask you," Old Uncle smacked his lips here, "when can we restore the graves of Missionaries Bao, Luo and Rong?"

"Ah," said Mingyen. Old Uncle was speaking of the British and American missionaries who had lived and evangelized in this area in the 1930s and '40s, long before the Liberation. The two British missionaries had died in Yunnan and were laid to rest here, as was the American family's six-month-old baby boy. The three graves, however, had been destroyed during the Cultural Revolution and were currently in ruins.

"I knew them all," Old Uncle went on. "Missionary Rong was particularly special to me. She never lost her patience with me, no matter how many questions I asked."

They never forget, thought Mingyen again. And now they wanted to honor those who had left their home countries so distant to come and think of them. The request touched him, stirred him profoundly. Tears almost came to his eyes.

Yuman interrupted Mingyen's thoughts. "I'm sorry Pastor. I was going to talk to you about that later." The elder's eyes moved from Mingyen to Old Uncle, then back to Mingyen. He was concerned they were making a mess of this request and he felt half-apologetic towards their guest. "You see, . . ."

Mingyen raised his hand to his friend to stop. No apology was necessary. "It is noble, what you are asking to do," he said. "We will do what we can to help you accomplish this."

"I can't do this."

"Yes you can."

"But it's swinging!"

"Of course it is. It's a suspension bridge."

Winnie looked out at the rope, cable and wood-slatted connection to the other side. She and Mingyen had finished two days of meetings in the first Lisu village, and now the way to the next destination involved traversing this span. Far below, she could hear the powerful rapids of the Lanchang River as they pummeled their way through the gorge. She looked back at the monument that had been erected by the locals, naming the bridge and paying tribute to the one who had made this crossing possible—Mingyen Chen. "Is it safe?"

"Safer than what used to be here," replied the one.

"Are you sure?"

Mingyen nodded his head patiently. "Here. Give me your hand." He was standing part way on the bridge already. Seeing she still hesitated, he said, "Remember how you felt when I first asked you to do a little bit of Bible teaching?"

Winnie nodded. She had insisted she couldn't do it yet; she wasn't ready.

"Well, look what happened yesterday. You did very

well!" he encouraged her. "The people really responded to you."

"Yeah, but teaching isn't the same as crossing this thing!" she nearly shrieked.

The mentor remained patient with his protégé. "Have I ever asked you to do something you couldn't?"

Regretfully Winnie shook her head.

"Come then." He reached out his hand to her again.

Winnie gingerly tried to step out on the wobbly bridge again. She clenched Mingyen's hand tightly with one hand while grasping the rope with the other. "So what used to be here, and what makes this better?" she asked in her nervousness.

"Don't look down. Just look at me." He turned and began to lead her across.

The bridge was only wide enough for one person. Winnie followed as closely as she could without stepping on Mingyen's heels, her eyes glued to his every step. Eventually they made it across.

Winnie wanted to hug the solid ground. She exercised some self-control though and contented herself with a huge sigh of relief. She tipped her baseball cap back, then took off her backpack, sat down on a rock and grabbed her bottle of water. "Well?" she said, after she had a sip and replaced the bottle.

"Well, what?"

"Well, what used to be here and why's this better?"

Mingyen sighed. She was always asking why. What ever happened to the good old days, when life was simpler and people didn't feel the constant need for information? He resigned himself, however, to the difference between their generations. This time though, she was forcing him to remember, and this was something he preferred not to think of. And yet, here he was. How could he not? He took off his backpack too and sat down. "There used to be a manual cable and pulley system here."

Ever the city girl, Winnie asked, "What's that?"

"Imagine a swing with a wooden seat. Instead of a tree, it's attached to a cable that runs across to the other side. You sit in the swing, which slides along when you pull the cable." Mingyen kept the explanation short and sweet, deducing she probably wouldn't care for a full mechanical description.

"Pull?" asked Winnie skeptically. "With your hands?"

How else? Mingyen replied in his head. But still, with ever so much calm forbearance, "Yes."

"Oh." Winnie looked back at the bridge and tried to picture what used to be there. "So what—did the old system break?"

"You could say that." Mingyen decided he wasn't going to explain anything more. It was too hurtful to him. His good friend's nephew had accidentally fallen off the old cable and pulley, and his body was never found. Afterwards Mingyen had the rusted and ill-maintained contraption taken down and the new bridge installed in its place. It was the least he could do—Ho's nephew only wanted to help build up the churches in the area and died trying to get there. It was a disastrous accident, fatal. These people aren't criminals, God! he questioned again. They are not evil. They only want to serve you! Why do you let things like this happen?

Winnie noticed that Pastor Chen had gone more quiet than usual. She surmised there was something personal in the building of the bridge, but she didn't pursue the matter any further. She sat there, respectfully silent. In her way she understood: Pastor Chen just wanted to make it easier for the Christian workers up here to do what they had to do. "So, Pastor," she began after a couple of minutes, "were you pleased with the meetings we just had?" She sensed a change of subject was probably in order.

"If people are encouraged to know and love God more, that is all that matters." Mingyen took his water out and had a sip. "But there is still much to be done there, I'm afraid."

"Their church is packed," said Winnie.

"It sure is. They won't be able to fit in there much longer."

"Are you planning to build another church?"

"We're always planning to build another church," replied Mingyen as he prepared to resume walking. "But, as ever, we need to raise the funds. I think for Elder Song and his village though, they have other equally pressing matters to consider."

"You mean the logging restrictions."

"Yes." Mingyen sighed as he said this. New policies by the government had been implemented a few years ago. They had mounted immense pressure on the ethnic minorities who traditionally lived off the land in these mountains. With growing urgency, it was vital they find new ways to earn their livelihoods, particularly as the government subsidies were running out. Employment, however, was not the only issue. The high elevation these communities subsisted at was a logistical nightmare for the efficient import and export of any goods and supplies to and from the area. It was downright expensive, and the means of transporting goods and supplies was limited to human labor and donkeys. At the end of the day the start-up costs of a new venture were often insurmountable.

Mingyen knew he could not ignore the reality: There remained so much need. It was all very well to talk about building a high speed train between Shanghai and Beijing, constructing the world's largest hydroelectric project in the Three Gorges, and hosting the Olympic Games and World Expo. But what about the rest of the country? Couldn't they have enough to live on?

SAIMEN LIANG

1980. Saimen stared out at the fields as his train rumbled along the tracks in a constant, repetitive rhythm. He fiddled absently with the window's latch in time with the beat as one by one he watched the wheat fields pass by. Up, down, all around, the carriage was full to capacity—seats were occupied, overhead racks stuffed to the rim with luggage, and hats and loose bags hung from every available hook. A three-year-old boy screamed across the aisle from Saimen, petulant that he was losing his toy; a rooster crowed somewhere in the rear; a roar of triumph arose from the men entrenched in their poker game a few aisles up; and *snap!*—every now and then, interspersed in the hum of chatter, one could hear the sound of roasted melon seeds being cracked open and flicked to the floor. Saimen was glad for the relative peace and quiet in his four-seat compartment. He scanned the elderly couple across from him, both of whom had fallen asleep, and the young man beside him (perhaps a university student?) thoroughly engrossed in his book. Only a few more hours and he'd be home—well, barring a bus ride and a three hour hike up the mountain to his house.

What would home be like now? It'd been six years since he'd seen Kaiyang county. The mother across the aisle opened a parcel and the little boy scrambled onto her hungrily. Steamed buns! Yanyan makes delicious steamed buns—Saimen's mouth watered at the thought of eating them again.

Yanyan was a good wife, really. It couldn't have been very easy for her all these years. When Saimen had been sent to prison she had been left with their six-month-old son. He knew she and baby Ren would have been stigmatized, even ostracized because of him. And she didn't know Jesus when he was arrested! How would she cope? But God works in mysterious ways. Yanyan finally became a believer a year into Saimen's labor camp tenure, when she was overwhelmed by the love and care shown to her and Ren by her husband's church members. What a relief! When she visited Saimen next, they were both so encouraged to learn that they each had "brothers and sisters" looking out for them. God thought of everything!

Across the aisle the little boy chomped away greedily on his bun, his pudgy, round cheeks bulging with every chew. I never saw Ren at that age—was he like this? Saimen winced a bit as some self-reproach hit him. But it's not as if he had had a choice about going to prison. Still . . . Ren would be seven now, in school. Hopefully he'll be able to study longer than I did, thought Saimen as he looked over at the student, maybe even go to university like this guy.

Saimen remembered his schooling, brief though those four years were: They were hard times. It had started with so much promise and excitement too—the new communes, the dawn of the Great Leap Forward movement! But then there was the great famine, and so many villagers starved. He *himself* had almost perished! His father, though, died. Saimen felt some pain again inside. It was, in fact, a very sad time for many people. Death had become so commonplace, so regular an event. And then he had had to stop studying. He was only twelve, but Ma could no longer afford to pay for school.

The young man beside Saimen closed his book on a

finger and gazed ahead, as if the better comprehension of a perplexing concept could be found in the cluster of people in view.

"That looks like a serious book," said Saimen. He stopped playing with the window latch. "What is it?"

"Huh?" The student turned his head to see who was interrupting his thoughts. "Oh, uh, just some biology."

"Biology, hm? So where d'you study?"

"Nowhere at the moment, but I'm hoping to again soon."

"Oh? What happened?" His interest perked, Saimen sat up in his seat.

"I was at Pingdingshan Normal College in 1970," the student began to explain, "but then our whole class got sent to the national farms. It's taken me and my family several years to get my paperwork right just so I can return to the city."

"That where you goin' now?"

"Yeah. I'm finally on my way back home." The student sat back and brushed his fingers through his thick mass of hair as he said this. "Hopefully I can re-enroll quickly and then, with a bit of hard work, catch up with the program."

"What program?"

"Medicine. I want to be a doctor."

"That's a good thing, to work at a job that can help people."

"Yeah. But I fear I might not make it. I've lost so much time and I'm so far behind. It'll be hard to catch up."

"But don't they start new programs every semester? So what if you start a few months later?"

"It's just, you know," the student looked down on the floor here, ashamed to meet Saimen's eyes, "I'll be older than new students starting out. They're coming straight out of high school and I'm coming back from the farm. What if I can't keep up? Then I'd lose face."

"Why let that bother you?" said Saimen encouragingly. "You know, when you care too much about people's opinions, it can stop you from doing what you have to do. Sometimes you have to not care so much. Besides, there will be others like you returning from national farms. I'm sure there will be some your own age."

"You think so? Really?"

"I do."

The young man beamed at the prospect. "Yeah, maybe you're right. I guess things *are* getting better these days. Wouldn't you agree?" Then, with renewed eagerness, he opened his book again.

Yes, thought Saimen, and hopefully it will be better for Ren too.

Saimen stepped into his house. He put his pack down on the floor, walked over to the table and poured himself a cup of tea from the thermos. He sat down as he sipped, perusing the place, trying to spot the changes since he'd seen it last. Instantly he spotted the single light bulb on a wire strung across the room—electricity!—that's new. A ball, a few kiddie trinkets, children's clothes hung in the corner, signs of the addition to the household he'd been forced to leave behind. The mandatory Mao paraphernalia of the early 1970s—posters, badges, books—was no longer visible on the shelf—thank God!

It was mid-afternoon and the neighborhood was still. Guess everyone's still at market and school, Saimen thought. He poured himself some more tea and decided he'd take the few moments of peace and quiet to read the Bible—that is, what few bits of it that they had. Now where did Yanyan keep it these days? He rummaged through the items on the shelf, dug through the rice barrel, and eventually managed to find a part of Matthew in the folds of a pile of his mother's clothes. Carefully he took out the three pages, tenderly placed them on the table and began to read, "Then Jesus said to his disciples, 'If anyone would come after me, he must deny himself and take up his cross and follow me. For whoever wants to save his life will lose it, but whoever loses his life for me will find it . . .'" This is what it costs, Saimen thought, this is what is required, then so be it. He closed his eyes and meditated deeper on the words. It was hard, yes, to be apart from the family, but it's for Jesus. Jesus never said it'd be easy; he just said he'd be with us . . .

Suddenly there was a gleeful burst through the door and Saimen's reflections were interrupted. Lost in his thoughts, he hadn't heard the patter of little feet running towards the house. Saimen found himself face to face with a little boy.

The boy had a small stubby nose, ruddy cheeks and hair that was disheveled in a manner similar to his father's, although the child himself was unaware of it. He stood there upright, legs shoulder-width apart with arms by his side, seemingly a lad who knew his place. The boy was obviously surprised at the sight of an intruder yet he remained firm, almost defiant. He was not afraid to confront the stranger. "Who are you?" he demanded, "and what are you doing in my house?"

"Ren!" The sight of his son moved Saimen. He could see the physical similarities between the boy and himself. He saw, too, the stout-hearted nature of the child's character. It was amazing to him how strong the emotional pull of flesh and blood could be. He knew he didn't know Ren when he last saw him as an infant in his mother's arms; he also hadn't seen the boy in any of his early formative years. Yet in this moment Saimen knew that he had not just missed his son all these years; he loved him. He loved him deeply. "Ren!" he repeated his boy's name again. "Hi! It's me—your father!"

"Who?" The little boy cocked his head to the side as he said this.

"Your father!"

"My father isn't here." Ren stamped his foot in a determined manner, as if to emphasize his point. "He's far away in prison."

"Tha-, that's not-. Not anymore, Ren," Saimen stammered. The bold and daring resistance in the boy's tone and manner was somewhat of a surprise to him. Is this how I sound to those in authority? he asked himself. For the first time Saimen realized how difficult it could be to have someone like himself working against himself. "I-, I was in prison, but now I'm home."

"No! You are not my father! He is not here! Get out of my house! Get out!" Ren shouted as he ran towards his father, hitting him with his childish fists, trying to chase him out of the house.

Hearing her son, Yanyan ran quickly to the house to see what was wrong. "Saimen!"

Saimen lay awake in bed that night. Beside him, in her sleep, Yanyan snuggled up closer to his side. She was a strong mother. Thank God for that! Saimen had been impressed by Yanyan's soothing of the little boy, her ability to calm and reassure him, to help him accept and welcome his father. But the heartache, the agony of his son not recognizing him—it was too much. For a second he felt as if he couldn't breathe. He struggled in his effort to take a normal deep breath. But somehow he managed to find oxygen again. He gently disengaged himself from his wife and rolled over on his side.

I should have taken better care of both of them, he reproached himself. I shouldn't have just brushed them aside like they didn't matter. Saimen thought back to the days when Yanyan was pregnant, in 1973.

"Is there a meeting again?" asked his wife. She was still seated at the dinner table, her left hand slowly feeling her large tummy. The baby would be due in a month.

"Yup," replied Saimen, beginning to tie up his shoes. "Three, in fact."

"Why do you have to go so often? Why can't you just stay home and spend some time with me?" She twiddled the chopsticks in her right hand as she asked this.

"It's only a few times a week, Yan. Why don't you come with me if you want me there with you? God's really marvelous at these meetings."

"Look at me, Saimen," she said, pointing to her belly. "I'm hardly in a condition to hike three hours each way up and down our mountain, let alone to who knows where else you tramp off to in the dark of night . . . Come on. Stay home. Our baby will be here soon and our life will change. Let's enjoy these final moments alone together."

"This is my work, Yan. I've got to go."

"Your work is building the dam. You've just come back from a whole day there. This church stuff is, is . . . It'll get you into trouble. It'll get us all into trouble!"

Saimen looked up from his shoes, surprised by the tension he heard in his wife's voice. "You don't understand," he said. She couldn't, he thought sadly, not unless she became a believer herself.

"I understand that you're taking a huge risk. The authorities have warned you, Saimen. If they find out you're still going to these meetings—" She stopped mid-sentence. Calm down, she told herself, putting the chopsticks aside and opening her hands slowly. Don't get overly excited; otherwise he won't listen to you. She took a deep breath. Then, "Saimen, they like you. The county secretary loves you, even like a son. You have such a promising future with the party. Why ruin it with such risky involvement in the church?"

"Yan, I'm going. God is my life. Understand? You can't talk me out of it." With that, he stepped out of the door and was gone.

Yanyan was left alone at the table, heartbroken. Her lower lip trembled as she tried to fight back the tears. This wasn't how she expected her husband to turn out. Despite her best efforts she had failed. She had failed to dissuade him from his chosen career in the church. She had failed to convince him to lead a more 'normal life' for the safety of their family. Instead, Saimen's zeal for God and the church had grown to an unfathomable depth, and the harshness of the times had only served to seal his commitment. It was all or nothing these days—and the way he was going, it looked like they were going to end up with nothing.

How could I have stopped loving God or even loved him less? Saimen asked himself again, lying there in the dark. How could I just not care anymore? It was impossible. Furthermore, God called me to be a fisher of men. I couldn't just ignore that; it'd be like disobeying a command. But then he was arrested and sentenced . . .

Saimen drifted into a kind of half-sleep . . . They hit me . . . My son hit me . . . They hit him . . . He wanted me out of the house . . . No one wanted him around . . . My own son rejected me . . . denied me . . . despair . . . deep . . . crushing . . . despair . . . Visions flashed of a young man riding in the back of an army truck, on the way to a denunciation meeting. Also along for the ride, about twenty elderly believers. The atmosphere was tense, apprehensive; there was fear, even dread, for all had seen and heard what happened at such assemblies. Their eyes, the elders' eyes spoke what their mouths did not—worry for themselves, yes, but also for this young man of twenty-three years beside them. He was only an up-and-comer in the church, not an experienced veteran—how would he be able to withstand the struggle? Yet simultaneously there seemed to be encouragement: "Stand firm. Don't be afraid, young one," all the captive hands joined together seemed to say, gripping his hands so tightly, so very, very tightly. In his youth and naiveté, Saimen then and there determined that *nothing* would ever make him deny his faith. Then came the reality and the despair: Five hundred accusers pointing their fingers at him, jeering, condemning, spitting, stomping on him . . . including all but two of the elders who rode in the truck with him . . . and this is what it costs . . .

BANG! The front door was kicked open in the middle of the night. Saimen and Yanyan bolted straight up out of bed. Ren began crying, and Grandma Liang hurried to comfort him across the room. It was several months since Saimen had returned home.

"W-What is it, Saimen?" Yanyan trembled.

"PSB!" a voice boomed from the front room. Saimen ran into the room. There he found four PSB officers ransacking the entire place, mindlessly turning and tossing items around, heedless of where or how they landed, stuffing their bags with whatever objects appealed.

"What are you doing?" Saimen asked. His voice sounded reasonable but inside he was seething. How could they just treat people's property like that? It took all his self control not to react with violence.

"We're here to search for anything subversive to the government! Now, get out of our way!" the officer replied.

"But what is subversive about that umbrella?"

"Shut up and move away if you don't want any trouble!"

Two more officers moved into the other rooms of the house, turning bed covers over, flinging clothes over their shoulders, pillaging papers and books.

"That's my ball!" Ren shrieked, as he saw an officer drop it into his bag. Grandma Liang clasped the boy firmly in her arms, simultaneously trying to pacify and protect him.

In little more than fifteen minutes they were gone. The house was left an utter mess.

Ren sobbed hysterically in the arms of Grandma Liang, who sighed resignedly. A single tear rolled down Yanyan's cheek. And Saimen, resolute, stared straight ahead. Yet another cost.

"You know there's no other way."

"I know."

"It means I won't be around much."

"Yeah."

"That's six times now this year that our house has been raided."

"Mm."

"In some ways it's even safer for you, Ren and Ma."

"Yeah."

Saimen and Yanyan were sitting at the table. Grandma

Liang had taken Ren out for an after dinner walk.

"If I stay I make it easier for them to watch me, but if I go I can try to shake them. But the most important thing is that the churches need encouragement and teaching. I've got to go anyway."

"You're right."

Husband and wife both sat there, silent for a few moments, each lost in their own thoughts. Then Yanyan stifled a laugh.

"What? What is it?"

"Oh, nothing."

"No, tell me Yan. What're you laughing at?"

"I was jus—nah!" Her hand brushed the air in one wide sweep.

"C'mon."

Wife looked at husband for a moment. Okay, she thought. "I was just remembering, you know, remembering when I found out I was going to be married—that they'd actually found a match for me—I was so excited because I'd have a husband, and he'd be a successful member of the party. And then, and then maybe I could be a mother and we could have a family. Such girlish dreams!" Yanyan giggled.

Saimen chuckled along with her. "I was excited too! I was so happy that someone would even want to marry me!"

"Your village elder, the guy who first came to tell Pa and Mama about you—what was his name again?—oh yeah! Old Uncle Pao—he had such a big nose and was so loud! He scared me!"

"Well, *your* village elder didn't look much better!" Husband and wife laughed over the memories of their first meeting. "Look, Yan, we *are* a family, and God is our Father. He'll take care of us whether we're together or apart. He wouldn't put this urge in my heart, this desperation to go help the churches without providing for you, Ren and Ma. I don't know how he'll do it but somehow everything will work out all right. We've got to believe that, okay?"

Yanyan sighed. "Then so be it."

I made an interesting discovery one day: My mother has more children than my siblings and me. She also has spiritual children. And she's just as proud of them as she is of us.

We were sitting in our home in Hong Kong at the dinner table when she asked, "So, how was your day?"

"Pretty good," I replied.

"What happened?"

"Well, I met an interesting candidate for pastor of our church."

"Tell me about him."

"Well, he's from the Mainland, has a great heart for Chinese people, and I'd love to support him. Only problem is, I'm not sure the church elders will think his Cantonese is good enough. You know how particular Hong Kong people are about their language."

"Hm . . ." she reflected, "from the Mainland, you say? Where?"

"Shanghai."

"Shanghai?" A native of the city, Ma's interest perked up doubly. "What's his name? What does he look like?"

"Maaa," I said, "just because he's from Shanghai doesn't mean you know him. Lots of people come from there."

"I know, but just humor an old lady. Tell me anyway."

What could I do? I thought with a sigh. So I gave her

a description and concluded with his name. "Chen. Mingyen Chen. There. Satisfied?"

"Hm . . ." she reflected again, "Chen . . . Mingyen . . . Chen . . . I know him! I do! Met him when he was a boy! He was in my Sunday School class!"

LILI TANG

1972. Yangzi sat on the steps alone. She was in no mood to play with her fellow students today. If she had had her way she'd have stayed at home. But Mama had insisted. In one corner of the school yard she couldn't help but notice a bunch of girls huddled together. They're all around Yulin. Again. Wonder why this time? She's always such a show-off, Yangzi said to herself.

"Hey, Yangzi! What's up?" Lili trudged up to her classmate and plopped down beside her. It was an overcast day and the two eleven-year-olds were on their lunch break.

"Oh, hi Lili," replied a gloomy Yangzi.

Lili raised her eyebrows. This wasn't chatty, spunky Yangzi. "What's wrong with you today? Why are you all by yourself?"

"Just feel like it."

"Oh . . . Want to play hopscotch?"

"Nah."

"What about Big 2?" Lili pulled out her deck of cards as she asked this.

"Nah."

Lili peered closer at her friend. "Hey, you've been crying!"

"No I haven't."

"Your eyes are red."

"No they aren't."

"Okay. Whatever you say. But they look red to me."

Both girls sat and watched the action in the yard. Most

of the boys were involved in the soccer match that took up most of the field; those that weren't stood on the sidelines shouting strategic tips to their friends, cheering them on or practicing ball handling drills. Pockets of girls stood or walked around the field, some watching the boys, others playing less athletic games, still others engrossed in their own conversations. The largest group of girls, however, surrounded Yulin. "What's Yulin got today?" asked Yangzi, trying to divert the attention from herself. "Why's the crowd around her?"

"Some new hair ribbons. I don't know what the big deal is. They're just pink," Lili replied. "I'm surprised her mom actually lets her wear them. My mom won't let me wear mine anymore."

"Me too."

Lili sighed. "I guess it's because her dad's an important cadre and he just came back from Beijing."

"Your father's a cadre."

"But he doesn't go to Beijing."

The conversation lapsed again.

"What's up, Yangzi?" Lili repeated. "You're so quiet today."

Yangzi studied the face of her friend. "Lili," she lowered her voice, "can you keep a secret?"

Lili nodded, her eyes widening.

Maintaining the low voice, Yangzi said, "My daddy died yesterday."

Lili was horrified. "What? How? Oh . . ."

Yangzi looked around to make sure no one was within hearing. "Red Guards came to our village yesterday. They came to our house."

Lili shuddered as she pictured the horde of Red Guards rolling up to Yangzi's house with their banging drums and clanging cymbals.

"Papa made a mistake. He wore his Mao badge on the right of his jacket instead of the left. They said Papa must have something to hide from Chairman Mao because he wouldn't let the Chairman see his heart.[5]" Yangzi gulped here to stifle a sob that wanted to come out. "And then they dragged him into our house, and then they saw we didn't have a portrait of Chairman Mao on our wall—but Mama and Auntie were moving some furniture around yesterday and something fell and ripped our poster, so they had to take it down and get a new one. And then they said Papa didn't love Chairman Mao and then they just started kicking and kicking him . . ." Yangzi started to cry again.

Lili didn't know what to say.

Lili tossed and turned in her bed. The drums boomed like thunder, every beat resounding within her frail body. The gongs and cymbals rang in her ears, reverberating unceasingly. They're here! They're here! A six-year-old Lili bawled. She clung with all her might to Mommy and Daddy's hands in mortal fear. She tried to pull them back, to stop them from opening the door. Don't let them in! Don't let them in! Then they were in the house. Shouting. So much shouting. Lili wailed . . .

"Wake up! Lili, wake up!"

Lili woke with a start. "Mama!"

It was a dream. A bad one. Except it was real. It was real because it had happened.

---

[5] During the Cultural Revolution devotion to Chairman Mao was shown by wearing the badge on the left side of the chest so that Mao's profile would be facing the person's heart.

"*Ge*[6] Min."

"Yeah, Lil."

"Are you going again?"

"Yeah. I have to."

"I wish you didn't."

"Me too. But if I don't go it won't look right, and then it could mean trouble for Pa and the family."

Lili was talking to her big brother. Min was eight years older than her.

"Yangzi's dad was killed by them."

"I heard."

"Why didn't you tell me?"

"Lil, it's horrible-, what they do. You just try and forget it." Min checked himself in the mirror, to make sure his Mao badge was straight.

"*Ge* Min," Lili paused slightly, "do you hit people? Grandpa said we should never hit people."

"I know. And no, I don't hit people."

Lili watched as Min tied the red band around his upper arm.

"But they all do, don't they? It seems like it anyway . . ."

"Look, Lil, I hate what they do as much as you and Ma and Pa, but if I don't even pretend to like it, they'll attack us. Get it?"

"So is, is that what you do—pretend?"

"Yeah. But don't tell anyone."

"No."

Min began to tie up his shoes.

"*Ge*, I had a bad dream last night."

"Mm."

"It was about that time a few years ago, when you tried to plant those flowers in the front window. Remember?"

---

[6] Mandarin for "elder brother".

"Mm-hm."

"And then the Red Guards came to our house and dug them out. Remember?

"Mm."

"Papa was very brave, wasn't he? He handled them well."

"Yeah."

"I hate those drums and gongs. I can't get them out of my head."

"Try to think happier thoughts, okay, sis? Think about good things instead. Like, think about how you like going to the flour mill after school to see Ma, how you have fun helping her grind the wheat and make the noodles."

"Yeah . . ." Lili became somewhat starry-eyed as she reflected on this. She was determined that anything Ma could do, she would learn to do. "But you know what she told me last week?"

"What?"

"She said she used to have to push the grinding wheel herself—she had no donkey like she does now!"

"Yeah, I remember that."

"You do?"

"Of course. I used to go to the flour mill too, like you. Those days were hard—no donkey and no food. I remember being hungry all the time. I would cry till I was hoarse but all they'd give me was water. My stomach was bloated out to here, so Grandma always tells me." Min was holding his hands way out in front of his stomach. "Yup, things are definitely better for Ma these days. Gotta go now, sis. See you later." Min left the house.

"Good morning class. Today we are going to talk about

superstition."

Not again! thought Lili as she sat at her desk. The topic of superstition was running deep into its second week at the newly reopened school, having been closed since 1966, the beginning of the Cultural Revolution.

"Superstition is old-fashioned," said Miss Zhou, the teacher, beginning in her usual, predictable way. "It's the way of the imperialists and we should not follow it. The imperialists brought some of the worst superstition into China many years ago, misleading and corrupting many people. But now the People's Liberation Army has defeated the imperialists! So we must do away with these old ways and destroy the wrong thinking!"

The class sat there motionless.

"One of their superstitions is to believe in a man called Jesus. This is wrong! There is no power in Jesus! There is no god in Jesus! Anyone who tells you otherwise must not be trusted. They're trying to deceive you . . ."

Who *is* this Jesus anyway? Lili asked herself. What's so special about him that she keeps harping on about him?

"These people who believe in Jesus, they are called Christians," the teacher continued.

Christians? Immediately Lili was alert.

"They are following something evil, something bad. We must do away with the Christians!" Miss Zhou proclaimed this adamantly, raising her right fist in the air.

How can she say that?! Mama is a Christian!

"The Christians must be destroyed!"

If she says that, then she's saying Mama must be destroyed too, isn't she? But Mama's so good—everyone in our village says so. How can the school say this? In her mind Lili chewed on these questions. But she could find no satisfactory answers. She decided to talk to her mother.

"Mama, you know what we're talking about at school these days?"

"What?"

"Superstition."

"Is that so." Mother sat at the table sewing a new shirt, while daughter stood on the other side cutting out a pattern that had been marked out for her.

"Yeah. But they keep going on about Jesus. Isn't that your God?"

"Yes, Lili." Perfect equanimity was maintained by the mother.

"They talk about him the most, you know. They say he's bad and that people who believe in him are bad. But how can he be bad? You're so good, Mama. You wouldn't believe in something bad, right?"

"Mm."

"Mama, I'm scared," the daughter went on, "What if they're trying to destroy Jesus? That means you might get in trouble too. What should we do?"

Mrs. Tang put down her sewing, reached across the table and cupped her daughter's chin in her hand. "Don't be afraid, Lili. Jesus can never be destroyed. He will never be defeated because he lives in my heart."

"But, but what if they, uh, come and punish you, like, make you wear a dunce cap and parade you through the streets?"

"It will be okay."

"It might be okay for you, but it's not okay for us!"

"Lili, you don't need to be afraid."

Mrs. Tang knew her daughter. She knew Lili would not rest until she had some answers.

"Come with me, Lili," she said one day.

"Where are we going?"

"Don't ask questions. Just get your jacket and let's go."

Mother and daughter stepped out into the night. The late autumn evenings were beginning to be tinged with the oncoming cooler winter air. Mrs. Tang kept Lili close to her side, glancing around her every now and then to make sure they weren't being watched or followed at a distance. Steadily they made their way to a house on the edge of the village.

Once inside, Lili noticed she was the only young person in the room. She respectfully remained quiet and tried not to be disruptive while six old ladies and her mother set up for their meeting. A couple of them made sure the windows and curtains were completely shut so no light could be seen from the outside; another checked that the door was locked; still two others silently arranged the chairs in a circle; another poured out some tea. One lady took a final peek out the front window.

"No one there." The women all breathed an inward sigh of relief. The last thing they needed was a band of Red Guards waiting to pounce on their meeting. Everyone sat down.

Grandma Zhong began to talk in a soft voice. "Jesus came to the earth to give us life. If we believe in him, we will go to heaven. If we don't, we will go to hell . . ."

Lili's curiosity was immediately aroused. She listened with some incredulity as the old woman went on to explain about what it meant to live in heaven and why you wouldn't want to go to hell. She had never heard such talk before in her life. What is this? This is not what they teach us at school. They say there is no heaven or hell. They say there is no God. What can this mean?

"I'm afraid that's all I've got to share today," Grandma Zhong concluded at length. "That's all I can remember from what the missionary taught us over twenty years ago. My memory is not as good as it used to be. But now, we should pray."

The adults knelt down on the floor to pray. Lili felt embarrassed. She was the only one still sitting in her chair. I don't want to pray, she thought. I don't even know who Jesus is. But then Mrs. Tang wrenched her daughter down beside her. Ouch! Lili winced, you don't have to pull so hard.

Lili watched in wonder as the women bowed their heads, clasped their hands together and closed their eyes. Silently they mouthed their petitions to God. Maybe I should try to pray, she thought. But what should I say? She decided to join her hands and close her eyes like the others. After a few seconds in that meditative pose though, she felt no inspiration. She scrunched her eyes tighter, as if that might help.

All of a sudden Lili was overwhelmed with a feeling of terror. I'm going to be destroyed! They're going to destroy me! I don't want to be destroyed! "Jesus, help me!" she cried out in desperation.

Immediately all eyes around the room were opened, startled by the outburst. "Sssh!" admonished a couple of the women.

"Quiet, little girl. Pray quietly," said Grandma Zhong.

Mrs. Tang laid a gentle hand on her daughter's hands for a short while. Soon calm ensued and she resumed her own prayers.

Lili felt the horror was gone, but now she was wretched. I'm such a bad person, she thought. I always scold my little sister. I steal my grandma's eggs and sugar to eat them myself. I hit my younger brother. I'm so mean to them, so selfish, so evil . . . I do deserve to be destroyed. Lili felt awful. She started to weep silently. "Oh, Jesus, help me! Please!" she pleaded in a murmur. The tears streamed down her cheeks as she pleaded with Jesus. "What's wrong with me? Please, please help me!"

Lili couldn't wait to get home. She was in a flutter as she walked briskly through the village at her mother's side later that evening. She was dying to talk about what happened, but she dared not open her mouth on the streets.

"What happened Mama?" Lili was exuberant as soon as their front door was shut. "It was so . . . It was so peaceful after I prayed. I don't know what happened but it feels like a new door has been opened to me and, and, and I've come through to the other side!"

Mrs. Tang beamed.

"It's like," Lili chattered on, "it's like I was always on the wrong side before, but, but now I'm on the right side." She paused to consider the meaning of her words. "Jesus allowed me to come in. He allowed me to come to his side. He's so good."

"Yes, Lili, he is good."

Then the girl had a thought: "Mama, those people, those people on the other side of the door . . ." her voice trailed off.

"Yes, dear?"

"They . . . they will die."

MINGYEN CHEN

1939. The onset of the Second World War was making life increasingly difficult for many people in Shanghai. While many of their countrymen had already been struggling with the Japanese imperial army for the past couple of years, the residents of the International Settlement and French Concession had not, as yet, been significantly inconvenienced. All they knew, for the most part, was prosperity and good times. Life on their streets revolved around serving their pleasure. Hence there could be no other purpose for the coolies encumbered by the weights hanging off the bamboo poles slung across their shoulders, than to be bearers of goods of desire. Likewise with the pesky and persistent street peddlers hawking their wares. It was fascinating too, to hear the array of foreign accents emanating from under the turbans of the Sikhs, the kimono-clad Japanese, parasol-carrying Europeans and Bible-holding British and American missionaries. They were, in all honesty, less offensive to the ear than the local sounds— the haggling (which tended to sound more like bickering), the rickshaw wheels spinning by, the odd automobile chugging along, and the early attempts at advertising— discordant musical bands, each of which were vying to draw shoppers to their employer's store. It seemed that everywhere, in whatever way, people here were doing every thing to cash in on the opportunities and riches of the "Paris of the East".

But slowly their landscape was changing. The mood on

the streets in the foreign administered neighborhoods was no longer purely of indulging one's desires. The single-minded greedy pursuit of wealth was increasingly becoming convoluted with the need for self-preservation, for survival. Rudely the reality and inconvenience of war, rationing and suffering were beginning to intrude on residents' lives. It was not pleasant to them to have to view the ragged refugees and war wounded cluttering their fine streets and squares, disturbing their pampered way of living.

"First they only allow you a miniscule amount of rice. And then what they give you is of such terrible quality! How can they expect people to eat this?" a six-year-old Mingyen heard his mother complain to Cook in the kitchen. He left them thinking she was saying that a lot lately. If it wasn't the rice she was grumbling about, then it was the flour or sugar. It seemed like none of the grown-ups were very happy these days. Except Cook and Amah. They were always nice to him. He couldn't say anything bad about them.

He wandered into the living room and sat down on the built-in bench in the bay window. Nestled in the crook of his bent leg was a red fire truck which boasted a bright yellow ladder; his other leg, meanwhile, lay stretched out beside him partially on the bench and half suspended in the air. With an elbow propped on the sill, he fingered the toy with his free hand as he gazed down yet again at street level from the third floor of the Chen house in the French Concession. He felt the bump of the siren on top, the rungs of the ladder running along the back, the unevenness of the side panels which indicated the truck's different cupboards and compartments. There were no fire trucks below, but there were ambulances and carts. It wasn't, he surmised, very happy down there either. In fact, the sight was a cause of anguish to him: In the square below the wounded and dead from the war were arriving and being sorted. Mingyen watched as stretcher upon stretcher of casualties was carried to and fro. Blood seeped through the bandages covering the heads, hands and bodies of those lying in obvious agony. Crimson blotches smeared the weary faces and rumpled clothing of the lucky few who were capable of sitting upright and of those endeavoring to bring aid and comfort. *They* couldn't think of eating rice, he thought. Some of them didn't even look like they could move. So many people were being hurt, hurting. Why? Why did they have to hurt?

The fire truck was stripped from Mingyen. "Hey! Give that back to me!"

"My turn!" yelled baby brother.

"It was in *my* hands, Yichun! I'm not finished yet!"

Mingyen made a dive for the toy. *Crash!* He banged heavily into the corner table which sent the delicate porcelain vase perched atop toppling over and breaking into two pieces. In the process he also knocked over Yichun. The two brothers started to tussle, one grabbing for the truck, another trying to flatten his brother's face in the floor. A foot flew into a stomach, and intermittently grunts and screams of anger and frustration erupted from their mouths.

"Mingyen! Stop it! Yichun! Both of you stop it!" shouted Mrs. Chen as she rushed into the room after hearing the commotion. Not without a struggle, she succeeded in pulling her two boys apart. "Mingyen! I'm ashamed of you! You should know not to be so rough with your little brother—he's two years younger!"

"He stole the fire truck from me!"

"He didn't share!"

"Okay! Stop shouting, both of you! Mingyen, you should share. You know that. Give Yichun the truck."

"But Maaa . . ."

"Give him the truck. You've had it for a while now."

It was always like that. Yichun always got his way.

"Where's your homework?"

"Aww Ma!" moaned an eight-year-old Mingyen. He was sprawled out on the floor, carefully aiming his next shot. Why did she always have to ruin his fun? "Can't I just finish this game of marbles?"

"I think you've played long enough."

"Aww . . ."

"Look, what do you think would happen if you spent half as much time on your homework as you did playing your games?" She stood looking down at her son with her hands on her hips. "Your grades haven't been good. You know Father will be angry if you don't do better this term. Come on. Get your books." As she watched him drag himself up laboriously from the floor as if burdened by the greatest weight, Mrs. Chen continued, "How about your English? Why don't you start with that?"

"I don't see why we have to learn *that*. Such hard sounds to make."

Not appearing to notice his remark, Mrs. Chen looked over to her two oldest sons at the table. "Look at your brothers," she said referring to them. "They study hard and do well. You should learn from their example."

If it wasn't Yichun, then it was them. Why couldn't he just be accepted for who he was? Why was he always compared to his brothers? And why did she always have to nag him?

1946. Mingyen watched as Grandma Chen hobbled up to the household shrine in her tiny, bound feet. Didn't they hurt? In his mind the thirteen-year-old boy pictured her toes being bent under each foot all the way back to the heel, held in place by the two and a half meter long cotton cloth strips that were tightly wound up to each ankle. It was the way he visualized the explanation from his school friend anyway. The swathes, though, reminded him of the bandages he had seen being unwound in the square. Those grisly strips. Bandages always meant someone had suffered.

Respectfully the old lady bowed three times to the porcelain statue and planted the joss sticks she was holding firmly into the golden sand-filled bowl.

"Why do you do that?" Mingyen asked her.

"We want to keep the gods happy," Grandma replied. "Look how well your father's factories have been doing! We live in comfort in this beautiful apartment—this shows they have been pleased with us!"

The house had been given up shortly after the war for a 2,000 square foot apartment in a quieter part of the French Concession. Mrs. Chen had decided she did not like to go "up and down, up and down all the time", referring to the stairs in their previous house. Besides, there were now too many American sailors making too much noise at the nearby nightclubs in their old neighborhood.

The new apartment was spacious, airy, with an abundance of natural daylight. Mingyen was always wary of being in the living room. Mother was always nervous whenever any of the boys got "too rough" around her teapot collection and, of course, she and Grandma didn't want anyone to upset the shrine.

"Are they still pleased with us? Why is Mother sick in the hospital?"

"Ah, it's even more important now, Mingyen. We must pray to the gods so that she will be well again."

Secretly Grandma was glad they lived in the French Concession. It meant they could afford to have Xiaowen sent to a good hospital, one with foreign-trained staff, so she could be taken care of properly. After all, they did reside in the same neighborhood as Madame Sun Yat-Sen and Generalissimo Chiang Kai-Shek, the leader of the country.

"So they're not pleased with us now—is that it? Is that why Mother's sick?"

"Sometimes the gods are not happy. I don't know why. Maybe that's why the Japanese were allowed to invade China? I don't know. We were lucky though, Mingyen. We had no bombs fall on us. Remember? It was not that long ago."

Mingyen did remember. How could he not? It was like thunder, the sound of the explosions. Then there were the machine guns. They rattled away and some people would just go on drinking tea in their gardens, seemingly taking no notice of it, acting as if the sound were birds chirping in the trees. But you couldn't ignore the blare of the air raid sirens—they just wailed and wailed. Then—he'd never forget it—there were the stretchers. One by one they kept coming, and it was very distressful. But it didn't stop us from having to go to school.

"How're you supposed to know if you've made the gods unhappy? Why'd she have to get sick in the first place?" As he asked this, Mingyen thought of his mother. She could be very uptight at home, he knew, but she was a different person away from the place. He remembered fondly the good times he had spent with her on holidays. You could never get enough of holidays, he thought. They were always special, so much more relaxed than being at home, for

Mother was never as strict on vacation. She had taken him and his brothers to tour other cities, to go to the beach, and staying in hotels was always lots of fun. So were the trains, especially when you got your own cabin to sleep in.

"Aiyah! You have so many questions! But anyway, your mother is getting better now, Mingyen."

"She is? How do you know?"

"Your father told me."

"He did?"

"He did. See, you should always keep the gods happy."

Sure. But you always pray, and something bad still happened. Weren't the gods happy? How are you supposed to know when they're not?

The chauffeur opened the door and Mrs. Chen stepped out of the car. Mr. Chen followed.

"Will you be needing anything else, Mr. Chen?"

"No thank you, Ah-Jin. You can park the car and have the rest of the afternoon off."

"Mother! You're home!" Mingyen ran out of the apartment building along with his brothers. "You're all better!"

"Yes, I am!" she replied, warmly embracing each one of her sons. The whole family, with smiles and laughter on their faces, re-entered the apartment. As they all assembled in the living room, Mrs. Chen caught a glimpse of the household shrine. "Well, we will have to remove that," she pointed, "It's not needed anymore."

"What?!" Grandma exclaimed. Everyone else was shocked too.

"We don't need it anymore. I've found the best God of them all, the only true God—Jesus!"

Life in the Chen household changed dramatically after Mother returned home. *She* was changed. It had all begun in the hospital, when she was lying there in her bed. She found herself questioning the purpose of her life? Was there truly a power in the universe that could assure her healing? Where would her eternal destination be? And so her mind raced. Then one day a man came and spoke to her about a person named Jesus. She learned that Jesus had come to give her life, to show her the way and truth in life, and she had made the decision that she must believe in him. Her health started to improve and she knew that when she was well she must not live the same way she had before. Jesus had saved her!

In addition to disposing of the shrine, Mother began taking her boys with her to church each week. Mingyen and his brothers were enrolled in Sunday School classes where they heard many stories about this Jesus.

"Well, what story did you hear today, Mingyen?" Mrs. Chen would ask her son.

"We heard about how Jesus went to Zacchaeus' house for dinner."

"And what did you think of the story?"

"Zacchaeus was a very wealthy tax collector," the son replied, "but he got his wealth by cheating people. But Jesus forgave him, and Zacchaeus was willing to pay back to people what he stole and more."

"And?" the mother pressed.

"And what?"

"That's what the story's about. But what did you *think* of it?"

"Oh." Mingyen took a moment to consider his mother's question. "Jesus must have been pretty special if Zacchaeus was willing to give his riches to the poor and pay back more than he stole—I mean, they only just met."

The mother laughed with delight at her son's answer. "He *is* special, son."

The young Mingyen wasn't sure he agreed with his mother, but he was glad to have these one-on-one conversations with her nonetheless. They were happening with more frequency, and they made him feel like she cared specially about him. It was like being on vacation all the time.

Mother also hosted weekly dinners at home for her extended family and friends, many of whom were devout Buddhists like Grandma. These dinners would be lavish in their array and quality of vegetarian foods and fresh fruits, making them a hit with the Buddhists. After the meal, Mother invited her pastor to say a few words to her dinner guests and they too came to know of the True way of life.

Mingyen was confused. Was it possible there was a "best" God of all? Was there really only *one* true God? What about all those things Grandma had told him? Aren't the other gods going to be unhappy now that we've thrown away their shrine? Won't they be jealous?

Not surprisingly, Grandma was upset. "Luyen," she called Mr. Chen by his given name. "How can you let your wife do this?"

"Now, Ma, it's all right. Let's just be happy Xiaowen is well again," he replied, ever the modern business man, not minding either way about the shrine, not really believing in any deity himself.

"But we could be ruined! Your businesses!"

"Ma, don't worry about it. I'm not."

But still she fretted.

"Why don't we have a shrine anymore, Mother? I know Jesus is your God now, but shouldn't we have a shrine for him?"

Mingyen was sitting with his mother on the balcony after dinner. The sun was still out, and she loved sitting outside at this time of year, enjoying the long warm summer evenings. Below, on the street, an elderly couple were out for a stroll, a few neighborhood children played ball and a rickshaw with a passenger wheeled by.

"When Jesus shed his blood, when he died on the cross and rose again, he did away with the need to have shrines and burn incense, Mingyen."

"But how can we make him happy then? How can we please him? Grandma always talks about making the gods happy."

"The way you make Jesus happy is to listen to him, to follow what he says."

"That's it? No making special food, no bowing?"

Mother turned to face son. The leaves of the aged ginkgo tree towered over the balcony and shaded the side of her face as she gave him her answer. "Those were all ways the ancients used to show respect to God before Jesus came to the earth. But when he came, he changed all that." She paused a moment, amid the humming of a flying insect, and considered how best to help her son understand. "Jesus said the outward show of religion is not what's important. Instead, he's interested in what's inside us, in our hearts. To have a heart that is committed to him, that's more important." Here she took hold of her son's hand. "In his heart every person needs to make a decision about whether to follow him or not. When you make that decision, it's shown by how you live your life. Your love for God is shown through the things you do, say and think. You too, Mingyen, need to make that decision."

Mingyen pondered her words.

1948.

"Did you hear the news, Luyen?"

"What news?"

"The Gong family is moving to Hong Kong."

"Oh, that. Yes, I've heard."

Grandma had come to speak to Luyen in his study. "That's the fourth family from this street in the past couple of months." She stood beside him as he sat there and worked, waiting in expectation for what he had to say.

"Hm." Mr. Chen had not moved from his position at the desk. Bent over some books, he continued checking his accounts.

"Well, don't you think we should be thinking about it? The Communists are getting stronger in the country. It might be only a matter of time."

"Ma, don't worry. I'm working on some plans, okay?"

"But *when*, Luyen? When? We don't have forever." Then, not receiving a reply, "You should never have allowed Xiaowen to remove the shrine."

The son sighed, put down his pen and sat up to face his mother. She would not be easily assuaged. "You don't seriously believe that's got anything to do with it, do you?" He had a skeptical look on his face as he said this.

"Well, look all around us. People are running scared, panicking. It certainly couldn't have helped!"

"Ma, China is in the middle of a civil war—what do you

expect? Your shrine in or out of our apartment is not going to make a difference."

"Well, I don't agree." She began to pace the length of the room in an agitated manner, wringing her hands. Then, "What are your plans, then?"

"We'll move to Hong Kong too. But, you know, I've got to organize things for the factories before we can go."

"When do you think we'll go?"

"I don't know. Hopefully soon."

"Within this month?"

"It's not that easy, Ma," Luyen was getting impatient. "If we went to Hong Kong tomorrow I wouldn't have work, which means I wouldn't have an income. If the Communists do take over Shanghai, they could make it difficult for us to get anything from the factories. I need to make sure the family will have enough. Understand?"

Grandma nodded. But still she worried.

Mingyen strained to see through the fog. Where was it? Why didn't it come? Surely it should be here by now.

Mingyen was at the Hong Kong airport with his father and brothers. It was four days before Christmas, and they had come to meet their mother who was scheduled to arrive from Shanghai. The Chens had moved to Hong Kong two weeks earlier. Mother had stayed behind a couple of extra weeks to be with her ageing mother.

"Where's the plane, Father?"

"Be patient, Mingyen."

An hour went by. Two. All of the day's ten scheduled planes had come and gone. All, that is, except Mother's.

"Why hasn't it come yet?" One by one the boys echoed the question.

"I don't know boys. Let me ask someone."

But nobody knew. Father and sons continued to wait.

Finally Father said, "Let's go home, boys. I don't think the plane will come today."

The newspaper headlines screamed "AIR CRASH ON BASALT ISLAND" and "THEODORE ROOSEVELT'S GRANDSON KILLED IN PLANE CRASH". Basalt, one of Hong Kong's 235 outlying islands, was sixteen kilometers east of the British colony. Conditions were foggy and the Danish pilot of the Chinese National Aviation Corporation plane had failed in his landing attempt. There were no survivors, as all twenty-eight passengers, including five women and a child, and seven crew died. Quentin Roosevelt, vice-president of the airline; Xuepei Peng, former Minister of Information; and P. L. Fang, a famous Chinese movie director, were among the passengers.

Mingyen read the paper with disbelief. Five women! How could they say that?! One of them was Mother! Tears began to flood his eyes and roll down his cheeks at the realization of this fact. She was gone! She wasn't coming back to him! How could this happen? She was so at peace, so radiant in the past year, ever since she'd become a Christian. She was like a new person! Always smiling, always gracious, patient, gentle, warm . . . If God could change someone so much, why would he do it for only a short time? This couldn't be right.

And who would be his confidante now? He cast his head down in sorrow, his thoughts a whirl. She heard him when he spoke. She was encouragement when he was discouraged. She brought certainty when he was unsure. He could go to her and not be afraid of how she would react.

But Father was always busy with business. It seemed he never had time to notice him—only Lushun. As the oldest son, Lushun would carry on the family name. In his position as the middle third child, Mingyen had always felt he was insignificant in the family—that is, until Mother became a Christian. Yes, he would miss her very much. The grief he felt was almost too much for him, crushing him inside, and he became despondent.

The rest of the day and the ones that followed were bleak. Mingyen walked about in a kind of stupor, forlorn. Amah tried to comfort him. Even Cook's attempt to cheer him up with *lobak goh*[7] and other dimsum delicacies had no consoling effect. That was a first.

As the days and weeks dragged on, Mingyen thought of the many conversations he had had with Mother. She understood him fully. But did he understand her? Of late she had been urging him to follow Jesus, that he was the only way to heaven. Yet that was what Mingyen couldn't quite get. It just didn't make sense with all the other stuff he'd seen and heard—how did Buddha fit into this, for instance? Maybe he should read his Bible again, go back to church (he hadn't done either since his mother had died)— maybe that would help to make things a bit clearer. Mother always said these things helped her.

Mother would be in heaven now, according to what she said. Well, that was good. And then it hit him: If I ever want to see Mother again, it can only be through Jesus. I've got to find Jesus!

---

7 A Cantonese dish of fried mashed turnip cake.

SAIMEN LIANG

1955. The water was cool to his toe. It had a tickly ickly feeling. He pulled it back up, standing there momentarily on one leg like a flamingo. Timidly he dipped his toe back into the stream. It was a warm, sunny day in Kaiyang county, Henan, and Saimen was only four and half years old. A light breeze created an ever so subtle ripple on the surface of the water, and the sounds of content birds chirping could be heard in the distance.

"Jump in, Saimen!"

"What are you waiting for?"

"Are you a rat with no guts?"

Tiny Saimen *was* afraid. He wasn't nearly as big as his cousin and friends. They were seven and eight.

Chang got out of the water and grabbed Saimen's hand. "Come on, little cousin. There's nothing to be scared of."

Saimen was dragged into the water. It crept up to his knees, then to his waist. It rose over his chest and pretty soon he could no longer feel the ground under his feet. He started to flounder. "Help me, Chang!" he cried in a panic. "Help me!"

"You're doing all right! Keep moving! Keep moving!"

"I, I can't!" Saimen was terrified. His feeble diminutive hands and feet began to tire. "Help me!" Saimen's head slipped below the surface and bobbed back up. "Help!" He gulped in some water, choked on it and started to cough. The current washed over his head again and it seemed like everything light around him was fast becoming dark. I can't breathe! Inside he was hysterical. I can't see! Help! I'm dying! Help!

Suddenly Saimen felt a strong jerk and he was out of the water! "Granduncle." The weary boy was greatly relieved.

Good ol' Granduncle. He was always coming to the rescue. Saimen had a wistful look on his twelve-year-old face, as he looked out once again on that stream. It was now 1963, but how could he forget. Every time he walked by it. Every time he brought the goats here, like now. Saimen checked around him to make sure the animals were alright. He spotted a couple of kids further up, head-butting each other, jockeying for position by the water.

"Always fighting," Granduncle would say to little Saimen, dusting him off. "You're always fighting. You shouldn't let what they say get to you."

"But they called me a rat with no guts!"

"It's just some words. Don't take it to heart so much."

A few days later the taunts would start up again.

"A rat with no guts! A rat with no guts! Saimen's such a rat with no guts!" Chang's friends just wouldn't stop.

It rankled little Saimen so much, he would fling his small body at his hecklers in an attempt to teach them a lesson—*anything* to make them stop. "Stop making fun of me!" he would yell as he charged head-on at them.

With great hilarity, the older boys would hold off the runt at his head with one hand. Meanwhile the smaller boy would struggle to inch in closer to land his tormentors a wallop or two. If one actually managed to make contact, Saimen would be sure to get one back packed with considerably more power! But before anyone really got hurt Granduncle would somehow end up plucking him from the fray and saving him from a beating. That had happened too many times to count.

Thankfully those days are over, thought Saimen, as once again he took notice of the goats around him. He'd been at this job for the past three months now, since he'd left school. Pa had passed away nearly three years ago and Mama simply couldn't afford to pay for his education anymore. He had tried to help her with the school fees by catching field mice to sell to the local apothecary in their making of herbal medicines but it wasn't enough. That is, there weren't enough mice. Four years of avid hunting had rendered the rodents no longer plentiful in these fields. Darn. He was good at catching them! And at 5 *fen*[8] a mouse . . . But she just didn't have anything left to spare. It was a pity really. Just when he was starting to get the hang of his studies. He didn't know if it was coincidence or not, but he felt like he got a better grip on his subjects around the time he met Jesus, about nine or so months ago. Prior to that, his classmates seemed to delight in reminding him that he was "slow" compared to them; indeed he did not have an easy time memorizing all those characters and doing mental arithmetic. But then one day it began to click for him. Understanding new concepts wasn't so complicated or abstract anymore. Things became easier in his mind. Instead of struggling to make sense of his math, he could now answer every question. And his writing improved too. Teacher really liked that last essay of mine, Saimen thought fondly, the one about how Granduncle's life was changed when he gave up his joss sticks and sacrificing to idols, and how all that was just a waste of money. I got 99 out of 100! Saimen was chuffed. They can't call me slow anymore!

Goat herding wasn't so bad though, he thought as he sat

---

[8] Less than 1 U.S. cent.

on the gentle slope of the hill, splitting a few long strands of grass. In fact, it was turning out to be quite a pleasant occupation. The animals pretty much took care of themselves, and it was agreeable to be able to enjoy the countryside in a leisurely manner each day. It sure beat backbreaking labor in a field! *And* you didn't have to talk to anyone. Saimen, by nature, never felt comfortable with strangers. He would actually go out of his way, hide in bushes, run up a mountain, anything to avoid talking to a grown-up he didn't know.

Saimen became aware that the afternoon was getting on. Better make sure I'm back on time today, he told himself. Don't want to be late for Granduncle. He began the process of rounding up the herd.

Saimen was looking forward to tonight. Then again, he always did when Granduncle invited him to his meetings. This time, however, was extra special, because it would mark the first time Ma would come. It had taken some time to convince her but she had finally agreed. He was excited. As the man of the house now, it felt good to be able to introduce something good into her life.

Yes, Jesus was good. It was amazing really, God sent his one and only Son into the world to die for our sins, he thought as he steered the goats back to their home. Jesus had been slaughtered, his blood had been spilled, much in the way we butcher our own animals in preparation for our household shrines and graves. Saimen remembered the first time he heard that idea, when he listened to Granduncle preach. The elderly man spoke of things he had never heard of before. Wow! I could go to heaven! he had thought. I'd give anything to go there! . . . But then Granduncle started talking about something called "sin". He couldn't understand, at first, what it was. He always thought he was a good person—it wasn't like he cheated or stole things. He didn't bully people either—in fact, they bullied him! And what about Ma and Pa? Pa didn't do bad things; neither did Ma . . . And then it dawned on him. It was about an attitude inside, about recognizing that every person in the world had sin and needed the gift of forgiveness that Jesus offered—himself included! The truth couldn't have been plainer: I can't go to heaven with sin! I need this Jesus. I need his blood sacrifice! I will accept him.

Saimen swung the gate in and locked the goats in the pen for the night. He made his way home, collected his mother and the two of them set off for the meeting.

"I'm so glad you're coming, Mama," Saimen said excitedly as they were walking. "Jesus is really someone you need to know."

Mama smiled at her son in response.

"Granduncle is really a good teacher. He'll be able to explain Jesus a lot better than me," the son continued.

"You've told me a lot already, son."

"But he can tell you more. I can't always remember everything."

She smiled again.

They arrived at Farmer Gu's courtyard. About forty people were already congregated there and, as usual, there was no one Saimen's age. They were always grown ups. That was the only "disappointment" he felt when he came. There would be no new playmates.

Granduncle stood up to begin the meeting. He led the singing of a couple of hymns and then he opened his Bible to begin speaking.

"Jesus was the Son of God," his preaching began. "Yet

he was also a man who walked on the earth. Why, you may ask, did he lower himself, leave his palatial home in heaven, and come to live among men? It was because he wanted to share how we human beings felt—the joy, the sorrows, the laughter and tears . . ."

Saimen glanced sideways at his mother to see if she was being gripped by the message as he was. She looked like she was listening: Her eyes were focused straight ahead, intent on understanding.

"If he hadn't suffered on the cross," Granduncle continued, "man would always say that he couldn't understand how we feel. But that's not true—he does understand. He understands because he's been through excruciating pain himself . . ."

Saimen felt the tears well up in his eyes. He forgot about his mother as he considered his granduncle's words. He thought about the hard times he had had in his young life already, the near brushes with death, the humiliation of having to beg, the tyranny he experienced at the hands of Chang's friends and "smarter" classmates at school . . . He was so engrossed in his ruminations, he was slow to notice his mother raising her hand to receive Jesus into her life. But when he realized it, he was filled anew with joy. His prayers had been answered!

Wow! thought Saimen the next day as he led the goats to their grazing ground. God actually answered my prayers for Ma. Imagine that! He spotted a friend walking to his work place in a sorghum field. "Hey, Jun!" he called out. Similar to him in age, Jun had left school too, only a year earlier.

Jun looked around to see who was calling, a piece of straw dangling from the left corner of his mouth. "Saimen!

How's it going?"

Saimen stopped walking momentarily, waiting for Jun to come over, meanwhile letting the goats continue down the road unattended. "Guess what happened last night?" he asked excitedly.

"What?"

"My mother became a believer!" The goatherd was impassioned as he spoke.

Jun wasn't impressed. "What's the big deal about that?"

"She's going to go to heaven when she dies!" Saimen flung his arms out wide in an animated manner.

"Nobody goes to heaven," replied Jun, spitting out the piece of straw he was chewing. "Only the gods live there."

"No, that's not true. You can go to heaven too! Don't you know that?"

"I can go to heaven," he said skeptically.

"Yeah!"

Jun stood there, staring at Saimen. He sounds so sure. Was he for real? "So what do you have to do then, if you want to go to heaven?"

"Believe in Jesus!"

Saimen, it appeared, was gifted at convincing people of their need for Jesus. He soon managed to win Jun over and, eventually, also many other village children. After initial doubts they almost always came around to believing what he said, and, quite unwittingly, he found he had converted a group of young people who wanted to have their own meetings. So Saimen and a couple of others began organizing them.

For the first time in his life, Saimen felt like he belonged. He was on even footing with the youth here. He had a voice. They listened to him. And no one pushed him around or ridiculed him. Everything seemed to be at ease and everyone managed to agree peacefully with each other. That's the way it always ought to be, he thought.

The year 1966 brought about the introduction of a new campaign in the country: "Down with the Four Olds". It was the kick-off to the violent decade-long Cultural Revolution. The poster's headline caught the fifteen-year-old Saimen's attention as it was being hung up by a uniformed cadre on the high street notice board. The old thought, old culture, old customs and old habits had to be abolished in order for the country to revolutionize and develop further and faster. Furthermore, the authorities encouraged the participation of young people in the movement. Ever the idealistic, romantic adolescent, Saimen thought this sounded positively fantastic!

"Excuse me, Comrade," said Saimen to the uniformed man.

"What do you want, kid?" The interruption did not deter the man from checking the remaining supply of nails he had in relation to posters. He just wanted to get all the stupid notices up before dark.

"Can you please tell me more about this?" Saimen pointed to the poster.

"What do you want to know?" he asked while recounting his posters.

"Well, what would the young people do specifically?"

"You know, all kinds of things—help people break away from old traditions and habits, help them learn to treat others with equality and fairness, help the poor—you know, that kind of thing." By now the man was beginning to collect his things and move on.

"That sounds great!"

The enthusiasm of the boy caught his attention. The lad's sincerely eager, he thought. The man paused to eye Saimen up and down. He adjusted his tone of voice to be more friendly. "It is! Why don't you join? You're a good-looking lad, strong and energetic. You'd be perfect!"

"You think so?" Saimen was glad at the compliment.

"Of course! And who knows? But something tells me you might even have the making of a leader."

Saimen beamed. Yeah, who knows? But nonetheless, it sounds so much like the things Granduncle teaches about helping people. Why not? So Saimen enlisted as a Red Guard.

The scene outside the window of the county PSB office portrayed a team of Red Guards patrolling the street, on the lookout for any capitalistic pigs and evil elements. They were, just several months into the revolution, well adjusted and accustomed to their new social responsibilities. Occasionally they would stop a housewife on her way to the market or a farmer, questioning them as if they were suspects in a criminal investigation. Some adults would try to avoid an encounter with the young people and walk by on the other side of the road. County party secretary Niu smirked as he looked on from his position, perched on the sill, a cigarette hanging from his lips. In his early forties, he was a man comfortable with his situation in life. He was derived from the common peasant stock, complete with thick, dark tanned skin and a solid build, and his father was a survivor of the Long March which he expected would go a long way to assuring the security of his own career.

"Do you like Chou? I think he'd be suitable." The voice

of his subordinate broke into the secretary's consciousness.

"No, Comrade Yang. That kid couldn't scare a mouse. We need someone who's not afraid to make noise."

"How about Hui then?"

"Oh, he sure can make a lot of noise—he only knows one volume! No, that boy always shouts so loud he gives me a headache. I couldn't deal with that on a regular basis. Besides, wasn't his grandfather a landowner? His background's too bourgeois."

Yang continued to flip through the files. His commanding officer sure was a hard one to please. They'd been at this for hours and still no one . . .

"What do you think about the Liang kid then, Sir?"

Niu took the cigarette out of his mouth and turned away from the window to face the direction of his junior officer. "Yes . . . Now there's a possibility. He *would* be good, wouldn't he? He's been doing a great job recruiting, I've heard, from his village and others—he knows how to get around." He nodded to himself as he mentally evaluated this qualification.

"And he comes from the perfect background too—dirt poor!" Yang added.

"You're right, Comrade. You're right," said the secretary nodding his head slowly. "I think we may have found our perfect model."

Party Secretary Niu went to Saimen's house personally to invite him to be the district leader of the Red Guards. He draped his full-length wool coat proudly on Saimen's shoulders in the presence of the Liang family and his accompanying officers. The teenager looked up at the county cadre, stunned. "You keep it, young comrade. It's yours now . . . You know," he mused, addressing the room in general, "children born in China must be the most blessed of all. Everywhere else in the world they suffer, but not here." He smiled in Saimen's direction.

Saimen couldn't have agreed with him more. He felt very honored and distinguished to have been given the party secretary's coat.

"So, young Comrade Liang," said Niu, standing at attention, "how many villages have you recruited Red Guards from now?"

"Sir! Thirty-three, Sir!" Saimen immediately straightened up and saluted his superior officer as he said this.

Niu chuckled with delight. "Keep up the good work!" he replied, patting Saimen on the arm. The party secretary turned to Saimen's mother. "You have raised a fine son, Mrs. Liang. We have strong families and a strong country. Long live Chairman Mao!"

"Long live Chairman Mao!" the people in the room echoed.

1968. SMACK! The slap across the head nearly knocked the thirty-nine-year-old man off his knees. A fresh red welt running down his face, he struggled to maintain his penitent position, all the while trembling with the fear of what yet might be.

"How dare you try to run away from us!" screamed Saimen at the man. With hands on his waist, he circled around the victim who had been hauled down from the courtyard wall in his attempt to escape. The model leader's Red Guard troop had then dragged the transgressor back to the front entrance of his house, where his mother and father were already prostrate.

The mother dared a peek at her son. A Red Guard roughly shoved her head back down. She had only wanted to ascertain that her son was all right. The victim couldn't help but return a glance at her.

SMACK! The back of Saimen's hand made violent contact with the victim's head again. "You dare to raise your eyes in our presence?"

The victim immediately lowered his eyes again.

As he inspected the trio of people on the ground before him, Saimen felt as if life couldn't get any better. Here he was, helping his country develop and move on from pointless traditions. Here he was, a revered figure in society, the leader of a Red Guard unit, and people took orders from him without question. "Rip out the shrine!" Saimen shouted to his subordinates, pointing to the wide open door of the house. "Bring it out here and burn it all! Make sure none of those false gods and idols are left behind!" He turned his attention back to the family. "Don't you know those gods are useless? They won't save you from hell!" He stepped aside as the first pieces of the shrine were brought into the courtyard. "Find all the fortune-telling books too!" he reminded his unit. He took a wooden statue from a pile one of his subordinates was carrying and hurled it to the ground. He trampled it under his foot, breaking it in two. "Down with the old customs!" he yelled boisterously.

"Down with the old customs!" repeated his troop.

Spring was in the air. The bleakness of winter was gone. The trees and flowers once again budded and bloomed, producing a rainbow of colors that made life appear so much more beautiful. Indeed, everything was coming up roses for Saimen. He was thoroughly in love with his country, and he was completely smitten with his God. He reveled in the fact that he was helping to build the people up within his community by day and within his church by night. He thrived on the feeling of being of use and respected both in society and in his fellowship. The county party secretary favored him. The church leaders relied on him. Taking his responsibilities with both the party and church seriously, Saimen went about his respective duties to "spread violence" and to "love your neighbor" conscientiously and wholeheartedly. He was good at what he did. People from both groups told him so. What could be more exhilarating to a seventeen-year-old than to be valued like that? In his utopian thinking he would be an exemplary Chinese citizen and Christian through and through all the time.

At the end of each day, as he prepared for bed, Saimen diligently remembered to pray to God, even if it was only brief. He made sure he wasn't negligent in this because he didn't want to be left behind when Jesus came back!

Saimen knelt on the floor. "Lord God," he began as per usual, "thank you for all that I have. Please help me not to do anything that is against you, or that is sin." As he finished this sentence tonight, however, a picture of the man he had struck earlier that day flashed before him, startling him momentarily. He brushed the image aside. "Help me not to do the wrong thing." Again, the face of his victim sprang up. He tried to ignore it. "Help me not to—" But he couldn't. It was just sitting there now. He saw the red welts stretching half way down the right side of the man's face. He remembered the sting he had felt in his own knuckles upon making contact. "Help me not to—" Then he saw the worried look of the mother. Her face had been shoved so low to the ground there was dirt on her nose and forehead.

He let go a long, slow breath. "It isn't right, Lord, is it?" He couldn't help thinking how each member of that family must have suffered, not knowing what was going to happen. He remembered the power he had felt as he had them there on their knees, at his mercy, and how he had basked in it. He realized he was in a position to do good but he had, instead, inflicted pain. "Forgive me, Lord. Forgive me." He took a moment to gather himself before he continued. "Lord, it's so hard. It's getting so hard. I don't know what happens—it's so easy to hit people." He gulped here, admitting to himself that it wasn't just easy; he actually enjoyed it. "Lord, forgive me. Help me. Help me not to hurt people in my position as a leader, especially my brothers and sisters, or their families. Help me to be a good leader, a leader who does not bring destruction. Help me know what to do. Amen."

Saimen crawled onto his bed. He lay there for some time in the dark perturbed. It wasn't right. He was thinking this more and more, and tonight this thought reignited an argument with himself that had become all too familiar lately. Tonight the prevailing point was proving impossible to drive away though: It just wasn't right to be beating all these people all the time. Deep inside he knew this. And yet . . . And yet the number of reports he had heard about Red Guards in other districts being even more aggressive and violent was increasing. It seemed as if everyone was doing it. Why shouldn't he? But he had heard too, that some of their actions had even led to deaths. This unsettled him. What if that should happen in his group?

So far, however, he had managed to keep his troop in check—they assailed but they didn't kill. Thank God for that! (Yet he knew now they would have to stop even the beatings.) He restricted their raids to houses with "old habits", that is, ancestral shrines that required demolition. They also did away with "foreign fashion". On the street or in a home they chopped off any woman's long hair worn in braids or other such flamboyant styles, and confiscated any jewelry they found. His Red Guard unit had delivered enough gold and silver to the county party headquarters to keep Comrade Niu more than pleased.

But more than the violence, the thing that was really troubling Saimen these days was the religious meetings. Rather, it was the distinct lack of them. They had all been completely shut down. It was no longer legal to hold or attend them. Furthermore, the Bible was now a banned item. If found anywhere, it was sure to be hurled into the pyre with every other "foreign" book that was being burned. This was one thing he couldn't abide in the current policy. It disturbed him to think that society was trying to obliterate the one true living God. This was not right.

He noticed lately that with each passing day the struggle within his soul seemed to be growing in intensity. If truth be told, he felt it had escalated into war. The conviction he felt of his wrongdoing tonight only underscored the reality of the conflicts within him. For the most part, he enjoyed his assignments from the Communist Party; and yet he felt a deep need to do God's bidding too. Within him, there had developed an indescribably strong urge to tell people about Jesus. He would even go so far as to say it was an unshakable compulsion. He had never experienced a feeling like this before. But how could he actually do it? The current environment was hardly inviting. It was going to be hard enough to deter his troop from hitting people! More importantly though, he had never consciously planned to evangelize before, and he felt acutely, for the first time, his distinct lack of knowledge. He didn't, for example, know how to talk about the Bible like his granduncle. He didn't even know what it said. It was unlikely too, that he would get a chance to know any time soon. The book was being destroyed if found, and some people had actually been beaten to death when they were caught with one in their hands. What to do?

Well, he finally concluded, the only thing I do know are a few songs. I'll just sing them. I'll sing "The Kingdom of God is Near" and "Don't Sink in the Lake of Fire". And then I'll just tell people they need the blood of Jesus to clean themselves from their sins. Yes, that's what I'll do.

LILI TANG

1973. The students marched into the school yard for assembly. Lili stepped into place with her classmates. Several months had passed since she had gone to her first secret meeting.

"The school will make first bow to Chairman Mao!" the principal called out.

The entire student body and staff bowed in unison before the portrait of the venerated leader hanging on the exterior of the school building.

"Second bow!"

Again they bowed.

"Third bow!"

And again.

Comrade Fu, the principal, turned to make his address to the students, whose gazes slid down from Mao to him. He cleared his throat. "Now," he began, "it has come to our attention that there are some students in our school who have superstitious beliefs."

The students kept their heads straight, resisting the urge to glance around. Where could they be—behind me? In front? Over there? A few eyes darted to the left and right, trying to spot the culprits.

"Furthermore, there is one student among us who is trying to convince others to believe in these superstitions."

Lili's heart leapt within her. He's talking about me!

"Superstitions, as you should all know by now, are not real. There is no truth or relevance about them. Our homeland prospers today not because of God, but because of our great helmsman!" Comrade Fu pointed to the portrait hanging behind him. "It is Chairman Mao Thought that we believe! Chairman Mao Thought that we follow! And it is Chairman Mao Thought that will continue to guide us along the road to success and development!"

Lili became anxious. It took all of her self-control not to move or cry out. What should I do? I don't want to get in trouble, but I can't help it . . .

"For those of you who are superstitious, we will give you a warning: Turn away from these beliefs. And if you are the one trying to convert others to believe in superstitions, you must stop. If you don't, you will have to bear responsibility for your actions."

Lili was aghast. I could get kicked out of school. Maybe worse. But I can't stop, she thought. Jesus is real and he is in me, deep inside me. Nothing can make him come out of me. Nothing.

Over the next week Lili was in a quandary. She knew she had to exercise caution, but she didn't feel it was right to stay completely quiet either. People could die, she said to herself. What should I do, God?

"Lil!"

Lost in her thoughts as she made her way to school, Lili didn't hear a thing.

"Hey, Lil! Wait up! Lil!"

Abruptly Lili turned in her tracks. "Yangzi!"

"I was calling you for miles back there! Are you deaf?"

"Sorry."

"Forget it." The two girls stepped into stride with each other. "Did you write your essay?"

"Uh-huh. You?"

"Yeah. Took me all night practically."

Lili kicked at a rock on the road.

"My mama always scolds me when I do that," Yangzi said, beginning to take a kick herself. "Don't ruin your shoes! Do you know how long it takes to make a pair?" She gave her voice a nasally tone in an attempt to imitate her mother.

"My mama too," said Lili, kicking another one. "But *Ge* Min and his friends always say girls can't kick as far as boys. They always tease me. Chairman Mao says girls hold up half the sky, but I don't think they believe it."

The two girls concentrated on kicking rocks down the road for a while.

"Lil?"

"Uh-huh?"

"I wanted to ask you: Can you come over for dinner?"

"Uh, sure. Whose birthday is it?"

"No one's."

Lili was confused. She stopped her foot mid-air, her rhythm put off. "Then what's the occasion?"

"We're just inviting you for dinner."

"Just me?"

"Yeah."

"What—you and your parents . . ."

"Yeah."

"Are inviting me?"

"Yeah."

"Your parents?" Lili said this more as a sarcastic statement than as a question.

"Yeah." Then, somewhat exasperated, "Well? Do you want to come or not?"

Lili still thought it was strange, but, "I guess . . . Okay.

When?"

"How 'bout tomorrow?"

"Tomorrow? Uh, okay. I'll have to check with my parents, but I think it's okay."

"Great." The two girls resumed kicking until they arrived at school.

"Again? That's the fourth time this month! You must be the most popular girl in school!" Shaking his head as he said this, Mr. Tang had a stern expression on his face.

Lili sat at the dinner table in suspense, her hands gripped on the edge, legs swinging nervously back and forth underneath. Please say yes. Please say yes, she pleaded in her mind.

"Our daughter's been invited to another dinner, Anlin," he said to his wife. "Can you believe that?"

Mrs. Tang, returning from the kitchen, smiled in response as she set the fresh oolong tea on the table and reseated herself.

"Don't you have homework?" he asked Lili.

"I'll finish it after school. I always do." She was ready with her answer.

"What about your chores?"

"I always get them done—I do, don't I, Mama?" she appealed to Mrs. Tang, expecting favorable support from that corner.

Mrs. Tang smiled.

"Well, what do you think, Anlin?" asked Mr. Tang. "Should she go?"

Mrs. Tang was in the middle of pouring tea. She set the pot down, as if to give her full attention to scrutinizing the question. She leaned left to shoo away the cat which had just jumped up on the table. Then Mrs. Tang glanced over to her husband, resting her eyes on him momentarily, then moved them to her daughter. All this occurred in the span of only a few seconds, though Lili thought it felt like an eternity. Then, "I don't see why not."

"Your mama seems to think there's no problem."

There *is* no problem, Lili said to herself, knowing mama's word alone wasn't enough. Please say I can go . . .

"But you know the rule." With a serious mien, Mr. Tang leaned forward to look his daughter straight in the eye. "You don't talk about anything that goes on in this house, right?"

"Right," said Lili, looking straight back at him.

"You don't mention what we eat. You don't mention what we wear. You don't mention what we have. And you don't mention what we talk about. Got it?"

"Got it." It was all she could do to suppress the squeal of delight she wanted to make.

Then Mr. Tang relaxed. "Anlin, imagine that—our daughter gets invited to dinner after dinner like a party cadre! She's turning into quite a socialite!"

Mrs. Tang smiled. Lili smiled.

"There she is."

"I don't know . . ."

"Why are you so chicken?"

"I'm not. I just feel like it's imposing."

"Well, don't. Lil won't mind at all. She's already been to my house, and Chun's, Su's, Shan's and . . . Just ask her. Go on."

Yangzi and Lingmei were talking in the school yard.

"You're sure?" Lingmei asked.

"Of course. If you ask her to your house, I promise you'll be in for a surprise."

At first Lili thought it was strange that her school friends, one by one, asked her over for dinner. But after a few times she began to see exactly what it all meant: She wouldn't have to remain silent at all.

"So, Auntie," began Lili, as was now her custom, "have you ever heard about Jesus?" She turned to face Lingmei's mother, who had begun peeling an apple for dessert. It was a couple of nights later.

"What are you talking about, little girl?" she exclaimed with dread, nearly dropping the fruit and knife. "The Red Guards would have our heads if they could hear us now!"

"You know," the little girl resumed calmly, not seeming to notice the last comment, "I used to steal food and lie about it. I was angry all the time with my little brother and sister—I even used to beat them up. And I was just so mean and selfish. But when I told Jesus about what I did bad, he was so good about it. He allowed me to live, to come to him, to cross over to his side!" The little girl was so purely honest when she spoke, so clearly unaffected. There was something soothing about her, Lingmei's mother observed, and she seemed to ooze such peace and hope—two commodities which were in rare supply these days indeed. Everything's just topsy-turvy around here now.

"He forgave everything I did wrong," the little girl continued. "Do you know how good that feels? Before I met Jesus, I used to be afraid about doing something wrong. Sometimes I felt like I couldn't help myself. Even if I didn't want to do something mean, somehow I ended up doing it. Have you ever felt like that? No matter how hard you try?"

There were murmurs of agreement from Lingmei's mother and the rest of the family around the table.

"Anyway, I was afraid 'cause I didn't like it when someone got mad at me or punished me. That always made me nervous to do things."

Don't I know that feeling, thought Lingmei's mother. It's just like Anyi was saying earlier today. She thought of the conversation she had had with her neighbor. "Everyone's so paranoid around here now. Everyone's so afraid of offending." Lingmei's mother had nodded her head earnestly to concur with her friend. "Who knows when tying your shoes or eating rice could become a reason for an attack against you? One minute you could be a hero, the next a criminal." Exactly.

"And sometimes when I tried to do the right thing," said Lili, "it still didn't seem like enough. Someone still got upset with me. Couldn't they just see that I was trying, honestly?"

Lingmei's mother found herself nodding again, this time in agreement with the little girl. She's so right! Can't the Red Guards see that we're all trying? Maybe we're slow learners but we are trying!

"But Jesus says it's okay. He forgives us when we do the wrong thing and He knows when we are trying. Since I met Jesus, I don't live in that fear or nervousness anymore."

Is this possible? Lingmei's mother asked herself. Could it really be? But everything else the little girl's said makes so much sense, and she's so full of confidence in him . . . "Stop!" she broke out. "Don't say anything else!"

Everyone in the room stared at the mistress of the house, startled at the interruption.

"Hua," Lingmei's mother continued, calling to her oldest son, "go and get Anyi, and her family! Go get the rest of the neighbors!"

Lili froze in her seat. "Wha-What?"

"Go, Hua! Get them! They need to hear this!" Hua

obeyed his mother. She couldn't explain it. She was overwhelmed with this sense that there was Truth coming out of this little girl, and her friends needed to hear it too. Lili was only speaking simple words, sharing her experience, but when she talked the woman felt like her heart was burning and something resonated within her that *here* was a way for them. We're all worn out, she realized. We have nothing left to give in our lives, nothing *in* our lives. But there's something *here*. Could this be the way?

"Uh, ar-are you sure?" asked Lili with a slight tremble in her voice. "What if, uh, what if the Red Guards find out?"

"Oh, don't worry about that, little girl!" Lingmei's mother said. "Our neighbors won't tell. You just tell them what you've told us and anything else you've got to say." She gave Lili a warm smile.

In a very short time, twenty-odd people were gathered in Lingmei's home and the hostess signaled the girl to resume. Recapping what she had said earlier, Lili went on to share further personal experiences with Jesus for another twenty minutes. Then she concluded with, "Jesus is the answer. Only he can save you from hopelessness and discouragement. Only he can save you from your sins. He promises to be with you always. You only have to ask him and he'll give you peace like you've never known." She stopped and looked around the room.

It was silent. Each person was weighing and considering the words of the little girl. There didn't seem to be anything spectacular in her manner, but somehow her words were moving them. They had never encountered that in anyone among them before. More than that though, like Lingmei's mother, they felt something in their hearts, a tugging, a compulsion, like someone or something was trying to get in to their lives.

Lingmei was the first to cry. Then, one by one, around the room, the eyes of the young people began to fill with tears, and then the adults. Each person became aware of the fact that they were sinful and that this created a void in their lives, a lack. They knew they needed to find peace and hope like Lili had. "What do we do?" they asked her. "How can we know Jesus more? How can we please him?"

Lili was stumped for a second. She leaned her head to one side, the tip of her right index finger on her cheek. Then, smiling brightly, she had an idea. "You should come together every week. You should meet together like this."

"Okay," they said. "But what can we do when we meet?"

"Well," she replied with growing eagerness as more ideas began to fill her mind, "you can pray together."

"What should we pray about?"

"Did you ever steal eggs from your grandma or grandpa? Did you ever hit anyone or shout angrily at them? Did you ever think bad thoughts in your heart? So you can just tell Jesus these things that you've done. Just keep telling him and he'll take the bad things away."

1978. Mr. Tang strolled through the village high street. Market day was buzzing. He was hoping to find a new yoke for his oxen. It was certainly pleasant to have some selection around here again, he thought, as he browsed through the wares on sale. Comrade Deng Xiaoping is doing some good things for the country.

"Comrade Tang!"

"Farmer Ting! Long time no see! How are you?"

"I am well, thank you. And you?"

"Very well, as you can see," said Mr. Tang, patting his full stomach.

"You must be proud of your daughter."

Mr. Tang raised his eyebrows, mildly surprised. "My daughter? Well, yes. I'm proud of all my children."

"Yes, but your elder daughter in particular. She's made quite an impact around here."

Mr. Tang's curiosity was piqued. "Are you talking about Lili?"

"Of course! She's such an excellent speaker, so eloquent. You'd have thought she'd have gone on to college!"

Mr. Tang was pleased in an irksome way by this comment. Lili had only just completed high school the year before, but he had a growing suspicion that his friend's compliment was not due to his daughter's academic prowess. "Whe-, where did you hear her speak?" Mr. Tang asked, making every effort to maintain his composure.

"Why, all over! She's been speaking in villages throughout the district! Where has she *not* been? And not only that—the most wonderful things happen when she speaks!"

"Wonderful things? Like what?"

"Miraculous things! Sick people get healed! Cripples— they can walk! The deaf, they hear! Crooked backs become straight! And hey—did you hear about Old Hongwu?"

"You mean the loony over in Changtai Village?"

"Yeah! Well, he's not crazy anymore!"

"He's not." Mr. Tang said this with considerable doubt in his voice.

"Yeah! He's perfectly sane now! Happened just the other night! I tell you—you name it—it's happened!" Farmer Ting could see that his friend was still skeptical. "Haven't you heard about all these incredible things?"

"I have," answered Mr. Tang slowly. "I just thought it was people talking though, you know, making up stories."

"No sir," said the exuberant farmer. "You really have an amazing daughter, Comrade!"

"Yeah." Mr. Tang agreed.

"Lili! Lili Tang! Come out here this instant!" Mr. Tang yelled as soon as he got home. "Lili Tang!"

"What are you in a huff about?" asked Mrs. Tang, as she came into the courtyard with a dripping bowl of watercress.

"Where is that girl? Lili!"

"Calm down. She's working out in the wheat field. Where else do you think she'd be at this time of the day?"

"Meimei," Mr. Tang ignored his wife's question and called to his younger daughter huddled in the corner, "go get your sister. Tell her I want to see her right now." Meimei dropped her book and quickly obeyed.

"What is going on?" asked Mrs. Tang.

"That daughter of ours is making a fool out of me."

"What do you mean?"

"She's been sneaking off at night, preaching again! After I expressly forbade her! She's got some nerve!"

"It's not that bad, dear, surely . . ."

"You're always protecting her! But this time she will not get away with it!"

"People like her. They welcome her. She does good, Wenli. Why stop her from that?"

"Why stop her?!" Mr. Tang was nearly at his wits' end. "If the higher authorities find out, do you know what could happen? Maybe we're going through a lenient time right now, but haven't the last twenty-five years taught you anything, Anlin? Policies could change at any time and that daughter of ours is a time bomb waiting to explode!"

Mrs. Tang kept silent. She knew her husband was in no mood to listen.

"I told her I don't mind her believing, but can't she keep it to herself?" he continued his harangue. "Why does she have to go slinking off in the middle of the night? No respectable girl does that! People could think she's having a dalliance or, or that she's loose! No one will want to marry her then and they'll say we're such terrible parents because we don't protect or check our daughter!"

"Lili is not loose! You know that. Do not say such things of our daughter!"

"I'm not! But people will think that when she's dashing off in the middle of the night!"

Mr. Tang paced the courtyard like a mad man, back and forth, back and forth. Mrs. Tang sorted through her watercress. Eventually Lili arrived.

"What have you got to say for yourself, young lady?" Mr. Tang was in no mood to be trifled with.

"About what, Father?" There was an artlessness in the teenaged girl's question. Inwardly, however, Lili's mind was calculating how much her father's latest displeasure would cost her. It was the natural course of events whenever she appeared before him in this way. She quickly concluded that the cost was irrelevant though; obeying Jesus was what mattered. Lives were at stake, she reminded herself. She must never be afraid to speak out. And besides, she knew deep down inside that the Son of God was real and alive within her—how could she act like he wasn't? It'd be like ignoring him, and she felt like she shouldn't—couldn't—do that. Not now. Not ever.

"Don't act so innocent with me! Why have you been sneaking off at night to your meetings when I strictly forbade you? What's your excuse?"

"I have no excuse." Lili bowed her head as she stood there, her hands held together in front, one knee slightly knocked. She looked momentarily as if she were a little girl trying to worm her way out of discipline. "I'm sorry, Father."

"Sorry! You have made a fool of me for the last time!" Mr. Tang grabbed the child-sized wooden stool beside him and raised it to strike at Lili. Lili ducked, rolled aside and scrambled towards the front gate.

"Please, Wenli!" Mrs. Tang pleaded with her husband.

"Stay out of this, Anlin! I'm warning you!" Mrs. Tang backed into her corner and watched with horror as her husband chased their daughter around the courtyard. But Mr. Tang was too wily for his daughter, cutting off her exit. He grabbed a hold of her flailing long hair and with one sharp tug, yanked her till she tumbled to the ground. Then he beat her with the stool, and all Lili could do was try to shield herself with her arms.

MINGYEN CHEN

1950. Hong Kong is in a state of chaos. British patrols tightly monitor the border, fearful the Chinese Red Army might attempt to cross. Refugees from the Mainland wander the streets in futility, desperately searching for food and employment. Enterprising entrepreneurs hope to capitalize on the times and cash in big time—and not necessarily by legal means.

Mingyen's mind was in chaos too. No matter how hard he tried, this calculus just didn't figure rightly in his brain. Why did I choose this course? he asked himself. Why did I ever think civil engineering would be good for me? Mingyen looked up and saw the photo of his mother on his desk. He needed a pep talk, a reminder of why he was doing this. She was always good for that. How I miss you, he said inwardly.

He decided to get a drink from the kitchen. As he wandered down the hall, he observed a forlorn figure sitting alone in the living room. Crouched over in the armchair, Mr. Chen held his head in his hands.

"Are you all right, Father?" Mingyen asked gently.

There was no response.

"Father, are you all right? Are, are you sick?"

Slowly Mr. Chen raised himself. Staring straight ahead, there was no visible sign he noticed his son. But, "I'm all right, son. Just leave me alone for now, please."

"Is there anything I can get for you, do for you?"

"No, thank you. I just want to be alone."

Mingyen was mystified. This was happening more and

more lately. Finding Father by himself, obviously with some kind of inner turmoil, but he would never say what it was. Mingyen would have asked his brothers to talk to him since they were the favored older sons, but they weren't around. They had gone off to study in universities in America and Australia.

Mingyen poured himself a glass of soya milk. What can I do? He's never talked to me. Mingyen sighed, feeling helpless. Lord, please help him.

1951. The Chens moved back to Shanghai. Mingyen looked around at his old bedroom—his desk under the window, bed to the right against the wall, oak wardrobe to the immediate right of the door—it was all familiar to him. Well, he thought, two good things have come out of the past year: I'm forever free of the problems of partial differentiation and I got baptized!

There was a smile on Mingyen's face. His father's financial speculations hadn't worked out well in Hong Kong and he had had to move the family back to the Mainland, but Mingyen was optimistic about his own future. He had been accepted into St. John's University in Shanghai, a far more reputable school than the college he had attended in Hong Kong. He looked forward to beginning his new economics program in September.

The past year had also brought him closer in his relationship with Jesus, and water baptism was only a natural course. Since his mother had died, Mingyen had decided to attend church and read the Bible of his own accord, to see for himself if what she had been saying was really true. And it was! Never did he think it possible that a Book could come so alive as this one had! Never did he think that words could warm his heart the way these ones had! Jesus was real and so were his words. Now, with each day that passed, he found that he loved to attend church. He loved to help the church, and he loved learning all he could from the pastor. And he would continue to do just that back here in Shanghai too.

"What would you say to preaching, Mingyen?" Pastor Liu asked one day.

"Me?" The eighteen-year-old Mingyen was incredulous.

"Yes, you."

"What—you mean on a Sunday?"

"Of course. What else?"

Mingyen sat there, still overawed at the idea. "What would I talk about?"

"You can just talk about whatever God's teaching you at the moment."

"But, but I feel like it's hardly anything."

"So take some time to study and prepare a bit—say, two months? You already do your own Bible studies anyway, right?"

Mingyen nodded his head slowly.

"Well, this won't be much different. And besides, you've been a Christian for a few years now. I think you'll discover there are things inside you already that you don't even know are there!"

A dubious look appeared on Mingyen's face. He wasn't convinced about that.

"Sure! Sometimes it's the challenges in life that bring those gems out of us." Pastor Liu paused to give Mingyen a moment to digest the idea. "You've been a great help in the church since you've returned from Hong Kong—leading the hymn singing, helping the people in practical ways . . . They like you, you know. I think you could do it. Why not give it a try?"

"You really think I could?"

"Mingyen, you will find in this life that many things are possible with God, and, therefore, for you. You've just got to be open to the opportunities and to his creativity. He doesn't always think or see things the way a human being does."

Mingyen considered his pastor's words. "Well, if you really think so, I'll give it a go."

1952. Preaching isn't so bad, Mingyen thought. The people really seem to take it to heart, to consider my words. He thought of the compliments a couple of people had paid him last weekend and beamed. I would never have imagined that anyone could be interested in anything I have to say. But then only God could make that happen.

Mingyen lay awake in his bed. It had been another full night of studying—both for the church and for university. He was beginning to feel lately that his coursework at St. John's was a bit of a nuisance. It was much more interesting, really, to read what Oswald J. Smith had to say about the revival we need, than how Joseph Schumpeter explained business cycles. But finals were around the corner. The only good thing about them, Mingyen thought, is that it means a summer of freedom is near!

He rolled over on to his left side. As he did so, he felt the hollowness of hunger in his stomach, reminding him of how late he had arrived home. Very little dinner had been left. Yichun's such a pig, Mingyen thought. The leftovers could hardly have been in the kitchen cabinet an hour.

Mingyen had been with Pastor Liu. In fact, he'd been spending a lot of time with the old man lately, following him around, after lectures, on his visits to the elderly and the sick in their church. Pastor Liu was so patient, so meticulously conscious of every one in need in his congregation. Mingyen imagined this must have been the type of compassion that Jesus exemplified while on the earth and had said so to the older man.

Pastor Liu had smiled in response.

"How do you do it?" Mingyen had gone on to ask. "Don't you ever get tired of visiting so many people and trying to help them?" The university student was thinking of the thing he found particularly trying when he was with the pastor—the trips to the hospitals. Mingyen was pained by the sight of suffering and he didn't like the sickly smells that infested the wards. What a depressing place, he couldn't help thinking. And yet it was while Mother was in the hospital that she got saved. Someone had bothered to take the time to go and talk to her and other patients about Jesus. Mingyen was chastised.

The pastor had delayed so long before answering the question Mingyen thought he hadn't heard it. But then he spoke. "You know, Mingyen," he began, "you are still a young man, but you will see many things yet in this life and draw your own conclusions. For me, however"—here he opened his hands as if he were offering something—"I've seen that no matter how hard people work, whether it be building a business or farming a field, or how well they plan, they still can't control what happens to them. Even if they are 'good' people, just trying to live out their lives in an honest way." Liu shrugged his shoulders, the picture of someone still trying to find an answer. "War comes, or some kind of other disaster, and it destroys everything they've built. People are left with nothing. What was all the work for then? What was the point?" The older man paused to push his glasses further up the bridge of his nose and to sigh as he remembered those he had seen who had been left with nothing. "It didn't matter how hard they worked," he reiterated, "it still amounted to nothing. Having enough money wasn't the answer. Neither was having the largest or most powerful army. Living in the country or the city didn't guarantee stability either."

"But maybe people didn't make the right choices for themselves," the university student knowingly interjected.

"Sure. That could have happened," replied Liu. "But even if you pick the right side in a war one time, there's no guaranteeing the next time a stronger army won't come along and overthrow the existing one. Just look at China's history. Bigger or newer isn't always better." The pastor looked over to the lad to see what he had to say.

Mingyen couldn't argue with the minister and remained silent.

"The only thing that I've found to be secure," the older man continued, "is the Word of God. It never changes and it never fails. Therefore His goals are the only goals worth pursuing. Because you're building something that *lasts*, regardless of what happens around you." The more experienced man looked at Mingyen here to see if he understood. "Many people will make you promises but don't count on them to keep them. Only God can do this unfailingly."

Mingyen nodded his agreement with this statement.

"Furthermore," Pastor Liu went on to say with growing passion, "his Word is alive. When I say this I mean it has this supernatural ability to be relevant no matter what the time or situation, no matter if you think you already know it. It grows and grows in its depth of meaning. But one only sees this over time." Pastor Liu paused in wonder as he reflected on his experience of this truth. Then, as if he suddenly remembered Mingyen was there, "So you see, it is crucial in my life to know more of his Word," he resumed. "The more I know his Word, the more I know him. He is, after all, the Word made flesh. And there is no other purpose in life except to adhere to his Word. So it is my mission in life to encourage others to do the same. Jesus is the only constant we will find in life, in good times and bad."

The zeal of the pastor's passion in talking about the value of the Word and its constancy had made an impression on Mingyen. And there, in his bed, the student was forced to reevaluate his own life. Did he have that kind of depth of love and commitment? Hitherto he had enjoyed his responsibilities in the church and was genuinely committed to the people and, of course, to God, but Pastor Liu had expressed something that involved more than mere service or duties. It was the reason for being, for living. Did God really mean that much to him?

As he pondered this, Mingyen's mind turned to something he'd read earlier in the Bible. "The Spirit of the Lord is on me because he has anointed me to preach good news to the poor." As his eyes had passed over the words he felt like a challenge was being issued to him. Was this what Pastor Liu meant when he said the Word was 'alive'? If so, then how is this relevant to my life? thought Mingyen. How, for instance, would my plans to start my own business fit into this? He couldn't come up with any workable ideas so he considered the consequences of doing something without Jesus. What would be the point? he concluded. What would be the point of having a business if you didn't have Jesus? You'd still be poor if you didn't know him, no matter how much money you made. Mingyen recalled again Pastor Liu's own comments on the matter earlier that day and was struck by the wisdom of the older man. He's so right.

Mingyen sighed and rolled over on to his right. He considered his upcoming exams and refined his studying schedule. One year down, two more to go. Then time to go into busi . . . He drifted off to sleep.

Grandma Chen was wringing her hands as she hobbled her way up and down the length of the living room. Upon returning home, Mingyen could see right away that she was worried about something.

"What's wrong, Grandma?" He went over to stand by her side.

She sat down on the sofa, still holding her hands. "Oh," she moaned, "it's your Father."

Immediately Mingyen's spine stiffened. "Father? What's happened?"

"He's been detained."

"Detained? Where?"

"At his factory."

"Why?"

"The authorities are investigating to see if he has evaded paying his taxes."

Mingyen was stunned. He had heard the rumors, that the clampdown on business people or "capitalist pigs", as they were being called, had begun . . . He shouldn't have been surprised but he was . . . because now it was his father. How could this be? Father is an honest businessman. I'm sure of it. "Surely Father pays his taxes."

"Of course he does."

"Then why the investigation?"

"Oh, Mingyen!" the old lady snapped. "Do you have to ask in these days?"

Mingyen felt sheepish for asking but he didn't know what else to say.

The family waited anxiously at home for the next three days. Mingyen couldn't study. He didn't even have the heart to go out with Pastor Liu. Both he and Yichun had tried to get into the factory to see their father but they weren't allowed in. Filled with foreboding and fear, they had reluctantly made their way home.

"What do you think they're doing to him?" asked Yichun, scurrying to keep up with his big brother. Mingyen was walking at a furious pace, like a man on a mission. His hands were stuffed deep in his trouser pockets and his eyes were focused straight ahead.

"How should I know?" came the exasperated answer. This was not a good time for little brother to break into his thoughts.

"Well, do you think he's all right?"

"I don't know."

"I've heard some pretty bad things can happen—"

"Don't talk about it," Mingyen cut in sharply.

"Yeah, but they can be pretty brutal . . ."

"I said don't talk about it." Mingyen took a deep breath and stopped walking. "Look, Yichun, I'm sorry I snapped at you. We're all worried about Father but it doesn't help to think the worst, all right?" He resumed walking. "This is the first time the authorities have detained him. I'm sure he's going to be fine. We'll just have to pray and trust God, okay?"

"Okay."

The two continued walking in silence.

Finally Father came home. It was to the great relief of

Mingyen, Yichun, Grandma and Cook. But he hardly appeared normal to them. He seemed to have aged ten years since the beginning of the week. He was haggard, his shoulders slouched, and his fedora was flattened and sat crookedly on his head. His silk tie was stuffed messily in the breast pocket of his Shanghai tailored, Italian wool jacket, and his usually pristine white shirt, now streaked with dirt and grease, was half tucked in in a haphazard way and half left hanging out at the waist. This was not their usual dapper dad.

In attitude Mr. Chen was also a changed man. From that point forward, he led a decidedly less visible life, trying to "relate more closely to the people," as he would say. The first thing he did en route to meeting this objective was to donate his chauffeur and automobile to his factory "for the good of the masses". He would no longer use them for personal reasons. He threw away his western cut business suits, hats and shoes and donned the fashion of the time, complete with Mao jacket, cap and soft soled, cloth shoes. Business owners, he rationalized, did tend towards capitalistic notions and needed to develop more awareness of socialist values.

Maybe going into business isn't such a good idea, Mingyen thought. Look at Father. Besides, how can I get closer to the poor if I'm locked in an office or plant somewhere?

The idea of working with the poor had weighed more and more heavily on Mingyen's mind lately. In particular, he had a deep longing to help them know about Jesus. He had begun to have a recurring dream which disturbed him: Many people in many villages were suffering because they didn't know there was Hope, and he felt that he must do his part in making Him known. Is that it, God? Is that what you're telling me? If so, then how can it be done? And where would my economics degree fit into this?

At first he thought he could just start his own business. Then he'd have control over his schedule to go and tell people about Jesus in rural areas. But there were two reasons why this didn't work for him. First, it would mean a part time commitment to the business, leaving only a limited time to teach. He felt he needed to dedicate himself completely to the latter task, especially if he was serious about building relationships with people which, to him, was what the church was all about. Second, private businesses were under a lot of pressure these days, even to the point of being forced to shut down. I don't want to have to deal with all that red tape, Mingyen thought.

There was another dilemma too, but of a completely different nature. The authorities were becoming stricter about "religious activities", placing limitations on what could and could not be done. Virtually all foreign missionaries had already left China, and he had heard that some local pastors and church leaders were being arrested and put in prison, accused of being counterrevolutionary. A new push was being made in the country to rid it of "enemies of the state", and this included targeting Christian leaders as they were seen as propagating "foreign" and "imperialist" ideas.

Mingyen decided it was best not to be a church worker in official title. He would have to go undercover. But what kind of cover? A businessman was out—it worked theory-wise, but not in practical terms . . . A teacher? But that would mean he'd have to be willing to spend at least a term in one school . . . No, that wouldn't do. He needed to be able to move from area to area, if necessary, without the constraints of a calendar . . . What would allow him to travel without raising suspicions?

A doctor! It was a hard decision for him, especially since he didn't like seeing people in pain, but Mingyen decided he would learn Chinese medicine. It was practical, helpful, and villagers always welcomed doctors because they were so scarce in rural communities. It would be the perfect excuse to travel from place to place and would raise no suspicion with the authorities. Yes, he concluded, that would be the plan.

LILI TANG

1978. Lili stood at the side of the grave of her cousin Tao. She watched as his parents lovingly laid the platter of boiled chicken, bowl of oranges and cups of rice wine down in front of the newly covered plot. That could be me, she thought. I could be in the ground, ashes and all. But I'm not. For some reason, God has healed me and allowed me to live longer than the doctor predicted. But why couldn't Tao have been healed too? I don't get it, Lord. Sometimes I just don't understand you.

Mr. and Mrs. Tang and Min began the descent home. Lili followed, gingerly making her way down the mountain behind them. She was still smarting from a few of the bruises her dad had inflicted last week. Tao had only just turned nineteen when he passed away, a year and a half older than Lili. She remembered, as children, going to the doctor for that first medical with him, and then to the hospital afterwards for x-rays. Dr. Ni had said they both had weak hearts, that it would take a lot of luck for them to make it to their mid-teens. It would be a *miracle* if they lived beyond them. He had seen it before, this condition in their family, he continued. It seemed to be a hereditary problem. They both regularly suffered from poor blood circulation, their fingernails frequently turning purple, their breathing often labored.

"Look at this child," Lili recalled the comments her grandparents used to make, "there's nothing to her! Even if you threw her to the dogs, they wouldn't have enough to eat!" This had disheartened the seven-year-old girl. What made them think she didn't know they were talking about her?

The sight of children running at the foot of the hill reminded Lili of physical exercise class. Chugging along at what seemed to her an aggravatingly slow pace, she would jog, pleading with all her heart inside, "Lord, help me! I don't want to stop! I don't want to have to give up! I want to run with my classmates! Please help me!" Then one day in her final year of high school, at age sixteen, she noticed that she wasn't fighting for breath the way she normally did after exercise or climbing the stairs. What's happened?

Earlier this year she and Tao had gone for another check-up. They had had the routine x-rays done. Tao's came back showing the usual problems. But Dr. Ni couldn't believe what he saw on Lili's. Her heart now appeared to be growing like that of a normal seventeen-year-old girl and her arteries were healthy. He thought she was looking more robust than usual when she came into his office but he never expected this!

Lili closed her bedroom door that night. She was still housebound, forbidden to go out. Her father maintained a close watch on her, knocking on her door every half hour or so and requiring her to respond verbally. He'd had enough of her trickery—a light through the crack in her door was no longer sufficient proof she was in her room. She couldn't even sleep uninterrupted if she wanted to.

She pulled out her most precious possession, an incomplete New Testament consisting of a mere five books—Luke, John, Acts and the two letters to the Corinthians. It had taken numerous nights and long hours to copy every single character by hand, but it had been worth it. It was to her as if Jesus himself were sitting there beside her, conversing with her face to face.

She was grateful for the person or persons (she still didn't know which) who had managed somehow to keep hidden even these few books throughout the tumultuous Cultural Revolution and so save them from the fires. Otherwise she would be sitting there with literally nothing in her hands. Lili knew there were many other believers who felt the same way she did, who were starving for knowledge of the Bible. In the madness and chaos of recent times, it was the only truth that had meaning to them, that cultivated life and inspired purpose. The core of the converts were, in essence, farmers, peasants, the simple country folk, and they clamored to her, begging her to make copies for them as soon as they found out she could write. Writer's cramp set in long before she had completed her furious rewriting of four more editions, yet demand remained great. She could not go on in this way. Finally she undertook to engage more scribes, namely her school friends who had become Christians.

Lili sat down at the table with her condensed Bible. Unusually, she was not overly eager to open up the volume this evening. She had been having a difference of opinion with Jesus lately and, quite frankly, Lili didn't feel like hearing what he was saying at the moment. She thought she could better ignore him by not opening the book. But as it sat there on the table it seemed to beckon her and she could no longer resist. I guess I can't avoid you forever. She exhaled. Okay. I'll hear you out. I'll give what you're saying proper consideration.

She began to read. "A man said to him, 'I will follow you wherever you go.' Jesus replied, 'Foxes have holes and birds of the air have nests, but the Son of Man has no place to lay his head . . . Follow me.'" Lili slammed the book shut. It was happening again—those words were jumping out of the page! She clenched her eyes shut, as if she had been struck by a fist. You can't be saying this! she shouted in her head.

Why not? What if that's what I want you to do?

I can't! Lili argued. You know what it's like here. I can't just leave home like that. It's, it's so improper for girls to be seen like that, traveling here, there and everywhere with no family or husband. What would the neighbors say? Mother and Father would lose face. Besides, I've got to help them on the farm. They count on me. And anyways, what's wrong with what I'm doing now? I'm following you at night . . . well, when Father isn't aware . . . I give you my all at night. You know I do. Can't you be content with that?

Lili got up from the table and began to pace the floor. She paused by the window, glanced out into the darkness, wishing, truly, she was out there instead of in here. The truth was, she loved talking about Jesus. The desire in her to speak burned like a wildfire. If she didn't do it, she felt like she would explode.

Then she sighed. Lord, she prayed, you know deep down inside there's nothing more I want to do than to please you, but I just can't do this. At least not yet. It's only been a year since I've left school. I've got to show my father I'm a good daughter, that he doesn't have to be ashamed of me. You know he doesn't trust me already. Give me some time to do that first.

The sun was scorching. Lili crouched down on her hands and knees in the sweet potato field, determined to get the better of the weeds today. A couple of weeks had gone by since she had come to terms with Jesus about their issue. Her father was loosening his guard a bit, so maybe she'd be able to slip out again for some meetings soon.

She missed going. There was something about being able to walk together from village to village with seventy or so other believers, most of whom were from Lili's year at school. There was such camaraderie and solidarity, such encouragement in being with people of like mind and faith . . . And then the atmosphere at the meetings was so electric. Whole villages were flooding the courtyards in anticipation, spilling over into the lanes. Hundreds, upwards to a thousand, could be there. You never knew what was going to happen. One by one, different teens would jump up, impromptu, and speak about whatever Bible lesson they were learning at the time or the most recent thing Jesus had done for them. The villagers didn't know what came over them. But they would be moved to tears, the words, flowing with such passion from youths unlearned and untrained, inexplicably gripping their hearts and shaking them to the core of their being. It was an amazing phenomenon!

Phew! It's hot today, Lili thought. She raised her head and her brow with the back of her hand. A few farmers, she observed, were working in the next field over. She focused back on her weeding. But she couldn't find them. All she could see were Bibles. At least she thought they were Bibles. She figured they must be Bibles. What else could they be? Stacks and stacks of them, in fact, packed in towers and towers of cartons. Being loaded on to planes. Many more being carried on to trains and boats. What is this?

This is so strange. What are these paper-like boxes?

We don't have them around here. We only use cloth bags to carry things. And those planes and trains—where are they? There aren't any of those around here either, except in pictures. What can this mean?

"Ma."

"Yes, Lili."

Mother and daughter sat with their sewing after dinner.

"I think God was trying to tell me something today."

"Oh?" Mrs. Tang raised her head. "What?"

"I think there are going to be many Bibles in China in the future. I saw them in the ships, in the planes and the trains."

Mrs. Tang laughed. "Oh, Lili, I think you've been copying too many verses lately. All you've got is Bible on the brain! I wouldn't be surprised if you've actually gone a bit loony!"

"I'm serious, Ma! I saw them—more than you could count! Tons of them! God's going to make it happen."

Mrs. Tang saw her daughter was not laughing. She was, in fact, very earnest. "You're possessed."

"I am not!"

"I'll have to pray for your deliverance."

"Don't say that, Ma! I'm not possessed!"

"All right." Mrs. Tang was growing concerned. Maybe being stuck at home so much recently was having a delusional effect on her daughter. "Then describe it. Tell me what the Bible looks like."

"Well . . . it's a small book, a thin book." Lili held her left thumb and index finger a hand span apart. "The pages are wafer thin too."

"That's wrong! A Bible is very big and thick—this thick!" Mrs. Tang held her hands fifteen centimeters apart. "What you saw were not Bibles."

"But they were! They were Bibles!" Lili insisted.

"Please do not talk such nonsense anymore, dear."

"I can't help it. They've been popping up in front of me all day!"

Mrs. Tang was disquieted. Every day for the past two weeks, her daughter claimed to have the same apparition. She became convinced that her daughter was indeed possessed by demons. She prayed for Lili daily, to exorcise them. But afterwards, always, Lili would say she could still see the piles of books.

Lili began to sneak out at night again. As much as Mrs. Tang disliked seeing her husband upset, she hoped the meetings would fix whatever was wrong with her daughter. After all, healings were such a common occurrence it was quite likely she would be made well too. Or perhaps the problem's just that she's been cooped up too long. Whatever. As long as she doesn't keep talking about seeing things that aren't there!

Lili took several deep breaths as soon as she got on to the main road. The night air was like a tonic to her, quickly reinvigorating her spirits. She didn't think she could have handled another night indoors. She stepped into a light jog, eventually catching up with a growing group of teenagers on their way to one of their thrice weekly meetings. This one was scheduled to be in Xushan village.

"Oh, Lil! So glad you could make it!" Yangzi said.

"Yeah! Long time no see!" Lingmei chimed in. "How'd you do it without your dad knowing?"

"He wasn't feeling well today, went to bed early."

"I don't know how you do it," Lingmei said, "I mean, how can you live in a house with that kind of tension?"

Lili remained silent. Her recent conversations with Jesus sprang to mind. *Okay, Lord! I said I'll follow you and I will. Just let me get on better terms with my father first!*

"What would you have her do?" Yangzi retorted, "Run off and live on her own? As if any self-respecting girl can do that!"

"Hey, don't get excited," Lili said, trying to preempt an argument between the two girls. "Jesus said there'd be persecutions and, well, at the moment I guess the test is my dad."

"Well, I don't know if I could live like that. I'm just glad my dad is a believer," Lingmei said.

"We weren't always believers before, you know," replied Lili.

"True," said Lingmei, snatching at a branch of a tree that was just about to brush her across her face, "but still. He beats you, Lili. How can you stand it?"

"I'm not the only kid to be beaten by their father." Her response was rather matter of fact. But then, with greater depth of feeling, "I don't hate him; I love him. I really do. He's just concerned about the family."

"But how much can you take?" Lingmei's question was a stern response to the issue at hand. "How much should anyone take?"

"'If anyone comes to me," Lili began to quote, "and does not hate his father and mother, his brothers and sisters—yes, even his own life—he cannot be my disciple.' Those are the words of Jesus." Lili was reverent at the mention of his name. "We've got to be willing to put up with difficult circumstances. We've got to love him more than our families, Lingmei."

"That's an awful high price to pay," said Lingmei.

"Maybe," said Lili.

The girls walked a few steps in silence.

"You know," continued Lili, "it's not that Jesus wants to make you hate your family, but there are lots of people who don't understand or know about Jesus. My father is one of them right now. He's just trying to do what he thinks is best. I can put up with that. I can." These last words were more a declaration to herself than to her friends, and she looked straight ahead with an unwavering focus, her determination renewed to face whatever came her way.

"What do you think you're doing?"

"What do you mean?"

"I heard when we broke into small groups tonight, your group prayed that God would provide one Bible for every believer."

Grandma Zhong and Lili were walking home from Xushan village later that evening.

"Aiyah! Slow down, girl," the old lady moaned, "I can't walk as fast as you young people."

"I'm just happy you decided to join us tonight, Grandma."

"Well, my grandson wouldn't stop nagging me to come. And now my bones won't be happy. I'll need a week to recover from this journey!"

Lili laughed.

"You didn't answer me," said Grandma Zhong getting back to her original question.

"What did you say again?"

Grandma Zhong sighed, exasperated. These young people, always so flighty. "Is it true? Did you ask your group to pray for one Bible for every Christian?"

"Oh!" Lili giggled. "Yeah. We did."

"Aiyah! Why are you so greedy?"

"What do you mean?"

"If you ask God for that, you are making so much trouble for him!" the old lady scolded. "Why don't you just ask for one Bible for each village church? That would be enough. You shouldn't make so much work for him."

"But Grandma, if God can give a church one Bible, surely he can give it ten or even a hundred! He's God! He can do it!"

"Aiy! You are a greedy girl."

Lili laughed again. But she had seen them and she knew they were coming.

Lili parted from Grandma Zhong at their village gate. She made her way through the dark streets, completely buoyed by the fact that she had been out again. Let it rain! she said to herself as the drops began to fall. It was glorious to be free and nothing could dampen that feeling! She turned the corner to her street, dancing with arms open wide as a heavier drizzle began to fall.

The Tang household was silent. Lili tiptoed across the courtyard, careful not to wake anyone. She pushed at the front door to enter the house, but it didn't open. She pushed again, but still no. This is unusual, she thought. She leaned into the door with her body but still it remained shut. It did, however, creep a couple of centimeters, and Lili barely made out the faint glimmer of a bronze colored bar. Oh no! I'm locked out!

Lili took a step backwards in utter disbelief. The wind picked up and it began to pour. She was getting drenched so she grabbed the collar of her jacket and pressed the two ends closer together. Oh great! What am I going to do, God?

she panicked. I'm getting sopping wet. It's getting colder. And if I make a sound, Father is sure to beat me again!

She took a deep breath, trying to compose herself. Lord Jesus, please open the door, she silently prayed. I know you can do miracles. Please open these doors. She checked again. They didn't give. She pleaded again, her desperation growing with each failed attempt. An hour passed and her hands and feet grew numb with cold; her fingers and toes were hardly able to bend. She was soaked to the skin, yet her tears were many and she tasted their saltiness every time she opened her mouth to pray.

She had been standing outside the doors a couple of hours. I'm doomed, she thought. Father's going to beat me if I don't freeze first. Standing there in despair, a story she had read in Acts came to mind. Lord, she said closing her eyes, if you opened the prison gate for Peter, I know you can open this door. Please, please do it. She opened her eyes and looked at the door again. At first she was afraid to try— why should it open this time? But then she told herself, if you don't ask or try, you don't receive: She put her hand to the door again. To her astonishment, it opened!

The long, ancient Chinese-styled bronze lock dangled lopsided from the front door. Part of the doorframe, to which the lock was fastened, had broken off and sat loosely at the bottom of the crossbar. All Mr. Tang noticed was that the door was not locked as it should have been. He walked across the hall to Lili's bedroom and tried to open her door. It was locked from the inside. Blast!

"Anlin!" he shouted to his wife. "Anlin!"

"What is it, Wenli?" she answered, rushing into the front hall. "Why do you have to shout so loud at this time of the morning?"

"Why did you open the door for her?"

"What are you talking about?"

"Why did you open the door for Lili?" he repeated, pointing to the front door.

"I didn't."

"Don't go protecting her again, Anlin."

"I'm telling you, I didn't open any door last night. What are you talking about anyway? You never lock the door."

"Well, I did. Last night, when I woke up. I went to get a drink and found that our obstinate girl was doing her disappearing act again. And if it wasn't you who opened the door, then who did? 'Cause I know I certainly didn't."

Mrs. Tang could tell her husband was starting to get into one of his angry moods again. "You locked the door, you say? Then you must have the key. Where is it?"

"Uh-it-uh-" Mr. Tang sputtered momentarily, then patted the pockets around his body. He turned sheepish. "Oh. It's here . . ."

Lili tiptoed back to her bed from her listening post at the door, having been wakened by her father's ranting. She was relieved. Relieved that she got into the house last night. (Thank you, Lord!) Relieved that her parents were not going to argue about her. And last but not least, relieved that her father, confounded at the mystery of how she got in, momentarily forgot to pursue his inquiry with her. She crawled back under the covers. But, she thought with some trepidation, he could still do that yet.

SAIMEN LIANG

1970. Saimen sat on the bare, hard cement floor. It was three o'clock in the morning. His legs were crossed, elbows propped on the knees, chin planted on his fists. He had no wall to rest his back against. The room was cramped with sixty other believers.

How did this happen? he asked himself. How did the PSB know we'd be there? He mulled over the events of the late evening in his mind. Could someone have told? What a shock to find the normally still bushes by the river rustle to life at midnight, with officers charging out of them, surrounding him and his group instantly. It was impossible to think of escape. We didn't even get to baptize anyone, he thought with regret. We barely even finished the opening prayer.

Saimen stood up. His legs were getting pins and needles. They're sure to find out now, he said to himself. They're sure to find out about my faith. The enormity of the dilemma crashed down on him: What if they make me choose between one or the other? . . . No. Christ must be bigger than Communist party membership. It couldn't be any other way. As he came to this conclusion, Saimen couldn't help remembering with pride the day party secretary Niu had granted him that honor, for not just anyone qualified for party membership.

"You wanted to see me, Sir?" Saimen had poked his head into the county secretary's office only six months earlier.

"Ah! Comrade Liang! Come in! Come in!"

Saimen sat down in the chair Niu indicated in front of his desk.

"Well, young comrade," the secretary began, "I've been hearing very good reports about you."

"Uh, thank you, Sir."

"You've done good work over the last couple of years, supervising the railroad line. And now, I understand you're currently assigned to help with the construction of the new party headquarters."

"Yes Sir."

"They say that the masses respond well to you, respect you. You really know how to motivate them and get them going."

Saimen remained silent. What could he say? He couldn't very well tell the party secretary he'd been approaching people one on one, telling them there was a Savior and that their sins would be forgiven if they came to him. He couldn't very well tell him either, that his ability to rouse the people was entirely due to the fact that they were finding hope through Jesus in these unstable and unpredictable times.

"Well," Niu continued, "I'm happy to inform you, comrade, that I'm recommending you for party membership."

"Me?" Saimen's eyes widened in pleasant surprise.

"Yes, you."

"Wow! How can I—Wow! Thank you, Sir!"

Saimen was brought back to the overcrowded room by a kick in the back of his ankle.

"Sorry," he heard a female voice mumble behind him, "my leg's killing me . . . Just had to move it."

"It's all right." Saimen decided to sit down again. As he

did, he noticed Lin standing in the corner, praying silently. The elder brother, in his mid-fifties, had really taken Saimen under his wing in the past year. He saw in the lad potential to lead the church. "You know, Saimen," he had said only three weeks ago, "I don't know how much longer our church will go undetected by the authorities. You see how severe they are on any believers they find." The older man had licked his lips, trying to gain some time as he decided best how to phrase his next words to his young friend. "Some day, Saimen, I believe you are going to have to make a hard decision. Either God is the truth or he's isn't—"

"Of course he is!" the young man cried out impetuously.

Lin nodded his head patiently. "Here me out, Saimen."

Saimen calmed down and settled in to hear the rest of what the older man had to say.

"Either God is the truth or he isn't," repeated Lin. "Either God is the way and the reason you live, or he's not." Here the older man paused slightly to check Saimen's urge to respond, then continued. "These are dangerous times for Christians, and I expect that it will become more difficult for you to carry on as you are." Lin looked over to Saimen to see how he had received this last sentence.

The expression on the young party member's face had become opaque, unreadable, but inwardly Saimen was thinking, "It's already difficult!"

Observing the quiet air that had come over the lad, Lin carried on. "If I am caught, Saimen, you must continue the road of the cross. This is what God wants for you. It will be hard, very hard, but you must keep on encouraging the flock. You must keep on helping them. And you must never, never give up on God. He will take care of you and show you what to do."

Saimen looked at Lin again. It's like you knew, he said

to himself. Except I'm stuck in here with you. But maybe . . . maybe . . . Secretary Niu has always been favorably disposed to me, he thought. He's always made me feel so valued as a person. Saimen recalled the various occasions the cadre had given him gifts of clothes for himself and food for his family. Maybe I should just tell him the truth. Maybe he'll understand.

Saimen got up and walked over to the door. "Guard!" he banged.

The wooden panel slid open. "What do you want?"

"I want to speak to party secretary Niu, please."

"You want to speak to the secretary?" The young guard sneered. "And what makes you think he'd give a rat's ass to talk to you?"

"Comrade secretary Niu knows me and my family. He'll speak to me. Please."

At that moment, another guard noticed the discussion and came to garner a closer look. Instantly he recognized the face through the opening. "Comrade Liang! What are you doing in there?"

Saimen was visibly relieved. "Comrade Zi! Please, I was just trying to ask your partner here, could I please speak to secretary Niu?"

"Oh, let him out Comrade!" Zi said to his colleague. "I know him! He's perfectly fine!"

The door opened and Saimen stepped out into the hallway.

"So you want to speak to secretary Niu?" Zi asked.

"Yes, please."

"Well, for you Comrade, that can be arranged. No problem."

"So, I was at the river last night, Sir. I was one of those caught," Saimen confessed.

"Oh, young comrade, don't worry about that!" said Comrade Niu with a chuckle. "I'll fix that in no time! Comrade Yang!" he called to his junior officer. "Comrade Yang, come in here!"

Yang ran into the room, breathless. "Yes, sir!"

"Find the paper work on Comrade Liang here and arrange for his release from that group that was caught by the river last night."

"Yes, Sir!" Yang was out of the room as quickly as he had come in.

"There," Niu turned back to Saimen, "you see? No problem."

"But Sir, I'm telling you I'm a Christian."

"And I said don't worry about it! As long as you don't believe in the future! We all make mistakes once in a while . . . Why don't you just go home and rest now, eh? It must have been a long night for you."

Saimen couldn't believe his ears. They know I'm a Christian and I can go home!

"This is not bad. Not bad at all." Leaning back in his chair, elbows planted on the armrests, Secretary Niu held the report half an arm's length away in his left hand, a cigarette in his right. Eight months had passed and it was now well into spring 1971.

"However, Comrade Liang," he went on, "the whole point of the party reorganization and having everyone write a report, is to state our position. You haven't actually done that." He leaned over to tip some ashes into an ashtray. Then he resumed his comfortable position. "You've done an excellent job telling us how your granduncle first told you about God and how he was responsible for making you a Christian. But will you continue to believe in your granduncle's Jesus? That is the question." Secretary Niu laid the report down in front of Saimen, who was seated on the other side of the desk, and turned it around so it was facing the author. His short stumpy fingers continued to hold the paper in place as he braced his position over the desk with his right hand (and burning cigarette) on the arm of his chair. With penetrating eyes he looked his young comrade squarely in the face. "You only have to write one more sentence." Niu sat back completely in his seat.

Saimen didn't move. He continued in his upright posture, hands folded in his lap, outwardly appearing a placid young man. The only sign of the struggle going on within him was the slight rigidity around his mouth. Discernible only by his mother, it was the look Saimen had whenever he was contemplating something deeply.

"Did you hear me, Comrade?"

"Yes, Sir."

"Well?" Niu moved the pen closer to Saimen.

Still Saimen didn't move. And still the area around his mouth remained tight. It was a hard decision. The words of the elder Lin had come back to haunt the young party member. What had seemed, at the time, an exaggerated concern to Saimen had become a hard decision indeed.

"Okay. You don't have to write the sentence. Just tell me that you will not continue to believe in Jesus."

Saimen shifted in his chair, straightening his back again. He opened his mouth to say something, then hesitated. He closed his mouth. There was just no way around it anymore. No way. Either God is real or He isn't. He is! Either He's the truth or He isn't. He is! Saimen bit the bullet. "But I will."

Niu sighed. "You are a Communist Party member. You do realize that, don't you?"

"Yes . . . Comrade Secretary, I want to believe in both!" The young comrade was stout as he made this declaration.

"Communist Party members believe in Marxism, Comrade, not in Jesus. You have to make a choice."

Saimen remained silent.

"You know, Saimen," Niu began his next attempt on the basis of their four-year-old relationship, "you've always been rather special to me, kind of like a son. I think I've always made sure you were looked after and treated well. Wouldn't you agree?"

Saimen couldn't argue with that. He nodded his head.

"And have I ever given you any reason to doubt or mistrust me?"

Sadly Saimen shook his head.

"Then trust me when I say that, if you choose your Jesus, you will be in for a difficult life. The way of Jesus is not the way of the Communist Party." There was a hardness to the secretary's voice as he said this, and a hint of bitterness. If all my time and efforts on your behalf have been wasted, boy . . . His thought was not completed.

It was a tone Saimen had not heard him use before. It was shocking to his ears, yet deep down inside, he wasn't really surprised, for it had all suddenly become very clear. They were of two different worlds. Adhered to different codes of law. They answered to different leaders. And now the line was drawn. This was it. There could be no more denying. "I'm sorry, Comrade Niu," he began, "I am grateful to you for all that you have done for me and my family. But I must choose Jesus."

Niu was crestfallen. "Then so be it."

"Liang!" The guard had come for Saimen again. It had been like this every two or three days for the past twenty-eight days. He unlocked the cell door and proceeded to tie the prisoner's hands behind his back. Saimen was then directed out into the corridor.

"Any sign yet?" asked Comrade Niu gruffly, as he watched Saimen being taken to the nearby school from his office window.

"No, Sir," his assistant Yang answered, "no sign of cracking yet. He's been rock steady."

Blast. "How are you handling it?"

"The usual, Sir, just like you said—searched his house, organized denouncement meetings and spread the word the star's in detention. We put him in the 'show cell'."

"And how's that going?"

"Well, Sir," said Yang gleefully, "the officers have been happy with the supply of cigarettes they've been able to collect!"

Niu's eyes narrowed and darted across to his junior. Clearly the superior officer was not amused with the subordinate's reference to the bribery that went on in his jurisdiction.

Yang coughed. "Uh, sorry, Sir. Beg your pardon, Sir . . . Uh . . . There's been a steady stream of people coming in off the street to see for themselves. A panda in the zoo couldn't ask for more spectators."

"Hmph." Niu returned his eyes to the scene outside the window. "Did the search turn anything up?"

"Well, sir, we found a songbook with anti-revolutionary themes in it."

"For instance?"

"Like, what does it say, Sir?"

"Yes, Comrade," answered Niu with a slight edge in his voice.

"It mentions things like 'the kingdom of God is near' and 'nations will fight nations', Sir."

"So he believes there's a government better than socialism and supports war efforts towards it."

"Appears so, Sir."

"I assume you had him questioned about it."

"Yes, Sir."

"What did he say? Where'd he get the songs from?"

"Well, this is strange, Sir. First he said he wrote all twenty songs himself, but it doesn't look like his handwriting—it's too neat, too smooth. And he's had so few years of schooling—how could he possibly write songs?" Yang paused here, rather pleased with his own deductions. "So after that he said he got them from his granduncle. When we went to check the old geezer out, we found out he died in 1967. He's obviously protecting someone, and we think it highly unlikely the granduncle wrote them. But the case is still inconclusive, Sir."

"Why didn't you put more pressure on him to reveal the songwriter's name?"

"We did, Sir. But he was very stubborn. He said we could charge either him or his dead granduncle for being anti-revolutionary, but he didn't have any other names to give."

The look on Niu's face hardened. He took out a cigarette from the pack in his pocket. "And what's happening at the denouncement meetings?" he asked as he lit up.

"About a hundred are attending at the school courtyard, Sir, each time."

"Where are you getting them from?"

"All the people he used to work with over the last four years, Sir, they've been summoned and scheduled, Sir."

Niu remained silent for a while. Most cadres would have died of shame by now and begged for mercy . . . The superior officer swore under his breath. Why are you so stubborn, boy?

"Is it all right, Comrade Secretary? Should we be doing something different?"

"No, Comrade. You're doing fine . . . What do they accuse him of?"

"At the meetings, Sir?"

"Yes, Comrade." Niu resisted the urge to roll his eyes.

"What you would expect for a religious zealot, Sir—that Liang told them the world will come to an end and Jesus is returning to earth . . . all that kind of stuff."

"And how does he respond?"

"He preaches to them!" exclaimed Yang in wonderment. Then, collecting himself, "He tells them to confess their sin and God will not hold it against them. Sir."

"Hmph." Secretary Niu contemplated how he could have made such a gross error in judgment. Liang was supposed to be his star protégé! "All right, Comrade Yang. Make arrangements to send him to Village 14."

Saimen stood under the jujube tree. He was next in line to receive his bowl of rice topped with a few pickled vegetables. He appreciated resting, however brief, under the shelter of the branches on this blisteringly hot afternoon. It was difficult to find things to appreciate these days, but at least he didn't have to face the angry crowds in the school yard anymore. It had been a shock to the system to discover that peers who once worked so amicably with you could do such a complete about face, that they could twist your words so maliciously and vindictively. Saimen tried not to dwell on these negative thoughts.

He took his lunch from the kitchen crew and went to sit on a rock under the cover of a nearby bush. Most of the other laborers from the sesame field with Saimen had also planted themselves around there. It was about the only place with some shade.

"Hey there, sonny!" said a bow-legged seventy-two-year-old man, waddling up with his bowl of rice to join the group. He smiled in greeting, revealing a missing front tooth.

"Grandpa," said Saimen somberly, respectfully addressing the old man in the traditional way a younger person would.

"How'd a stripling like you end up here in Village 14? You don't look like you qualify to be an old, outcast landlord!" He extended his arms, with chopsticks and bowl in each hand, to indicate the group of hungry men around them, all in their sixties or older. Someone in the group stifled a snicker at the remark. "You couldn't have amassed a lot of wealth at your age!"

Despite his recent trials, a small grin crept onto Saimen's face at the man's attempt to be friendly. "I was sent here because I believe in Jesus."

"Oh . . . a Christian, are you? But other religious people aren't sent here."

"Well, I guess it's because I used to be a Communist party member."

"Oh . . . I see."

The men busied themselves with shoveling rice into their mouths and for a while that was the only sound that could be heard, bar the occasional buzz of a fly.

"Well," the toothless man resumed, "I suppose that explains last night's superstition theme in political study."

"How often do we have to attend that class?" asked Saimen, the night having been his initiation.

"Oh, only a couple of times a week."

Saimen didn't look too impressed with that answer, the impatience of youth coming to the surface.

"You know, sonny, after all the raids, the public beatings and struggle sessions, life in Village 14 is easier in comparison, I say," the elderly man began to say in response. "They think that by putting us on public display in these fields they can shame us further. Well, I ask you," he leaned in closer to Saimen here, "how much more face does a person have to lose after going through all that?" The man flashed his toothless smile again. He obviously had come to grips with his own situation.

But Saimen hadn't. He was melancholy for the rest of the afternoon and for many days after. Since he'd made that crucial choice in Secretary Niu's office, he had had only one thing on his mind: God, I've done it. I've given you my life to serve you. When will you get me out of here so I can do that?

Still: Gaining Maturity

Suffering isn't pleasant for anyone. The natural human tendency is to avoid such a prospect, if at all possible. But what if you can't? What do you do? Some choose to fight it, kicking and screaming all the way. Others, though, choose to look patiently for the lessons that can be learned through the painful times. They find, after having gone through it, that they now possess some of the deepest and most profound truths in life.

"Let's get some lunch," Saimen said to me one day when I was visiting.

"Okay."

"How about dog? Is that okay with you?"

"Sure. Whatever you want." I was quite happy, as usual, to defer to my host on the local cuisine.

Soon afterwards, seated in a restaurant, Saimen perused the menu. After several minutes he decided on the dish. "All right," he said, "Let's have dog head."

"Uh, okay," I responded, not exactly enamored with the choice, "whatever you want. But why do you want dog head?"

"Because I like to chew on the bones. It reminds me of being in prison. That's all you get when they give you 'meat'—bones."

MINGYEN CHEN

1995. Mingyen is seated on a stage, looking out at the couple of hundred cadres and party officials gathered in the audience, listening to the master of ceremonies drone on and on. When will this man finish? The air was warm in the Chinese People's Congress Hall, somewhat stuffy, and Mingyen subtly readjusted his bowtie to help him breathe a bit easier. It would be nice to have some tea right now, cooling.

In Anhui province, site of his fourteen and a half year labor camp imprisonment, Mingyen was being distinguished as Most Honorary Citizen. It's ironic, really, he thought: Branded a counterrevolutionary one day. Given the key to the city another. Who could figure it out?

The audience applauded. The mayor of Anqing stepped up to the microphone. Aiyah! Another speech! Mingyen hoped he didn't look bored.

Hu Xitong began his speech, "We are here today to honor Mingyen Chen for his great philanthropic love for the people of Anhui and China. As you all know, there was severe flooding in our province in 1991 and lives were lost, but many more people would have died and suffered had it not been for the help Chen brought to us."

Mingyen counted the number of dignitaries seated on the stage with him—two of them had already spoken, this was the third. At most there should only be one more speech, he reasoned. Thank goodness. He wasn't meaning to be ungracious, but sometimes, he thought, people really do go overboard with the formalities.

"In addition to raising generous support for the relief fund, he organized to have several containers full of medical equipment and supplies shipped from America to our province. As a result, thousands more people were able to receive treatment and be reunited with their families."

Mingyen's mind turned to a previous time that he had been able to see people in Anhui treated and returned to their families. That was when he was still imprisoned in the labor camp, in the mid-1970s, despite the fact that he had finished serving his full ten year sentence in 1970. Officials deemed that he hadn't reformed enough, that he was still counterrevolutionary in his thinking, so he hadn't been released. He wouldn't be for another eight years.

At least the last couple of years in the camp were a bit better. As the camp's head Chinese herbal doctor and pharmacist, he was given his own room in the medical clinic and he no longer had to live in the regular barracks, sleeping on the same *kang* with up to twenty-nine other men. He also received more humane treatment from the camp authorities and their families, as they respected him for his skills in Chinese medicine. That was a welcome change compared to the six years he had been assigned to the cesspool! Mingyen almost had to suppress a smile when he thought of that time.

Mingyen was arrested for the third time in his life in 1960. This was the charge that eventually landed him in the *laogai*, the Chinese gulag. He had been caught preaching in a village in Zhejiang, then sent back to his home city of Shanghai for interrogation, trial and sentencing.

Interrogation. What an ordeal. Terrible, horrifying, it

was a grim nightmare he hoped he would one day to be able to forget.

"Confess! Tell us who your foreign connections are!" shouted Comrade Rong, the investigator, a burly man of forty-two. His hair was too long, constantly having to be brushed aside after falling in front of his eyes, and he seemed too big for his clothes: The buttons looked ready to burst on his shirt and his sleeves and trousers tended on the short side. "We know you've been in contact with people in Hong Kong, America, outside. Who are you working for?"

"I don't work for anyone," a twenty-seven-year-old Mingyen replied, utterly exhausted. This was the third straight day of questioning and he hadn't been allowed to sleep, not even once. Every time he nodded off or was near doing so, a guard would slap him in the head several times or kick him in the shins. "I know people in Hong Kong—I lived there for a couple of years."

"That would've given you plenty of opportunity to be trained by British intelligence."

"I'm not a British spy! I was studying civil engineering at Canton College!"

"Yeah, and from your grades, it doesn't look like you did that well. Maybe you were up to something else—like learning spy tricks instead of civil engineering?" Rong gleefully sneered his question.

"Civil engineering is a hard course. There was more math involved than I expected and I'm not a natural mathematician. That's why I eventually transferred to economics at St. John's University here in Shanghai."

"Hmph! . . . In your file here, it says you were helped by a Canadian lady, a Helen Willis. You were arrested last in 1956 and she helped you then! She was trained by the Americans—I think *you* are working for the Americans! She tells you to give her information about China, doesn't she?"

"I'm not working for the Americans—or for anyone! Miss Willis, as you well know, came to China as a foreign investor, but she left years ago—you know that too. Yes, she helped me when she was here—she lent me some Biblical reference books from her bookshop. She helped me in my Bible studies! How can I teach the people in church if I don't study?" Of course Mingyen didn't mention that Miss Willis was actually a Christian who was kindhearted enough to source him the materials that enabled him to write and publish many Christian books in Chinese.

"You and your church," Rong spit out the words with disdain, "just a bunch of religious nonsense . . . Anyway, don't you know you shouldn't be relying on those capitalist dogs anymore? This is a new day for churches in China! No more foreigners dominating our churches! Instead, Chinese people should be governing their own churches, Chinese people supporting Chinese churches, Chinese people teaching Chinese churches! With the Three-Self Patriotic Movement, there's no need for foreigners to help your church! You shouldn't follow their doctrine, their ideas or their ways. Get with it!"

Rong paused for a moment, pleased with the fervor of his own speech—everyone should see it this way! Then he continued, "Let's say that maybe you aren't a spy—*maybe*. But you can't deny you do have foreign connections. Surely some of your friends *are* spies. Tell us which ones."

"Look, I don't have foreign friends living here anymore—you know they've all moved back to their home countries. So how could they possibly be spying?"

"They've assigned someone local to watch you secretly, to observe your methods. Which of your friends has been acting suspiciously?"

Mingyen would have laughed at the ludicrousness of the idea if he wasn't so worn out. "I don't have friends like that. And besides, if there were any such spies, how could they report overseas? It's not like they could meet with their fellow spies on the street or run down to the local post office to make a telephone call in front of everyone and transfer information."

"Hmph. You intellectuals all think you're so smart. But you've obviously got serious problems with your worldview. It's not right." Rong motioned to the guard by the door. "Take him back to his cell for now."

Mingyen fell flat on the floor when he got back to his cell, grateful for the respite. God, he prayed, how much longer will this go on? Interrogation was ruthless, brutal, and unrelenting. Every few days they would come and take him for questioning, usually waking him in the middle of the night, and he could be there for anywhere from one to three days straight.

Mingyen turned over in the tight cell—a mean feat considering four other men were sleeping on the roughly two meter long by one and a half meter wide floor beside him. The space was so cramped Mingyen could touch both walls with his hands if he stretched out his arms. But at least he could have a few moments rest, and he drifted off into a dreamless deep sleep.

RRRINGG! It was the wake up bell.

"Chen! Get up! The guard'll be here soon," whispered Zheng, a cellmate. He shook Mingyen. "Get up!"

"Leave him! If he gets in trouble that's his problem,"

grumbled Jiang, another cellmate.

Mingyen groggily lifted his head. "What time is it?"

"It's time for you to get up!" Zheng persisted.

A guard peeped his head into their cell. "4701! How was your sleep?" he mocked, knowing that Mingyen had only returned to his cell less than two hours ago. The guard's presence was a precursor to breakfast. It meant the food trolley was not too far behind. And sure enough, it rolled up to divvy out the standard fare, a bowl of congee—if you could call it that. It was more like lukewarm, milky colored water with a couple of grains of rice sprinkled in. The prisoners lined up with their enamel bowls at the front gate of the cell, waiting for the kitchen boy to ladle out their portion. Then carefully, so as not to spill any, each man would walk back to his corner and drink, perhaps imagining it was something more substantial in their mouths, something more tasty.

Mingyen was the last in line to receive his ladle this morning. As he waited he gazed through the iron bars before him, into the atrium of the British built prison which had originally been named after the famous battle at Waterloo. He wasn't exactly sure, but he estimated there were up to eight floors of cells in this block. He was somewhere in the middle. Opposite him, on the far side of the atrium, was a wall with a row of windows, the only source of daylight into this otherwise dreary place.

It took a couple of months but he was slowly beginning to get accustomed to its rules, ways and quirks. For the most part talking to other cell mates was not permitted. Just sit there and don't talk. Or, if it was "exercise" time, which consisted of a few minutes walking up and down a corridor (you couldn't even go outside for fresh air!), don't talk. About the only time you were permitted to talk was in study group.

Study group. Generally an article from a newspaper would be read aloud. Everyone was then expected to express what they thought about it. In essence, could the prison officials find any evidence that inmates were learning how to speak Chinese communist talk? That's not it *officially*, of course, but while they might get everyone to look and sound the same externally, how could anyone truly know what went on *inside* an individual? You had to be God to know—and communists don't believe in God!

Mingyen sighed. These days were hard because they were long. They were long because there wasn't much to do. And there wasn't much to eat, only two meager meals a day. Every second day or so, prisoners would actually get a bowl of rice with a few pickled vegetables. Otherwise, it was that watery thin soup they passed off as congee.

But at least the interrogations were starting to be spaced out. Or maybe he was just getting used to them. No, there were definitely starting to be longer gaps between the oppressive sessions now. They were slightly fewer in number. The first month felt like there was hardly any let up. It felt like he just got back to his cell and then he'd be dragged off again. It was taking all his mental resources and strength to remain focused—on the answers he gave, on getting through the unspeakable grind, and, when that was over, on trying not to scream from the boredom of a prison regimen of inactivity.

At least he could look forward to monthly family visits. Chi and Tai would be here next week! She was sure to bring some food—good! Nevertheless, it would be good to see them both. Mingyen wondered how much his son had grown since last month. Tai's four now and he's beginning school . . . Is Chi managing all right for the two of them?

She is resourceful though, and her family will help her.

Chi and Mingyen had been married five years. They met when he was teaching at a retreat for Sunday School teachers, and Mingyen had been struck by Chi's inner strength. She was the only Christian in a traditionally devout Buddhist family; however, her parents had agreed to their union with no fuss. Chi was also supportive of his work. They had spoken at length before the wedding of what that entailed, of the risks involved, that he could be arrested literally at any time. Yet she still wanted to marry him. He felt he was truly blessed.

"You don't look so good."

"What do you expect? I'm in prison. We only get two bowls of congee a day. But I'm surviving."

"But those bruises. Are you still being interrogated?"

"Yes, but not as often as at first." Thank God, he added in his mind.

Chi could finally ask Mingyen all her pent up questions now that her mother had taken Tai out to the waiting room so husband and wife could be alone. (Well, as alone as the presence of prison guards would allow you to be.) They spoke in low voices.

"Do you know when your trial will be?"

"No, not yet."

"What do you think they'll charge you with?"

"I don't know."

"Surely your case isn't that complicated—what's taking them so long?"

"I don't know." Mingyen was beginning to feel a bit impatient with these questions that he didn't have answers to, but he didn't want to waste this little time with Chi getting into a needless argument. "Look Chi, I know I'm not guilty of any crime. *You* know that too. This is just the way things are in China at the moment. You know we talked about this before, that I could be caught anytime and, and, what that could mean for us. Well, it's happened again. We just have to keep praying and believing that God will change the situation."

"Last time wasn't this hard though. You were out in a couple of months! It's past that now and we still don't know anything! And, and—and they're so much rougher this time with you!" Chi bit her lip to stop the tears from coming.

"I'm okay, Chi." Mingyen had to muster all of his self-control to say this calmly, especially as he knew his wife saw the cruel treatment he was being subjected to, but he knew he had to be strong for the two of them. "We just have to be patient," he continued. "God is in control. We know that in all things he works for our good. Trust him, okay?" The husband tried to divert the wife's mind from their troubles and looked into the bag she had given him. "What did you bring? Mmm, glutinous rice steamed in lotus leaves, an apple and boiled eggs. I'll enjoy these. Thank you."

"I'm sorry it's not much. It's getting harder to find food these days and more expensive. Ma helped me with the eggs though. I don't know how she did it, but she found some extra coupons so we could give you a couple. And I can't always get to the market on time, what with the office and Tai."

"It's great, Chi. Thank you."

"So you don't know when your trial will be? Maybe father will be able to help."

"I told you, Chi, I don't know. Don't trouble your father—we don't know what's happening yet anyway, okay?" Mingyen knew he had to prepare his wife somehow. He leaned forward a little closer to her. "Chi, listen. I won't lie to you: I think this is going to take some time. You think it's been long already, I know, but it could be longer yet. This time could be different, not like a few years ago. You understand?" Then, because she didn't answer, "Do you understand me, Chi?"

Slowly Chi nodded her head once, but she remained mute.

"You've got to steady yourself, prepare yourself if that's the case, you understand?"

Again Chi nodded her head.

"You and Tai will be all right. I'll be all right. God will take care of us. Understand?"

There was one final nod.

In 1961, more than a year after coming to Waterloo, Mingyen was charged and tried. He was labeled a counterrevolutionary for his preaching and evangelistic activities, for writing and publishing Christian articles, and for his Hong Kong connections and "imperialistic" tendencies. It was clear to the panel of judges that this *bourgeois* man had thought problems—and they cited his recent attempt to evangelize a fellow inmate as further evidence—and consequently they sentenced him to ten years in prison, to be served where he already was.

Inwardly Mingyen recoiled at the mention of that attempt. It's not that he regretted sharing his faith; it was just the memory of the "dark room"—where the attempt landed him—no light for twenty-four hours a day for countless days, except for the briefly opened door when they gave him food. The full blast of light, however, was too much for the eyes to absorb in that short moment, and just when one had overcome the shock and was ready to embrace it, the door was closed again. Heartbreak. There was no interaction of any kind with anyone from inside or outside the prison during this period. No letters either, writing or receiving. He thought he'd go insane. He still didn't know exactly how many days he had been in there, but it was definitely at least a month because he missed two family visits.

The tedium of life at Waterloo didn't change much for Mingyen after sentencing, except that those horrendous interrogation sessions were mercifully over. The food remained measly, study group was ongoing and exercise time left something to be desired. He didn't try to evangelize again. There was, of course, the dark room, but more than that, he had been discovered because the inmate had reported him. The betrayal still stung. It seemed you couldn't trust anyone anymore.

As the days wore on, Mingyen felt his strength draining away. He found he needed to focus more mental energy on surviving physically. There were days he felt so feeble all he could do was crawl across his cell. Even before he was arrested he had developed a problem with his stomach; the current diet provided insufficient nutrients and calories, and the stress of the interrogations had only served to aggravate it. Mingyen suspected he was developing an ulcer when he saw the color of his stool. It wasn't severe enough in the warden's eyes to allow him a visit to the clinic for proper medical attention though. Hopefully it wouldn't get any worse.

The incessant inactivity became an ever growing anxiety in Mingyen's mind. It's slowly killing me, he said to himself. He tried to think what he could do to slow the regression. There are factory wings in this prison. I will apply to do work there.

"4701! What do you think this is?" yelled Comrade Rong through the bars, flinging a piece of paper into the cell. Every member of the cell looked up at their interrogator, stunned by the sudden outburst of noise. "That's right! I'm talking to *you*!" Rong pointed at Mingyen. "You think you can make amends by working? You need much more than that, I can tell ya that!"

Mingyen picked up the piece of paper which had fallen on the floor. It was his letter of application to work in the prison factories.

"You're moving! Get your things. Let's go!" Rong unlocked the cell door.

Mingyen gathered his few belongings and stepped out into the corridor. Handcuffs were snapped on to his wrists and, with two guards on either side of him, he followed Rong down the hall. Mingyen was led down the stairs, through a series of doors, out of the block, across the courtyard and into another block.

Oh no! thought Mingyen to himself. This isn't a factory block. What is this? For a short while fear entered his mind again. Am I being interrogated further? Is something worse going to happen? But my trial's over. What can this be?

Rong stopped at the administration desk of the new building and signed some papers. He resumed leading Mingyen and the two guards up some more stairs, through some more doors, down a few corridors, until finally they stopped in front of a cell.

"In you go!" Rong hollered boisterously as he stepped aside after opening the door. "You need more rehabilitation!"

Mingyen looked around him, initially disconsolate at the turn of events. But then he was thankful. He was thankful that his worst fears had not been realized. Eventually he became aware that he was no longer being classified as a "criminal" prisoner; he was now locked up with the "thought" prisoners. And while it was common for criminal prisoners to be assigned work in the institution's factories or shipped out to a labor camp, thought prisoners in his newly assigned wing generally didn't go anywhere.

His new cell was similar in size to his previous one, but there was one less occupant. A positive—only slightly less crowded than before! The new regimen, however, included more study group sessions which lasted for longer durations. Dismay—even greater drudgery.

"But why do you want to go?"

"It's not so much that I want to go, Chi, but I can't go on doing nothing. I'm still young, but I'm wasting away here and it's only been three and a half years—how am I going to survive the ten? If I don't go, I'll die. My only chance is to have some work to do, anything, so my health can't just deteriorate like it is now."

"You'll lose your Shanghai residency."

"I realize that."

"You won't be able to come back here to live."

"I know. But pretty soon I won't be able to live at all if I stay here! We'll worry about residency later, okay?"

It was Mingyen and Chi's last meeting at Waterloo Prison. Mingyen was due to be shipped off to Anhui tomorrow. In a last ditch attempt to find himself something to do, to have some kind of occupation and "exercise", to have some kind of purpose to wake up each morning, he had decided to apply to serve the rest of his sentence out of province.

"I can't believe you actually applied to go to a labor camp."

"What else could I do? They wouldn't let me work in the factories here."

"You'll be so far away."

"We can write to each other. And anyway, it's not as if we can see each other everyday here."

"But who *chooses* to go to a labor camp?"

"Look Chi, I'm going. It's all approved. We can't change that now, so there's no point in questioning it. You must keep strong and take care of Tai, okay?"

"Mm." Husband and wife sat there, quiet. Then, "It's very hard—the conditions—isn't it?"

"Most likely, yes."

"People die there."

"Well, you'll have to pray for me. We'll both have to pray. God has helped me survive this place so far, I'm sure a labor camp is no different to him."

"Mm."

The next day, hands tied behind his back, Mingyen left the prison to catch a boat heading up the Yangtze River to Anhui.

LILI TANG

1983.

"Is she there?"

"Almost. Just wait . . . Okay, she's closed the door."

"'Kay. Quickly. We need to make some serious decisions here." Kuan lowered his voice slightly as he looked intently at the three other leaders seated in the room, all of whom were aged from thirty-three to fifty-three years. "What are we going to do if Lili gets shot?"

"Oh, it's terrible, isn't it?" said Sheng, who saw Lili as a little sister. "She's still just a girl—barely twenty-two. She shouldn't have to be in this position."

It was the month of August, and the central government had launched a new initiative—the Anti-Spiritualist Pollution campaign. In an effort to rid the country of corruption and "polluting elements", there were new requirements to be met by all levels of party leadership, from national through province, on down to the county and village. Quotas, for example, on criminal convictions, imprisonments and executions had to be filled as evidence that society was being cleaned up, and here, in Weining county, Shanxi, there was no exception.

The church leaders gathered here, including Lili, either former "convicts" or blacklisted because of their religious activities, had discovered that they were now targeted by the local PSB. They could, if they resisted, be executed on sight without arrest or trial. Moreover, if they *were* shot, their families would be charged with the cost of the bullet. (That wasn't an issue with the leaders now though. Earlier they had all coughed up the nine *yuan* and set it aside so their families wouldn't be burdened financially if that should turn out to be the case.) Local authorities had publicized all of their names, among a total of thirteen, in wanted posters that had been plastered throughout the county. The purpose of the meeting today was to discuss how to continue safely church operations. Until this moment, however— when she'd gone to the outhouse—no one had dared to raise the "Lili question".

"At least if one of us gets shot, we have husbands, wives or families who would come to claim our bodies. But she doesn't," Sheng continued. "She's not married. She's attached to no one."

"But what about her parents? Couldn't they claim her if she's killed?" asked Wan.

"No," Kuan interjected. "Don't you remember? Her father has all but disowned her because of her faith. Even before she left home, he used to beat her when he found out she'd gone to a meeting. We cannot expect her parents to take her back."

The room fell silent as they contemplated the girl's sorry situation. Sheng, the only woman in the room, broke into quiet sobbing. To be disowned! To have no one to claim you! She began to sniffle, let out a sob, and then she had to pull a hankie out of her bag to blow her nose. As she tried to stifle another sob, the men couldn't help but notice. They too began to feel their eyes water.

"Well," said Wan, "maybe I could talk to my wife, and we could find somewhere suitable to bury her."

"No, let her come to me," said Bai. "It'll be easier to find a place for burial on my farm. And then I'll get my wife to plant some flowers over her grave. We'll take care of her."

"Excuse me." All four heads swung around wildly, afraid that Lili had caught them unawares. Thank goodness! It was only Mrs. Chung, their hostess. "Dinner's going to be ready in about ten minutes. Just wanted to let you know."

Mrs. Chung left to make her final preparations, and Lili reentered the room. Oh no! Did she hear after all?

As Lili sat back down at the table, she noticed that no one would make eye contact with her. It was as if they were all purposely trying to avoid her. Kuan looked up at the ceiling; Sheng, out the window; Bai, at the floor; Wan, all around and anywhere but at her. Sometimes these older people were so strange, she thought.

"Well, where were we?" asked Kuan, turning his eyes to his twiddling thumbs.

"You know," Sheng scrambled up awkwardly, "I think I'll go help Mrs. Chung serve dinner."

"Oh, good idea. I'll join you," said Lili, half rising out of her chair.

"No! Uh—I mean—I think one of us helping will be enough." She left before Lili could make a reply.

Lili raised her eyebrows.

"I think I'll go to the toilet before dinner." Bai popped up and left immediately.

"I'll come with you," said Wan.

"Me too," said Kuan, not wanting to be left alone in the room with Lili.

Yup, really strange.

Sheng and Lili laid down to sleep in their room. The Chung family were always such wonderful hosts, Lili thought, as she pulled the bedcovers up to her ears. She couldn't stand the cold and preferred, when possible, to have the blankets just so.

Her thoughts turned to dinner. The other co-leaders had continued their awkward behavior throughout the meal and Lili could no longer believe it was merely due to their difference in age. They're hiding something from me, she realized. But what? They've never not talked about church issues with me before; they've always included me in the decision making.

"Sheng?"

There was no answer.

"Sheng? Are you awake?"

Sheng was determined not to be awake for conversation tonight.

"Sheng," said Lili, poking her with a finger.

Great, thought Sheng. As if I can ignore that. "I'm sleeping, Lili. Can't it wait till tomorrow?" The muffled voice beneath the covers had a trace of irritation in it.

"Sorry." Lili turned over. She really doesn't want to talk about it. All right. I'll let it go . . . for now . . .

Her mind turned to the meeting that day. The policy was forcing them to change the way their church worked. The leadership team had made the hard decision to disband the large courtyard gatherings. Although serving as a key life force of the body of believers over the last few years, it just wouldn't be safe to meet in this way anymore. Why draw the attention of local authorities if you didn't have to? For the protection of the church, they would need to exercise more prudence and greater discretion in how and where they now assembled . . . And what about Sheng? Kuan? Bai and Wan? It would be so awful if they were killed because of this new law. Lili couldn't, in particular, forget the look of concern that came over Kuan's face when they first read that dreaded poster on the street. He had been released from prison less than two years ago—eight years apart from his family. If only I could take their place, Lord, she said inside. They all have people that depend on them, that they need to care for . . . And yet . . . and yet they can't even go home. With the way things are at the moment, they can't even be there for their loved ones. Instead they're all—*we're* all on the run. What does this mean?

She searched for an answer in her mind as she lay there in the dark. She tossed over possible reasons, explanations, and then, slowly, she saw emerge a way that might be an answer: It was a river. The river was wide, stretching before her as far as she could see. But it was a sheet of ice. Lili cautiously stepped on to the frozen surface, unsure of its thickness and ability to hold her weight. She hesitated to take a second step. I don't want to fall into the freezing water. I might get swept away with the current underneath. I wouldn't be able to surface for air . . . But she felt she must take a step. Otherwise, how would she get to the other side?

She proceeded to step forward. She wobbled a bit. Her feet slid, fighting to get a grip, trying to find balance on the slippery surface. She had to put her hand down on the ice to steady herself. But at least she was still dry! So far, so good! She stood upright again and decided to take another step. A slighter slip, nothing a pair of waving arms couldn't control though. Then another step. And another.

As she found her footing, she decided to look back, to see how far she'd come. A few people were behind her, going through a similar first few nervous steps like her. She carried on walking. A little while later she looked back again. To her astonishment there were even more people now! Masses of them! Then she knew it was all right. All these people are on the ice. It's going to be strong enough. We're going to make it. We're going to make it to the other side!

Suddenly Lili woke up. It took her a second to remember where she was, but she relaxed as soon as she heard the even, deep breathing of a sleeping Sheng beside her. As it was still dark outside, she readjusted her blankets in preparation for more sleep.

In the stillness of the night she reflected on her dream. That's the way I felt when I first left home two and a half years ago, she realized. I didn't feel safe. I didn't know if I was going to be all right. But I've been fine. And now . . . Now I'm with the people. There's so many of us running around in different teams . . . We're going to be okay . . . Is that what you're saying, God? Even with this death threat hanging over our heads, we're going to be okay?

The gate of the Chung courtyard banged open at seven forty-five the next morning. "Did you hear?" asked an anxious Shulin, the nineteen-year-old daughter of Mr. and Mrs. Chung.

"What?" asked her mother, who was serving breakfast in the courtyard to the five guests.

"There were mass arrests over in Biru and Pucheng counties!"

"Mass arrests? What do you mean?" asked Kuan tensely, standing up from his chair.

"Last night. Christians. Lots of them, maybe several hundred. They even had to open an army barracks because the jails were too full."

"Who told you this? How'd you find out?" pressed Kuan.

"I was just down at the village market. That's the only thing people are talking about," the girl answered.

"We can't stay here," said Bai.

"You're right," said Kuan. "We need to leave. The sooner the better."

"But, but where?" asked Lili. "Where should we go?"

The four other church leaders looked over at the girl. She was the only one of them who had never been to prison. Yet. If only they could protect her. Somehow.

"Wan, Bai," Kuan said to the two oldest co-leaders, "I think maybe one of you should go with Lili. You could pretend you are a traveling father and daughter. Try to get out of the province if you can. Sheng, I think you should go home. Your husband will be able to help you."

Sheng nodded in agreement.

"I'll go with Lili," said Wan.

"Okay," said Kuan. "Bai, it's you and me."

Wan and Lili had been riding their bikes all day. They traveled roughly eighty kilometers and managed to make it into neighboring Hebei province.

"I know a Christian family in this village. Let's see if they can take us in for the night," said Wan.

"Okay," replied Lili.

They rode down the main street. The market was closing up for the day before sunset and very few stragglers remained. Wan and Lili looked at each other. That wasn't normal for a village. It should still be bustling with activity at this time of day.

"Here it is," said Wan. He got off his bike and rolled it up to the door, Lili following his lead. Wan knocked.

The door opened a crack. An eye peeked through suspiciously. "Brother Wan!" the owner of the eye said, opening the door wider.

"Brother Gao!"

"Come in. Quick." He seemed almost frantic as he waved the two visitors in.

"What's going on here?" Wan asked as soon as the door was closed. He hadn't failed to notice his friend's unnatural behavior.

"Not sure. It's felt kind of weird around here all day. Everyone's been edgy and nervous. What are you doing here?"

"I was hoping you'd be able to put me and my sister up for the night. Gao, this is Lili. Lili, Gao."

The two smiled polite greetings to each other.

"We've had to leave Shanxi because the PSB started arresting a lot of people last night," Wan continued. "Several hundred believers may already be in jail as we speak, and both our names are on our county wanted list."

"I'm sorry to hear that, brother." Wan's news did not make Gao feel any easier. "Maybe a crackdown's coming here too then, what with the way people have been behaving today. Something tells me it wouldn't be safe for you to stay here tonight."

"Is there anywhere else you could suggest then? It's getting dark."

Please suggest something, thought Lili. She was tired and didn't want to have to get back on the bike again.

Gao thought for a minute. "Okay. I have an idea, but you'll have to split up." He looked at the two of them, looking for some sign of agreement. Lili nodded at Wan. Wan nodded at Gao.

"Okay. Brother, you could stay in my shop tonight. If the PSB do any raiding, we shouldn't be connected—you'll just look like a worker. You, sister," he turned to face Lili, "I'll take you over to a widow friend of our family. Now she isn't a believer, but she's a kind lady. I think you should be safe with her. All right?" He looked again at the two of them.

Lili and Wan looked at each other, both glad and grateful for any assistance. "All right," said Wan for the two of them.

The night passed uneventfully at the widow's for Lili. Around seven in the morning though, there was a knock at the door. It was Gao's twelve-year-old daughter.

"Auntie!" she called Lili.

"What is it, Meijing?"

"My parents were arrested last night. And your bicycles were confiscated!"

Lili was in shock. What about Wan? Was he arrested? What do I do? I've got to find Wan. But is it safe? I can't stay here though. What if this kind widow comes under suspicion because of me? That settled it. She would go and look for Wan. "Meijing, can you help me? Please?"

The young girl nodded.

"Can you show me where your father's shop is? Then I think you should go home to be with your grandparents."

The girl nodded again.

The shop was empty. It was still closed and no one answered when she knocked. Has Wan been arrested?! The thought made Lili sick in the stomach. This is awful, God! Now what? She walked out of the village, out on to the road she and Wan had rode in on the day before. I don't know what to do, God. Should I stay or go? If I go, where to? Maybe I should stay around this road for a while and he'll show up. Yes, maybe he'll come to look for me here. Please

Lord, let him come.

Lili walked up and down a small stretch of road about ten kilometers outside of the village several times that day, keeping an eye out for Wan. It was an uneven dirt path, grooved roughly in the middle, where most single bikes tended to ride, and out wide for the donkey carts. Several short rows of poplars lined the country lane intermittently, while in other areas the grass grew wild and long. Whenever she saw people, Lili would quietly hum a song to herself, Psalm 23, in hopes that any passing Christian would recognize the tune and identify himself. Maybe then she could get some assistance from him. The long day passed but there was no sign of Wan or any other believer. Physically exhausted from the worry, the ceaseless walking and no food or drink, she spent a restless night under a tree, just off the dirt path. Her body begged for sleep but her mind remained active, jolting her awake every now and then. There was no rest that night.

Early the next morning, as soon as the sun was up, she resumed her pacing. Maybe Wan will come today. Please Lord, let him come. Or send someone to help me.

In the early afternoon, a couple of teenaged boys rode by on a bicycle. As was her habit, Lili hummed her song.

They stopped in their track. "Are you a Christian?" asked the one riding on the back.

"Yes, yes, I am," said Lili, hopeful. "Are you?"

"Yeah. We both are, me and my brother," he said, pointing in front of him.

"Are you from around here?"

"Yeah, Jincheng village, about fifteen kilometers that way," he said pointing his thumb backwards. "What about you? Where're you from?"

"I'm from Shanxi."

"You know it's not safe around here right now, don't you?" said the other boy. "Our parents were arrested last night. Lots of believers were arrested."

The grim look on Lili's face told them she was aware of the situation. "Would it," she began, unsure of what course of action to pursue, "would it be possible for me to stay at your house tonight? Do you think?"

The brothers looked at each other. "Normally it'd be all right," said the one riding on back. "But I don't think it's safe right now—for you."

"Oh." Lili thought for a bit. "Well, maybe I should go back to Shanxi. Is there any way you could help me?"

The two brothers looked at each other again. "Sure," said the one riding on back. "We'll give you a ride to the border. How about that?"

"All three of us on one bike?"

"Yeah!"

The brothers swapped over and took turns, one peddling, one on the front handle bars, while Lili rode on the back rack. Only stopping briefly for short breaks and for the brothers to switch positions, it took them the rest of the day to cycle the forty-odd kilometers to the border.

Lili prepared to spend another night under the stars after she left the brothers at the border. On edge, even more so after a second day without food, no sign of Wan and no certainty about what she was doing, she did her best to make her bed as comfortable as possible for the evening. As she laid back on the ground, she thanked God for the boys who had delivered her here today. She also asked him what she should do next. She just didn't know. An owl hooted in the distance. A light breeze blew, rustling the grass, causing

Lili to sit up immediately and wonder if someone or something was approaching. It would be another fitful night.

The next day, when she hadn't heard anything specific from God, she decided to head over to the nearby mountains. There was a Christian family she knew who lived up there, and perhaps it would be safe to stay with them for a while. It was the only thing she could think of. She had a few *yuan* in her bag and hoped it would be enough for the bus fare to the town at the base of the mountain. Her feet were blistered. She was going on almost three days without food or water, and she would need all the strength she could muster to find the trail and climb the mountain. She wasn't exactly sure where it was, having only been there once before a couple of years ago.

God, please help me, she prayed as she stood on the packed bus. Help me find the right trail. Help me know the right place to get off. Help me make it up . . . The bus stopped to pick up even more passengers. Mercifully several got off, giving her a bit more breathing room.

A couple of minutes later, Lili felt someone tugging at her shirt. "Hi, Lili!"

"Uh, hi." Lili didn't recognize the teenaged girl. "I'm sorry. Do I know you?"

"Oh, probably not, but I know you. I've heard you preach in our village. I'm Mrs. Kuang's daughter."

"From Pinglu county?" Lili asked hopefully.

"Yes! That's the one! I'm on my way home now in fact!"

You are amazing, God! Lili thought. Sending an angel to show me the way!

Mrs. Kuang suggested Lili rest in the bedroom for the few hours before dinner, but she couldn't sleep. Her mind was too full. She was still amazed at how she had managed to get to Pinglu. She was also still worried about Wan. What had happened to him? And what about Kuan and Bai? And where will I go next? Mrs. Kuang had only said she could stay for the night since it was so late in the afternoon; it was clear she was not keen on anything longer. The talk in the villages of the area was that Pinglu would be targeted for a crackdown soon.

It was four-thirty when Lili decided to pray. She poured out the problems that were troubling her, occupying her mind, her feelings of total helplessness and inability to decide on the next plan of action.

Eight o'clock tonight.

What's that? Did you say something, God? But she didn't hear anything else. She focused on the words: Eight o'clock tonight. Well, she thought, I suppose something's going to happen then. What? she asked God. But she didn't hear anything else.

Seven-thirty rolled around. "Dinner's in half an hour, Lili," Mrs. Kuang called through the bedroom door.

Lili got out of bed. She had managed to sleep a couple of hours after all. She looked at her watch. Her eyes popped open wide. Half an hour! Only half an hour! All of a sudden, the excitement within her that God was about to do something rose to a virtual frenzy. What's going to happen, God? Are you going to send a chariot to carry me to safety? The prospect was thrilling to her, and she tried to imagine how this would be effected. Oh, how I wish I could just change my watch and it'd be eight o'clock now! That last half hour felt like it would never pass.

Lili sat down to dinner with the Kuangs in their

courtyard at five minutes to the top of the hour. She had decided to bring her bag with her to the dinner table so she'd have it with her when the chariot came. Mrs. Kuang asked her to say grace. The eight diners around the circular table bowed their heads. Lili began to give thanks to God for the Kuang family, for their hospitality, for their faithfulness in helping the church . . .

BANG! The front gate of the Kuang courtyard slammed open. Startled, everyone around the table opened their eyes immediately.

It was Wan. Right on the hour.

"Wha-? How? How did you come?" asked a tremendously relieved Lili.

"Don't waste time talking. We've got to go. Now. Come on."

Lili grabbed her bag, quickly said thanks and good-bye to her hosts, and left immediately with Wan. She followed as he led the way higher up the mountain at a furious pace. On and on they walked, passing pine tree after pine tree. In the moonlight their branches stretched out ominously, creating eerie shadows, tempting the mind to imagine something that wasn't there. But Lili always quickly refocused. Why's he in such a rush? she thought, scrambling to keep up with him. Her foot slipped within her shoe, causing a painful rub against a blister. She didn't know what was worse to run into in the dark—long unpredictable tree trunks or hard loose rocks. She suppressed the exclamation of anguish she wanted to make with each contact. While Wan maintained this tenacious tempo, Lili didn't think it was appropriate to complain about her sores. He wouldn't persist in this way if it wasn't urgent. But after a few kilometers, she couldn't contain her curiosity anymore. She broke the silence between them.

"What's the hurry? What's going on?"

"The PSB are going to make arrests in this area tonight. That's the rumor I've been hearing all day. We'll just go a bit further up and spend the night in the woods."

Lili stopped still in her tracks, realizing how close she had been to being arrested. She only resumed walking when Wan beckoned her to keep moving.

The two trudged on for a few moments in silence. Then, "Wan, what happened? You weren't at the shop."

"And you weren't at the widow's. We must have passed each other without knowing."

"But how did you find me here?"

"Long story. I happened to run into your bike-riding brothers, and then eventually Kuang's daughter. She said something to someone who said something to someone else in the market this afternoon, but I had some problems finding the trail up to their place at first."

Lili's eyes clouded over with tears. She was overcome. God had truly carried her to safety.

SAIMEN LIANG

1971. Outside it was still pitch black as Saimen arose from his kang. It was 4 a.m. and, as was his established custom in Village 14, he washed his face, changed his clothes and then knelt down in preparation to pray. He'd been interned in the 'outcast' community for almost three months now.

Life had improved considerably after the first couple of weeks there. Saimen found that when he returned from the fields to his assigned home, many local Christians just happened to be sitting on the edge of the stepping stones he had to cross to enter the condemned village, refreshing their feet in the shallow stream at the end of a long, hard day. They wouldn't look at Saimen. They acted as though they didn't know him. But as he made his way across, one by one they would encourage him softly, under their breath, barely moving their lips. "May God help you." "May God be with you." "May God's peace be with you." Saimen immediately received a boost and he felt it was so amazing to be remembered in this way.

Saimen bowed his head and clasped his hands together. He gave thanks for the believers who had encouraged him at the stream yesterday. He prayed that they would find strength in their own time of need. He remembered his mother and sisters. And then he came to himself. When can I leave this place, God? When will you get me out? Should I escape? How can I be an evangelist if I'm stuck in here? They were the usual questions he had posed since he'd arrived and, admittedly, asked so many times now he didn't really expect an answer. But he felt better knowing he'd gone through the rhetorical routine.

He was just preparing to close off his conversation with God when he heard it. "In four days, I'll give you a bicycle." It was a still, small voice.

What? Saimen thought. Did you just say something, Lord? There was no response. Then he considered the words he heard. The more he thought about them, the more he was convinced he hadn't made them up himself. How could he? He'd never ridden a bike before in his life!

Wow! It hit the twenty-year-old: I get to ride a bicycle! I GET TO RIDE A BICYCLE! All my life I've never been able to do this. All my life I've never had a chance. I wonder what it'll be like? he thought with anticipation. I wonder if I'll get to pedal myself or if someone will double me. It seems so hard to stay upright on just two wheels. Will I be able to do it? Saimen was so giddy with excitement at either prospect he could hardly wait for the next three days to be over. He couldn't eat. He couldn't sleep. So he prayed even more for the days to go by faster!

Finally the fourth day came. Heightened excitement. Morning passed into afternoon. There was no sign of a bicycle. But do not despair. There's still half the day . . . Afternoon faded into evening. Still there was no sign. Now puzzlement.

The only thing that had broken the monotony of Saimen's daily chores was that he had been assigned to take the crop to town along with three other ex-landlords. It was a demeaning and arduous assignment, to be one of the 'mules' that would transport the sesame plants sixteen kilometers to the government warehouse. As one of the most physically demanding jobs in the village, everyone hoped that anyone else but he would be given it.

Collectively the four men had to propel manually the laden two-wheeled cart into motion and push the heavy load for four hours to make the delivery.

And now, because they had arrived so late in the afternoon and because the crop wasn't "dry enough" (so the snooty receiving clerk had said), they'd have to camp overnight outside the warehouse, as their goods would not be officially taken in until the next day. There was no way they could return to Village 14 with a full cart in the dark or without the official receipt showing they had made the delivery.

The four men sat on the ground, forlorn. There would be no dinner tonight and no shelter. (And no bicycle, thought Saimen gloomily.) But then the young man had an idea. He had a friend who lived nearby. Maybe he could go and borrow some blankets from him so at least they wouldn't be cold at night. Would they mind if he went to ask? Grateful for any succor, the ex-landlords agreed to the suggestion.

"So you're supposed to ride a bicycle today, eh?" Kachun asked Saimen this after the latter had explained what he thought he heard from God. The two friends were heading back to Kachun's home. Kachun, it turned out, was the 'friend' who had supplied the blankets. Furthermore he had just finished making a good show of fawning over Saimen, "the brother I never had", in front of the former landlords. He absolutely insisted that Saimen must stay at his house tonight—and how could the landlords object since they themselves had just received some provisions? "Well, I don't have one myself."

The two entered the house and Kachun called to his wife

to bring the dinner. "The only thing that comes to my mind, brother," said the host to his friend, "is that God's telling you to go on a self walk."

"A self walk?" Saimen asked.

"Yeah. You know, 'self walk vehicle'[9]—you're the vehicle. And I know the exact route for you to take."

After dinner, all through the night, Kachun led Saimen on a tour of neighboring villages, taking him from one believer's home to another. Kachun knocked silently on each door. They would enter the seemingly sleeping homes and Saimen would be surprised to find the household was actually awake, every member engrossed in their prayers. People would be kneeling either in the dark or with only one very dim kerosene lamp lit far from the well covered windows. As Saimen heard their words, tears welled up in his eyes. They're praying for me, he marveled. They're asking God to protect me, to release me.

There were many times too, that night (in which Saimen didn't sleep a wink), he imagined this must have been how Peter felt in the book of Acts, when the angel released him from prison, and afterwards the servant girl Rhoda answered the door of the house where all the believers had gathered to pray for him. No one could actually believe that he was standing there beside them. Their loving welcome overwhelmed him. God had not forgotten him.

He returned to Village 14 the next day with his fellow donkeys, much lighter in heart than when he had left.

"Report."

"Comrade Secretary, there's been no change, Sir," Yang

---

9 In Mandarin the three characters that make up the word "bicycle" literally translate into "self walk vehicle".

began. "Liang's been working in the fields and going to political study classes as directed. His attendance has been good and prompt at both, he doesn't complain about anything, but he hasn't changed either. Our man inside said he still believes in God."

Curse you, boy. Niu was disgruntled. He hated to be wrong about anything. "Move him to the reservoir."

His hands were coarse, severely chapped. They were perpetually coated with a chalky feeling from having to break stones with other stones to make them of manageable size. Initially the skin on the top of his back peeled from the constant friction of the manageable sized stones that he placed there for hauling to the place of removal. Now, however, he was beginning to develop calluses. Every breath he inhaled seemed to bring with it a choking layer of dust. But the reservoir was to be Saimen's assignment for the next two years.

Grueling though this new job was, his one consolation was that he was finally out of Village 14. He could eat and sleep in his own home at least. He could also attend secret meetings with believers once more. Of late, it was thrilling to be part of the current circle of believers that was sharing a recently recovered copy of the New Testament. The underground church had agreed to divide the volume into its twenty-seven separate books so that twenty-seven different people could read it simultaneously. Furthermore, if one book should be confiscated, at least the other twenty-six would still be protected. Having just finished the book of Romans, Saimen couldn't wait for the next epistle to be passed on to him. He had not yet been able to read the whole New Testament.

"Did you hear?" Mrs. Liang asked this as she walked into the room.

"What, Ma?"

"Mrs. Po's son used part of Colossians as toilet paper."

"What?!" Saimen was so shocked he didn't know what else to say.

"That's what she told me today. She's so upset."

"Why'd she let him get his hands on it? How could she?"

"Don't forget, son, Luhong was charged as a pickpocket—it's hardly surprising he was able to snatch it from her without her knowing."

"All the more reason she should have been more careful with it!" Saimen was indignant.

"Don't blame her, Saimen. She's feeling bad enough already. She couldn't stop apologizing."

"I don't mean to," said a half apologetic, half grumbling Saimen, "It's just, well, that guy is always trouble. Even at the reservoir. If he finds out someone's a Christian, he's sure to report them to the cadres!"

"Well, we can't really do anything about it now. What's done is done. We'll just have to trust that God will bring another Bible to our church."

Saimen couldn't help feeling bitter disappointment as he climbed into bed that night. So many people are desperate to read this book, God, he thought. Like bread to the body, we're starving for it. And like water, we're thirsting. It is the only thing that satisfies the hunger inside, the only thing that quenches the thirst in our souls. It's what is keeping us alive! What else is there to live for these days? And now this guy has so disrespectfully and sacrilegiously ruined a part of it. Why? Why did you let a thing like this happen, God? You know it's next to impossible to find a Bible these days.

Eventually he drifted off into a restless sleep. In the deep recesses of his mind he had a dream: He saw a man emerge. The man was healthy and everything appeared to be running smoothly in his life. The picture faded into another: The same man was now lying down, apparently dead. When he bent over for a closer look, Saimen saw the man was Luhong.

As Saimen walked to the reservoir the next morning, he suddenly remembered he had had a dream last night. Now what was it again? he asked himself. He vaguely recollected being shaken by something he had seen, but he couldn't think what it was. Oh well, he thought as he arrived at work.

The laborers and cadres were in a flurry all over the reservoir this morning. Saimen noticed it straight away. "What's going on?" he asked the nearest worker.

"An accident. A man died."

"What happened?"

"Dynamite didn't go off like usual. The guy went to check it. Idiot! Fool! It blew up in his face just as he got there."

A chill swept over Saimen. "Who, who was it? Do you know?"

"Po. Luhong Po."

At that instant Saimen remembered.

God's judgment can happen just like that, thought Saimen. It was 1974. I must not deny him. I must not betray my brothers and sisters. No matter what happens. Saimen reminded himself of these lessons as he was led like a dog down the village street. A rope tied loosely around his neck served as a collar and leash. The placard draped over his body kept banging his knees and the three-foot high hat they placed on his head was beginning to slip. But he couldn't move his hands to straighten it; they were tied behind his back. Let them fix it if it falls off, he thought with dismal pleasure.

It had been like this every day for the past twenty days, since he'd been reassigned to more re-education classes at the county detention center. Each day he was led to a couple of villages and paraded through the streets. He endured the morning and afternoon sessions, each of three hours duration, being displayed like a freak show to the general public. They don't even let you walk up on stage in a human manner, Saimen thought in disbelief. "Imperialistic religions are the way of dogs!" the Red Guards would shout, untying his hands, thrusting his neck down, compelling him to ascend the steps on all fours. Or they would forcibly drag him up by the armpits and dump him unceremoniously on the stage, not giving him an opportunity to find his feet.

But walking, even on all fours, was always less taxing than having to remain absolutely still on stage. Sometimes standing, sometimes bending in the "jet"[10], but more often he was commanded to kneel, including on a narrow bench. The batting of an eyelid was often enough to receive a punch, a nervous twitch sufficient provocation to warrant a kick.

Saimen tried his best to ignore the scoffing and shouts of derision from the masses. The street crowds, however, were relatively docile compared to those in the county hall. In the twice weekly evening meetings, in the dimly lit auditorium there was somehow a more frenzied, intensive

---

[10] During the Cultural Revolution, struggle victims were made to assume this position—bent over at the waist with arms forced back behind them.

insanity in the atmosphere. Perhaps the walls enclosing the place served as sound reflectors, incessantly bouncing the sneers and ridiculing back and forth, magnifying the madness and oppressiveness of the situation at the end of a very long day.

It was as if virtually everyone and anyone who had ever been in contact with Saimen before in his life had been assembled in the evenings. It had been disconcerting, at first, to recognize the faces of some, then most, even those he had met as a twelve-year-old at his granduncle's meetings. Fear had wrangled its way in at one point, shaking him to the core of his being. Had he known it would be like this, maybe he would have thought twice about pressing God so hard in the previous three years to use him, Saimen, to be his witness.

A battered and mud-spattered Saimen fell into the detention cell. When will this end, God? They're treating us like animals—how could this possibly be glorifying to you? These questions coursed through his mind as he crouched there on the floor on all fours. Meanwhile Grandma Wen and Grandma Ao had limped and staggered their way over to look after him. He allowed the two old women to help him up to his feet. They were each nursing their own injuries inflicted by the Red Guards, severely battered feet and a severely bruised back respectively.

"Oh, look at you," said the sixty-eight-year-old Grandma Wen, fussing over the boy as if he were her own grandson. "Let me get a cloth to wipe your face."

"How's that cut from yesterday?" asked Grandma Ao, four years Grandma Wen's junior. She turned over Saimen's left hand to have a look.

The young man was cut to the heart. He had dared to question God. How could he? Yet look at these two stalwarts. Barely able to stand themselves, they were faithfully cleaning and tending his wounds—they did this every day without fail—giving him whatever care they could. And then they would pray for him. How they could pray! The power he felt in their words was such that they brought tears to his eyes. His faith was always renewed by them.

But these two women, just like him, also had to endure the tours of the village streets. They too had to withstand the struggle meetings in the county hall. They never once, though, felt sorry for themselves (at least they didn't show it), and they never gave up in their belief that God was in control.

"God will change China," Grandma Wen would regularly state. "He will not allow it to go on like this forever."

"You just keep yourself clean before him, young man," Grandma Ao would urge. "Do not give up on him."

Saimen couldn't help but notice Grandma Wen's feet as she wiped the mud from his forehead. He had to bend his head so she could reach his face with the cloth. Grotesquely black and blue with patches of hardened blood, the woman's feet were mutilated, swollen and deformed, the stomping of the guard's army boots having been thorough indeed. He had seen the punishment being inflicted three days earlier at lunch. He couldn't bear to watch, so brutal it had been. He had had to turn his head away. Yet she bore the pain patiently and tottered her way across the room to think of him! Saimen was convicted, totally overwhelmed by the depth of what it meant to be a servant of God. He realized it was so much more than just talking about him.

"Excuse me, Grandma," he said all of a sudden. "I have to go to the toilet." He called for the guard, who let him out of the room.

Saimen ran across the compound, passed the grass that prisoners frequently pulled out in clumps to eat raw in their hunger, and into the communal, low-walled washroom. As soon as he saw he was alone he fell to his knees, completely broken and humbled. "Lord," he cried, "I haven't even begun to learn what it means to live for you." A picture of Grandma Wen's feet flashed across his mind again. "I have complained in my heart. Forgive me . . . If you want me to stay on in jail, I am willing. If you want me to suffer for the glory of your name, I will."

MINGYEN CHEN

1964. Mingyen hadn't been outside prison walls for three and a half years. He savored the sight of the city as the bus carried him and his fellow prisoners to the pier, his last view of Shanghai for who knows how long. They passed by the streets he knew so well, but something was different. They were cleaner than he remembered. The people in the streets looked happier too, he thought, the city apparently having rebounded from the disastrous collapse of Chairman Mao's failed attempt to communize the entire country. Mingyen inhaled deep breaths and thought he could smell the cooking of red stewed pork. What he'd give to taste that again! He remembered how well Cook used to make that dish (and many others). He and his brothers used to race to the table to get the biggest piece of fat. And then he boarded the flat bottomed barge. Soon after, the city of his birth and childhood began to drift away.

The barge headed west up the legendary Yangtze River for two days, approximately 400 kilometers, traveling through Anhui until they were not far from the borders of Hubei and Jiangxi provinces. Disembarking near Po Lake, the prisoners were forced to march for another two days, until they reached their new place of confinement in Susong county, the No. 9 Labor Camp, Anqing District. The first thing Mingyen noticed was the "fence" that separated the camp from the outside world: a deep moat. They had to cross a wooden bridge to enter the facility. The moat had walls which were steep, near vertical, and it was filled with muddy water. Armed PLA[11] soldiers were stationed along the banks and served, Mingyen couldn't help thinking, as a most effective deterrent to any attempt at escape.

Processing of the new arrivals followed the normal routine—requisite forms were filled in, and rules and regulations barked out as they stood at attention in the central courtyard. Mingyen was deployed to the central medical infirmary, since there was a shortage of Chinese herbal doctors. He didn't mind the placement at all. As an inmate, the infirmary and maybe the kitchen were arguably the most coveted assignments in a labor camp. The hours were long, beginning at sunrise, but at least it didn't require back-breaking hard labor in extremely hazardous conditions. Many inmates died in labor camps, Mingyen knew, and he had been bracing himself for that.

Then, barely a week had passed, and a desperate cry rang out in the infirmary halls. "Help! Help!" A cadre came running into the clinic carrying his unconscious, ten-year-old daughter in his arms. While a doctor examined the girl her father began pacing the hall, waiting for the diagnosis. Mingyen, meanwhile, not aware of this particular case, was busily employed, taking stock of the dried herbs in the Chinese pharmacy.

"Hey!" It was the father at the pharmacy window. "Hey you, behind the counter!"

Mingyen turned around, startled at the sudden, outburst in the usually quiet corridors. The white willow bark nearly spilled out of his hands.

"What are you doing?" the cadre asked grumpily.

"I'm taking inventory, Sir."

"I haven't seen you around here before. What's your name and how long have you been here?"

---

[11] People's Liberation Army.

"Chen, Sir. Mingyen Chen. I've been here for a week."

"What are you doing here?" This was asked brusquely.

"I'm sorry, Sir?" How rude this guy was!

"I said, what are you doing here?"

"I'm a Chinese herbal doctor, Sir." Mingyen hoped this was the right answer.

"Aren't you a little young to be a doctor?" The cadre eyed Mingyen up and down. "How old are you?"

"Thirty-one, Sir."

"Well, you look too young to me to be a doctor. You sure you know what you're doing?" He had an accusatory tone in his voice as he asked this.

Mingyen began to feel uneasy. This man is so volatile! He seems like he could just explode out of nothing! He told himself to stay calm and act normal. "I studied and apprenticed three years, Sir, with Dr. Feng in Shanghai."

"Well, that doesn't mean anything. Who the heck is Dr. Feng? What makes him so specially qualified?"

"Dr. Feng is very well respected in Shanghai for his skills and experience in Chinese medicine, Sir. He comes from a long line of doctors in his family, most of whom served previously in the Forbidden City, including himself. He served in the former Qing palace."

"Hmph. It figures—an imperialist. Wh-"

"Comrade Pei!" His next question was cut off by a nurse calling him from down the hall. "Comrade Pei! The doctor wishes to speak to you."

Before turning to address the nurse, Pei pointed at Mingyen with his index finger. "I still think you're too young to be a doctor."

Mingyen felt like he had just made an enemy.

A couple of days later Mingyen was transferred out of the medical clinic to a brigade in the southwest corner of the huge camp, to Team Eight.

"The guy is young and strong! He shouldn't be inside doing cushy work! He should be learning reform through labor in the fields!" Comrade Pei had argued with the camp authorities. They acquiesced.

Mingyen wasn't too upset, however. It was, after all, what he had originally anticipated. Working in the clinic for a week had been a bonus. And at least he still had something to keep him occupied and a chance to strengthen himself physically.

The labor camp was divided into multiple brigades. A brigade comprised roughly a thousand prisoners. It was divided into five groups of approximately 200 inmates each, which were in turn broken up into ten teams of twenty. Prisoners were housed in small "neighborhoods" which consisted of sleeping quarters, toilets and a small medical station for each group. Food was distributed to each group by the brigade kitchen.

Overseeing each brigade was a chief cadre, who oversaw the leaders of each group. Under a group leader were ten captains, each of whom led a team. These all lived in premises on camp ground with their families. All told, this could easily amount to several hundred additional people having contact with one brigade, if not more. Thus it was not uncommon to see prisoners serving in the households of the cadres.

Mingyen found himself adjusting to a new daily routine. Each morning he still awoke at daybreak, but this time it was with the rest of Team Eight in their straw-roofed, mud brick hut. Two giant *kangs* ran down the long walls of the hut, on each of which up to thirty prisoners would sleep, tightly packed close together—making it easier for the guards to keep watch. It was so cramped, you couldn't even turn over to adjust your position at night. Mingyen just tried to be thankful for the shelter.

The prisoners shuffled outside each morning to wash their faces in a huge, communal, wooden bucket which had water poured into it by a laborer. The kitchen crew came to distribute breakfast, which was either a bowl of plain rice or congee. Then the prisoners would each be handed a gardening tool at random, perhaps a hoe or a shovel, and march for ten to twenty minutes to the designated field for the day. The No. 9 Labor Camp's crops included cotton, rice, wheat, rapeseed, corn and a variety of vegetables.

At first Mingyen found farming more difficult than he anticipated. He didn't know how to handle many of the tools very skillfully, and some of them, not at all. He didn't know how to lift heavy loads efficiently either. And because he was known to be a counterrevolutionary, one of only two in their team, inmates were generally not that inclined to offer assistance of any kind. Counterrevolutionaries were either the intellectuals or thought criminals and were typically relegated to the lowest rung in the social hierarchy of the prison. They were the least fit to do hard labor, having had limited or no experience at using their hands for work. Therefore they became easy targets for bullying or abuse in a labor camp. Despite the hardships Mingyen quietly persevered, watching the more physically skilled and learning from their example along the way. He never complained. He never, in fact, said much at all. This impressed one or two of the men, who, over time, offered him advice on how to better hoe or carry things on his back.

The cotton fields were ripe for harvest. Fearful it wouldn't be collected in time, the labor camp announced a cotton picking contest for the inmates. Each worker's daily pickings would be weighed at the end of each day and the one who collected the most cotton would be rewarded with an extra bowl of rice at lunch for the next month. More food! What an incentive.

The prisoners primed themselves for the competition. Eager to win the prize, many of the experienced laborers knew that cotton was heaviest in the morning because of dew. It became a mad dash among them every morning to beat the sun—to stuff as much dew-laden cotton into your bag as possible before it dried and became lighter. The knowledge spread throughout the group, and soon many of the workers were employing this strategy in an attempt to get ahead of the others. Everyone in Team Eight was doing the same. Everyone except Mingyen.

"What are you doing, Mingyen?"

"I'm picking cotton."

"But you're squeezing and patting it dry," said Lu. Lu was the other counterrevolutionary in Team Eight. The two of them had become silent friends over the past month. They didn't actually say much to each other in public, but there was mutual understanding of the similar pressure they faced because of the way they had been labeled socially. It just so happened too, that both of them were Chinese herbal doctors.

"If you leave the dew on," Mingyen explained, "it will cause the cotton to turn yellow, lowering its quality. I couldn't submit poor work, especially if I knew how to prevent it. It wouldn't be right, and it'd be a waste of the crop."

That night at the weigh-in Mingyen was rebuked in

public by his team leader. "Chen, what's the matter with you? You're so far behind the rest of us! You're making Team Eight look bad!" said Shi. "What's the matter—is the work too rough for your delicate hands?" The group broke out into raucous laughter. Mingyen remained silent.

A few days later the labor camp authorities changed the cadres in charge of weighing the daily pickings. Instead of using the camp's internal personnel, they now brought in experienced inspectors of cotton to weigh the crop.

The group leader stepped forward. "For your information, we've been instructed by camp authorities to weigh and evaluate the cotton in accordance with government standards. Therefore you should be aware that there is now some unacceptable cotton for submission."

A hushed silence came over the crowd, each man wondering what this could possibly mean for him.

"Unacceptable cotton," the leader continued, "is that which we would not be able to sell at market for full price. Any 'yellowish' cotton, for example, is unacceptable and will be disqualified. The chief inspector will now show you a sample of that!" The chief inspector used a pair of chopsticks to pull a bunch out of the bag beside him and held it high in front of the whole group.

"This specimen, in fact, is the absolute worst kind of submission!" the group leader went on. "It was picked by the leader of Team Eight."

Every prisoner was stunned. They turned their heads to face the unfortunate man, who wished he could back away from the spotlight. But he had nowhere to go.

"Leader Shi, you should be ashamed of yourself! What kind of example are you setting for your group? Urinating on your cotton!"

Shi was rendered absolutely speechless at being found

out, his jaw literally hanging down.

"If I hadn't seen you doing it myself, I wouldn't have believed it! Guards! Lock him up!"

The guards took Shi away.

The group leader turned to face the prisoners again. "And here is a sample of good cotton." The chief inspector picked some up from another bag on cue. "This has been collected by prisoner Mingyen Chen. Not one single piece in his bags has been found to be yellow. Good work, Chen! You are now appointed the new leader of Team Eight."

His first winter in the labor camp came. Snow covered the ground and there was no farming to be done. The prisoners were marched two to three hours out of camp each day to build a dam on a tributary that flowed into the Yangtze. The sub-zero temperatures bit into Mingyen's fingers as he lifted the pails of dirt and trudged back with them to the dump spot. He had tried to wrap his hands with strips of material to provide some protection from the cold, but it was insufficient to prevent frostbite.

At least he was allowed to visit the infirmary though, his degenerating blackened thumb proving to be adequate evidence for the team captain. A few months ago Mingyen had tried to obtain permission to go for his stomach ulcer. It had begun bleeding regularly with the added physical stress and the coarse food they served in the camp. The staple they served at the time was field corn. It wasn't the tasty sweet corn he had tasted as a child. Elsewhere the lower grade cereal was grown primarily to be used as animal feed. But here in the camp, the rocklike, chunky corn served as the prisoners' sustenance. It was difficult to digest and sat hard in the stomach. It was a dilemma he could have done without: To eat or not to eat? If you don't eat, you'll starve and have no energy to work. If you do eat, you'll have wretched internal pain. Mingyen tried to explain his condition to the cadre but, because he didn't have a fever and he "looked fine", how could there be a need for him to see a doctor?

Mingyen had no other alternative. He prayed desperately to God with his hand on his stomach one day in the field when it was bleeding yet again. Please heal me, God. Please. As he went back to camp to eat dinner that evening, he went through the usual dread in his mind, trying to convince himself it was better to swallow the coarse morsels than not, telling himself it was important to his survival to eat. He picked up his bowl and chopsticks and began to eat. After a few mouthfuls he noticed that he wasn't starting to feel uncomfortable like he usually did. This is a change. He took a few more mouthfuls. Then a few more. Where was it? He had finished eating the whole bowl and still he felt nothing. An hour later, reading the newspaper, he continued to feel fine. Amazing! From that day onwards, Mingyen felt as if he had a new stomach. He no longer had problems eating and he lost all the symptoms of his ulcer!

But now his thumb was in trouble.

"We're going to have to cut it off."

"Cut it off?!" Mingyen was distraught.

"Just the tip," the doctor said. "It's rotten already. We can't save it. You'll still have most of your thumb though. You'll still be able to use it."

Mingyen sighed. "Do what you have to do."

LILI TANG

1989. Once again there was tension within the country. This time, because of the student demonstrations in Tiananmen Square. In 1983 a tight policy had been in effect for eight months before it was relaxed, and Lili and the other four could show their faces on local county streets again without fear. They weren't specifically on a wanted list this time but there was, nevertheless, a strained atmosphere, and local officials were only too pleased to placate Beijing in any way they could. How long would they have to lie low this time?

In September, a twenty-eight-year-old Lili sat on the train, her eyes closed, appearing to be asleep but, in actuality, she was praying. She was riding back to Shanxi from Guangdong on yet another one of her Bible runs. She looked up periodically, checking that everything was normal. I'm tired, she thought as she scanned the carriage, but I can't rest yet. Not until the papers have been handed over. Please, Lord, no matter what happens, let the Bibles be safe . . . And then it's off on a tour of some churches in Shaanxi and Gansu provinces, she reminded herself. The Three-Self Patriotic Movement had begun charting a new course lately, pushing beyond its traditional "big city only" boundaries and into the rural communities. Lili wanted to encourage the churches to be careful and wise in their dealings with them.

So many churches need more Bible teaching too, she thought. That challenge had become more apparent and more of an interest to her in the last couple of years. You know, Lord, she said inside as she thought of this, the day I'm arrested will be the last day I deliver Bibles.

The train rolled into Taiyuan city station at a quarter to five in the morning. Lili got up with the rest of the passengers and pulled her luggage down from the overhead rack, two large sacks filled with some books and audio-visual equipment, donated by Christians in Hong Kong and passed on through Han.

She stepped down from the train and began to make her way to the exit, an oversized bag in each hand. She eyed her contact coming towards her from the far end of the platform—always a welcome sight to her. Just before she reached him though, a couple of PSB officers stepped in front to block her path. Her heart sank within her.

"What have you got there, Miss?" asked the first officer, reaching over to take her bags. "Crap! That's heavy! Don't you agree, Comrade?" He looked over at his partner. The second officer lifted the bag and nodded.

Lili set the bags down completely on the ground. There was no evading these two. "It's just a few books, Officers, and some VCRs."

"Open it up," said the first officer.

Lili obeyed.

"Where have you just come from?" he asked as he perused the contents.

"Guangdong, Sir."

"Well, it looks like you have some interesting items," he said, as he pulled out a thickish reference book. "I suspect someone would do some serious studying with this."

Lili made no reply.

"Looks like some explaining is in order here, Miss. I think you should come back to the station with us."

Great, thought Lili. She spied her contact monitoring her situation at a safe distance, and protecting the Bibles became her biggest concern. She decided to make no fuss with the officers; they led her away. They soon came to a compact pick-up truck and Lili was directed to climb up the back of the open-topped vehicle, along with her bags. The only seats were benches over the rear wheel arches. Lili reached for the side of the truck to support herself as she sat down. Deliberately misjudging the distance, she clumsily overshot it, dropping her cloth handbag over the side and on to the ground in the process. Firmly grabbing hold of the side, she steadied herself and sat down. The whole event went unnoticed by the officer who sat down opposite her. As the vehicle drove away, Lili saw her contact pick up the handbag. It contained the cargo claim papers. She knew the Bibles would be all right. That was all that mattered.

Lili sat alone in the interrogation room. Midday had come and gone, and the rumblings in her stomach reminded her she hadn't eaten since they'd given her breakfast at seven-thirty that morning. Her interrogator had left the room an hour ago. It had been a three hour session and she thought that she had managed to keep the church safe. They still didn't know she was a resident of this province. With a little good fortune, she thought to herself, this might all just blow over in a couple of days and I'll be out of here. Or I might be able to escape.

She had a strange feeling about it though. Try as she might, she couldn't help but think that her time had finally come. She closed her eyes and sighed. I didn't think my Bible delivery trips would come to an end this fast! she said to herself. She refocused on the situation at hand. Give me wisdom, God.

"Well, Comrade, what do you make of it?"

"Comrade Superintendent, Sir! She has no ID," the interrogator began. "She's carrying an awful lot of books and equipment for one person—two VCRs and a dozen strange panels that no one around here has seen before. They could all very well be supplies to support a movement. And those panels—they look suspiciously to me like some kind of secret weapon." He paused here to let his information sink in. "The equipment is definitely from outside China, Sir, probably smuggled in through Hong Kong, seeing she just came from Guangdong."

"Foreign equipment, eh?" The plump balding superintendent took off his glasses and rubbed his eyes. "What else do you have to report?"

"Well, Sir, I think she's one of them."

"A student leader?"

"Yes, Sir."

"A student leader," he said this more to himself than to his subordinate. Why did it have to be the university students? The superintendent inspected his glasses in the ceiling light. Spots. He took out a cloth from his desk and began to clean them. "So what's her story then? What's she doing here?"

"She says she's visiting relatives, Sir, that the books and equipment are gifts for them."

"You are, I presume, having the relatives checked out?"

"As we speak, Sir. But it might take a while. They live on the other side of the province."

"It figures. Blast those kids—they always think they're so smart. What'd she say about the weapon—what'd you call them?—panels?"

"She says they're solar battery chargers."

"What the heck are they?"

"For recharging batteries, Sir, so she says. But whoever heard of reusing a battery?" The interrogator scoffed.

"Seems we need to do more investigating into our— what did you say her name was, Comrade?"

"Uh, Miss Wong, Sir. Her surname is Wong."

"Yes, Comrade. We need to further investigate our Miss Wong."

Yup, she was right. They fingerprinted Lili at the end of the day. They fed her dinner, some rice, vegetables, and a couple of scraggly pieces of pork. Then they drove her over to Taiyuan's largest jail. It was ten degrees Celsius outside, but it felt like freezing riding in the open air at the back of the pick-up truck that evening. Lili was still clothed in the light cotton, summer clothes she wore in sub-tropical Guangzhou. She didn't think she could be glad for the shelter of the county jail when she arrived, but she was, if only for a brief moment.

Then she was locked into her cell. Hearing the door shut and the key being turned brought the fact home to her. I'm here. I'm really, truly here.

She took her first hard look at the cell. It was roughly eight by four and a half meters, and had a glass ceiling through which every movement of the inmates could be observed by guards in the gallery above. A giant stone slab almost filled the drab concrete room, leaving just a narrow aisle on one side. This served as the inmates' collective bed, bench and table.

In the far corner was a small section cordoned off by

bricks which served as the toilet. There was no drainage; the human waste was pooled and removed only when the enclosure was full. It proved to be the perfect breeding environment for maggots, which could frequently be seen crawling around the cell. Oh God, help me! she prayed.

Then she noticed her fellow prisoners: A dozen women were staring at her, studying her with curiosity, perhaps even some wariness. Lili felt she could read that in their faces. This wasn't quite what she was expecting. Kuan and the others had told her it was not uncommon for a new arrival in prison to be harassed, bullied, made to know her place . . . But then, these women hadn't said anything yet. She steeled herself for what might yet come.

A broad shouldered woman, about five years older than Lili, sidled up to the new inmate, circled around her, trying to assess the probability of a long, skinny reed like this being trouble. Lili felt the woman's eyes boring into her body, sizing her up. She guessed this must be the cell leader.

"You don't look like a vicious murderer," the woman said in a coarse, scratchy voice.

Lili wasn't quite sure how to respond to this. She opened her mouth but nothing came out.

"You don't even look capable of doing it," she continued, her lip curled up at the left hand corner in a slight mocking tone. She completed her inspection of the new arrival and made her way casually back to her edge of the stone slab. She remained standing but leaned back against the wall. "What's the matter? Don't you have a tongue? What's your name?"

"Oh, uh, Lili."

"Lili . . ." The cell leader waved her hand in a circle to indicate she was expecting more information.

"Uh, Lili Wong."

"Lili Wong. Welcome to the cell." She continued the mocking tone in her manner, waving her hand, this time, to present the room.

Lili was still standing by the door. She hadn't moved from the same spot since she first entered the cell.

"Well, why don't you come in? We're not going to bite."

Lili singled out the nearest open space on the slab, calmly made her way over and sat down.

Hm, the cell leader observed, she's pretty sure of herself. She doesn't seem intimidated. They could be right. "So," she said, "this your first time in prison?"

"Uh, yeah. So what's your name?" Reconciling herself to her situation more with every passing minute, Lili was over the initial shock of being locked up. She was beginning to converse normally again.

The cell leader looked somewhat surprised at the genuine friendliness in Lili's voice. "I'm Shulei."

"Shulei. It's nice to meet you." Before Shulei could utter another word, Lili began making the verbal rounds of introduction around the room.

Hm, initiative. Yet she's natural, easygoing when she talks, Shulei couldn't help thinking. Is it possible? Could she be one of them? I wouldn't think they'd be like this.

"You're not even a criminal, are you?" Shulei broke into the final introduction.

Lili looked up at the abrupt interruption. "No," she said simply. "I am not."

There seemed to be a collective sigh of relief around the room.

"So why are you here then?" asked Shulei. "Honestly. What have you done?"

"Honestly. I'm a Christian. I had Christian books in my possession when they arrested me."

"That's it?"

"That's it."

Shulei's face broke into a wide grin, which triggered the release of similar smiles around the room.

"What?" asked Lili. "What are you all smiling about?"

"They told us not to trust you, that you were dangerous. They said you were part of the student movement, one of the leaders planning to overthrow the government. You even have a secret weapon to kill people. We're supposed to watch you closely and not let you commit suicide."

"Wha-, what?" Lili was at a loss for words. Overthrow the government? Secret weapon? How did they get that impression? She searched the recesses of her mind, trying to recall the questions and answers of her interrogation, trying to ascertain what she had in the sacks that could have been construed as a weapon.

"Well?" said the cell leader. "What do you think about that?"

"I, uh, I . . . I'm sorry—you've caught me off guard," said Lili. "I hadn't expected this. I was just trying to figure out how they got that idea."

SAIMEN LIANG

1974.

"Well, Comrade."

"Comrade Secretary, Sir," said Yang, beginning his report, "there's still no change."

It was mid-way through the year. The junior officer was standing in the superior's office.

"Still?" asked a skeptical Niu. He was seated at his desk, an arm slouched over the back of his chair.

"You saw for yourself, Sir, at that last meeting."

"And you're saying he's always like that?"

"Yes, Sir."

"Every time?"

"Every time. Sir."

"Incredible." Niu muttered this last word to himself. He got up out of his chair and walked over to the window, his hands clasped behind his back, revealing nicotine stained nails. The guy has no shame, he said to himself. He doesn't know the meaning of face. He doesn't flinch when he's on public display, even when he's being treated like a dog. And he doesn't gripe like the others when he's given degrading labor. What's it going to take to break this guy's spirit?

"Sir?" Yang ventured gently to break into his superior's thoughts.

"What is it, Yang?" He didn't turn from the window.

"If you don't mind my saying so, Sir, I don't think Liang is going to cave in."

"And I suppose you have some kind of theory or rationale to support this view."

"Well, Sir," said Yang, glad for the chance to explain himself, "I think there's something not quite right in his head—not meaning any disrespect to you, Sir," he added quickly, knowing how much the secretary used to value the boy. "When he's accused of being a Christian he says, 'Yes, that's what I am!' He makes no attempt to deny it. What kind of sane guy would do that? It's like Chairman Mao says, he's picking up a big rock to crush his own foot."

Niu kept his eyes fixed resolutely on the street outside. A unit of PLA soldiers was marching through on its way to a training ground. *Life should have progressed smoothly for you, Liang, as smooth as these troops are going through their drills.*

"And, Sir," continued Yang, although not quite as boldly as before, "if you don't do something, it could reflect badly on the party, especially since he's a member." The subordinate stood there for a while, looking anxiously at his boss. He hoped he hadn't been too presumptuous in saying this much. "Sir?"

Niu pursed his lips together. Yang was right. He hated to admit it, but that was the bitter truth. "Charge him. Charge him for being in possession of an anti-revolutionary book." He let out a deep breath. "Strip him of his party membership too."

"Yes, Sir."

The last of the troops disappeared from the secretary's view. "And Yang."

"Yes, Sir?"

"Move him out of my county."

"Where to, Sir?"

"Anywhere. Just get him out of here." *If he could help*

it, Niu didn't want to see, hear or think about Saimen Liang ever again.

Saimen's case was officially closed, after three futile years of trying to get the prodigal back on track. He was taken to a district on the other side of the province, to Mingshui, where he found himself confined in another prison. As the newcomer, he was allocated the spot in the back corner of the cell, beside the human waste bucket. The stench, needless to say, was foul. But after a few days Saimen saw it as a blessing in disguise. The reek often ensured he was left alone as the other prisoners were eager to keep their distance, and he could pray in peaceful obscurity, leaning his cheek on his hand, his head tilted against the wall for support. He felt it was wonderful that God had counted him worthy to suffer in prison.

In total there were ten men in his cell. A small window let in some daylight, but it was too high to see anything except the top of a tree outside, and Saimen kept watch of this to mark the seasons of the year. When the leaves budded he knew that spring was nigh; when the branches were bare, winter wasn't far behind.

There wasn't much daily activity for the inmates. They spent their days sitting on the same straw mats they slept on, and no talking was permitted in the cell. If a prisoner was discovered talking or walking in his cell (other than to use the waste bucket), the guards would beat him.

After a year and a half of this, he was moved to a *laogai*.

1976. It was early in the new year when Saimen entered the labor camp. Because of his previous party affiliation and success supervising projects, the warden designated him a group leader and apportioned him the thought prisoners that worked in the apple orchard. Watching over a hundred and eighty laborers as they picked fruit and pruned trees was a welcome change from the utter boredom of the previous eighteen months, and from the severity of the raucous reeducation classes and manual digging of reservoirs. Under the cover of the trees, Saimen considered it a treat to actually be able to pray out loud, even if it was only for a minute or two. He hadn't been able to do that in several years. And the food was better here. It was more substantial (he'd take a bowl of rice over two strands of noodles in flavorless soup any day) and you got more.

"Did you read it yet?" The cook asked the question under his breath, as he methodically scooped rice into a bowl.

"Yeah," replied Saimen, in just as low a voice. He was the last man in line to receive dinner tonight.

"What'd you think?"

"It was amazing! Insights I never had before."

The cook grinned, as if he were pleased there were no more meals to be served that day. He had lent Saimen a hand-sized devotional called "Spring in the Valley" after discovering he was a Christian. He was pleased someone could benefit from the booklet, he himself being illiterate. "Later on I'll be peeling some turnips out back for tomorrow. Why don't you stop by on your way to the latrine?"

The stars illuminated the night sky, as Saimen stepped out for his rendezvous. He walked around the corner of the sleeping quarters, past the medical station and in the direction of the kitchen. Hong had already peeled half a bowl's worth of turnips. In just a brief time, the two men had become friends, after Hong had noticed some inmates badgering the new boy about his superstitions.

Saimen squatted down and picked up a root vegetable and knife, attempting to imitate the skilled hands of the middle-aged Hong. He wasn't very adept, however, carving huge chunks of turnip out with the skin as well.

"So, what passage were you studying?"

"Second Corinthians, chapter eight, verse nine. I never realized how much it cost Jesus to come down to earth," Saimen began in wonder. "Think of it—he had all the riches in heaven and he chose to be poor! Heaven, the source of the river of life, and yet he had to ask the Samaritan woman for water." The large turnip slipped out of his grip, causing him to gauge out another considerably large lump of vegetable again. He fished the turnip out of the bowl, where it had landed, again. "When he died, he was left with absolutely nothing; even his clothes were divided. What's more, he was buried in someone else's tomb." Saimen's eyes began to water, just like the first time he read the devotional. "Can you imagine?"

Hong shook his head in answer, his eyes no longer dry either. Every time this guy shared what he was learning, the cook seemed to experience it along with him.

"You know, your booklet has really been encouraging me, Hong. Thanks again."

"Hm." The cook was much too modest to say anything else.

"I feel like I'm understanding God better lately," Saimen continued, "but I also feel like I'm still so far away from him. It just makes me even hungrier to know him."

"Me too."

"I've been praying, Hong."

"What about?"

"That—that I'll know him better, more intimately. It's so hard, you know, to pray in the barracks with thirty of us in there . . . I'm thankful for the couple minutes I get in the orchard, but it really isn't enough. At least you have only a couple of guys with you in the kitchen rooms."

"Hm."

"I just wish I could spend time with him in private, with no interruption from others."

The cook nodded, tossing a peeled turnip into the bowl and reaching for another. "Well, I'll pray for that for you too."

1978. One night, after one of his clandestine meetings with Hong, Saimen returned to his sleeping quarters.

"Liang! Hey Liang!" the camp guard on night duty called. "The warden wants to see you."

Saimen followed him, wondering what this could possibly mean. He entered the warden's office, which was purely functional in its furnishings—a wooden desk, a cabinet and a few chairs. It was full of the smell of cigarette smoke, the warden easily polishing off a couple of packs every day. Even now he signaled to Saimen to sit with a burning cigarette in his right hand.

"Don't tell anyone, Liang," he said behind a billow of smoke, "but tomorrow we're moving you out of your unit. We've reassigned your duties. You're now going to look after the pigs."

Saimen was elated. This was as good as receiving a promotion! The pigs lived in a large building located on the outer wall of the labor camp. The pens, which comprised the bulk of the building, were flanked on either end by two rooms for the two attendants who looked after the animals. This meant Saimen would have his own private room. Furthermore, because of the location on the outer wall, he would be able to have outside visitors without them having to register with the labor camp office. Saimen was very grateful to God for this favor from the prison officials.

"Here."

"What's this?"

"Some food. It's a gift from Farmer Shu."

"Again? He's so generous."

"Yes, he is." Ying sat down as Saimen set the burlap sack down on the side. "He's only been a believer for a year, but he's keen to help when he knows there's a need."

"You've all been so wonderful to me, since I've come. I couldn't expect more kindness if you were my own family. Hong wasn't lying when he said you guys were the best."

Ying waved his arm. No need for thanks, the gesture said. He was happy to be of service anytime he could. "So I was thinking," he went on, "Hong says you're a good teacher of the Bible. Maybe you could come and teach some of our brothers and sisters in the area sometime."

"I'd be honored. But how can it be done? The guards won't just let me leave."

"Easy. There's no way they can keep watch over you when you're out picking wild grass and plants, right?"

"Picking wild grass and plants?" Saimen had a puzzled look on his face.

"In the nearby woods, outside, you know . . ."

"In the woods?"

"For the kitchen . . ." Ying waved his hand in circles, trying to help Saimen get the hint. "You know, helping gather some stuff for the kitchen . . ."

"Oh! Oh yeah! For the kitchen." Saimen was beginning to see the light. "Okay. When's the best time to do this?"

"What's your schedule with the pigs?"

"I just have to feed them twice a day—first thing in the morning and at dusk."

"Great—that gives us at least eight or nine hours in between. No problem."

The expectation of what this could amount to aroused Saimen's excitement. He was going to be able to serve God's church after all. "When should we start?"

"How about tomorrow?"

"Uh, okay. How do we do it?"

"Well, when you're out in the woods gathering your plants, a couple of brothers will come by on their bikes and help you. When you've collected enough, they'll make like to leave. One of them will walk away while the other leaves on his bike. You follow on the other bike to the meeting place. Sound okay to you?"

Saimen stood there, his finger tip on his lips, not making any answer.

"Saimen? Sound okay to you?" Ying repeated the question.

"Well . . ."

"Well, what?"

"Well . . . not really."

"Why? What's the problem?" Ying was becoming concerned.

"Well . . . you see . . ." Saimen became rather embarrassed. "I can't ride a bike."

Ying laughed out loud. So that was all. "Oh, don't worry about that! I'll just get them to double you!"

Living in the swine hut proved to be an enriching time

for Saimen. The local believers would regularly come and help him "collect wild grass and plants", which was a totally acceptable activity to the labor camp, as it meant the pig attendant was "being productive" when he wasn't taking care of the animals. And, as it turned out, pigs were even simpler to take care of than goats, in that they remained in their pens all the time—you didn't have to chase them down to corral them at the end of the day. As long as they were healthy and Saimen came back with his daily pickings, the camp officials were happy.

The secret churches in the area were full of recent converts, people who didn't have Bibles but were keen to hear stories from it. So Saimen told what he knew and what he had read about, of Mary breaking the bottle of perfume over Jesus, how it was a symbol of sacrifice; of Lazarus being raised from the dead because Jesus was so powerful; and more. Together, they had the holiest of communions with an apple, cut up into little chunks, for their bread. The local believers wanted to share not only in Jesus' suffering, but in Saimen's too. They would visit him at the pigpen and scoop some dirt from there to take home with them. It was a symbol and a reminder to them that a fellow brother was suffering in prison, and it prompted them to pray for him.

The year 1978 also saw a new feeling of optimism and hope arise in the nation, which subsequently filtered into the labor camp. Strongman Deng Xiaoping was re-installed in power and people were being reinstated into society.

"So you'll be cleared of all charges, Comrade Liang," said the warden, smiling behind his cloud of cigarette smoke. "How does that sound to you?"

"It sounds great, Sir. But I wasn't put here because I

was counterrevolutionary. It was because I was a Christian."

"Then don't be a Christian anymore. It's that simple."

"Well, Sir, then I'm afraid I don't want to be reinstated. I can't just not be a Christian."

The cigarette fell out of the warden's mouth. He scrambled to pick up the burning end from the papers on his desk. "Don't want to be reinstated?" he asked incredulously. "Are you out of your mind?"

"No, Sir."

"Your dossier will be cleared. Don't you understand?"

"Yes. But a clear conscience is better than a cleared dossier."

The warden took a second to register Saimen's answer. Evidently this was not a rational man. "You have a chance to go home to your family, Liang, to live a normal life again. Don't you want that?"

"Yes, Sir, but not at the cost of renouncing my faith."

"You know," the warden sighed, thereby releasing yet another puff of smoke into the air, "I never understand you Christians. You never make sense. My mother's a Christian and it's the same with her. You always go and make things so much harder for yourselves. Why? So God can perform a greater miracle? Ha! What kind of miracle is it to live in a labor camp?"

Saimen remained silent.

"Don't you know how many men would die to be in your position right now?"

"Look, Sir, not meaning any disrespect, but please don't talk to me anymore about this. The truth is, I am a Christian. Nothing is going to change that. And if it means I can't be reinstated, then so be it."

Saimen completed his sentence in early 1980. You know, God, he prayed upon exiting the labor camp, you've been so wonderful to me all these years. First of all, you counted me worthy to suffer for you. Next, you taught me new things from your Word. Then you gave me such sweet fellowship with the believers in this area. I am honored to be so blessed.

As he strolled through the streets of Mingshui town, Saimen marveled at how much it had developed since he was first driven through the place on his moving to the labor camp. The department store window seemed to have a vaster array of goods for sale than four years ago. Brightly colored articles of clothing were on display, providing a sharp contrast to the rack of drab army green and morbid blue items inspired by the Cultural Revolution. He noticed that the people on the streets also seemed to be venturing into trendier fashions; there were less traditional Chinese collars and buttons visible and more European-influenced styles. There were more people milling around on street corners and sidewalks, chatting, catching up on the gossip of the day, enjoying an unexpected run-in to a friend. All around a hum of pleasurable activity filled the air, as the old fear of officials possibly questioning their presence or purpose for being out was diminished.

Bikes abounded on the roads, overtaking the donkey carts in swarms. He had to zigzag his way across the street, exercising more caution than in the past. Next he came up to the shop showcasing electrical goods. Here he saw televisions, transistor radios and cassette players were now available to the general public in greater quantities.

He turned into the wet market. It was immediately apparent that meat was more readily available from the butcher and a larger assortment of fruits and vegetables from the produce merchants could be found too. The line-ups no longer existed for mere staples. Street stalls abounded, selling cooked food and featuring more diverse menus. Wow, he thought, as he saw a man spit a chicken bone out at his table, is it like this all over China?

God, all these new items are wonderful, he continued to pray, but whenever you feel it keeps me from getting closer to you or being disciplined in my walk with you, send me back to prison. Then I'll remember all the lessons you've taught me there. Or, he added on further thought, when my son turns eighteen years of age—whichever comes first—send me back to prison. I never want to be far away from you.

MINGYEN CHEN

April 12, 1971

To Mingyen Chen:

    This is to inform you that your wife, Mrs. Chi Chou Chen, has divorced you on account of your label as a counterrevolutionary. Mrs. Chen has requested and been granted the legal custody of your one and only son, Tai Chen, as your status was deemed to be less beneficial to his growth and development as a citizen of China.

Yours truly,

The Fu Hong National Company

So this is why she hasn't written lately. Mingyen sat down on the *kang*, dumbfounded. The letter, which had been lying open on his lap, drifted down to the floor. He felt—he didn't know what—helpless? Miserable beyond words. What could he do stuck in here? It's not as if he could just go and try to talk her out of it. He felt like crying. He longed to scream in anger. You couldn't even tell me yourself! I would never have imagined this of you!

    God, it's hard enough. Don't you think? First of all I'm still stuck in here—even though my sentence was officially completed last year. And now this! I don't need this! Mingyen's eyes filled with tears. What have I been surviving these last five years for?

He thought of the summer day in 1966 that led to the past several years. There was a mass brigade meeting out in the field, the prisoners all standing at attention by teams and groups. Then came the announcement that the Cultural Revolution was now under way. After that he was transferred to a new brigade. His new captain was none other than Comrade Pei. The comrade, it turned out, still had it in for him.

"Chen. Mingyen Chen. So we meet again."

Mingyen remained silent as he stood in the cadre's office.

"I've been reading over your file. Team leader . . . commendable, at one point, and yet . . . and yet there's an asterisk here." Pei looked at Mingyen's face as he said this.

Mingyen knew what that was all about. As the leader of Team Eight, it had been his responsibility to ensure the quality of work for his team and to integrate the new members. One day, Old Robber was assigned to Team Eight. Old Robber was notorious throughout the camp for being trouble with a capital T. He was violent, ruthless and totally uncooperative, so much so that cadres had him moved out of their jurisdiction as soon as they could. In his previous group, Old Robber had cut off a fellow prisoner's ear with a broken plate just because he wouldn't give him extra food.

Wang, as he was known before his misnomer, was a fifty-two-year-old butcher from Shandong province. He was sent to the *laogai* because he found out his wife was having an affair and then he murdered her lover.

And now Mingyen had to deal with the guy. Through patience, however, kindness and some tough negotiating with the kitchen to secure extra rice for the man, Mingyen managed over time to tame Old Robber. In fact, Old Robber had turned such a new leaf, he ended up becoming an outstanding worker in the field. The camp officials wanted to make him their new "model inmate", to showcase the effectiveness of reform through labor. A brigade meeting was planned where Wang would be honored. An officially approved acceptance speech was written and Mingyen helped him memorize it.

The day of the grand ceremony came. Wang stepped up on the stage and began to recite his speech. After the first couple of sentences, Wang turned to the cadres seated on the platform. "Sirs," he said, "I can't really read and I have a bad memory. Could I just say what I feel?"

The beaming cadres, proud of their protégé, nodded their consent.

Wang began, "From the bottom of my heart, I would like to thank my team leader, Mingyen Chen. I wouldn't be standing here today if it wasn't for his help. Chen is such a good, good person. Chen is so kind to me. He doesn't shout at me. He doesn't hit me. Chen is so patient. No one's ever been like that to me before. I learn a lot from him. Chen taught me how to . . ."

The speech was never finished. The cadres yanked him off. And hence, the asterisk.

"You know, Mingyen Chen," Pei continued, "I don't know what kind of game you're trying to play here, but you won't be making any converts in my team. Understand? In fact, you're going to have to prove yourself to me. You'll work in the cesspool."

It was five years now and counting. I'm still up to my neck in human excrement. I have no release date to look forward to. And now I have no wife and son to go home to. Mingyen wasn't sure how much more heartbreak he could take. He laid down and pretended to sleep as prisoners drifted in and out of the dorm in the early evening.

"Hey, Chen!" an inmate yelled across the room. "Chen! Movie's about to start outside. You coming?"

"No, not tonight," he replied without turning over. Who'd want to see it anyway? Ever since the Cultural Revolution started, they've been playing the same two propaganda films over and over, "The Red Lantern Story" and "The Red Female Army". Don't people get tired of them?

"Chen!" another voice called a few minutes later. "Newspaper!" He dropped it on the *kang* near Mingyen's feet and walked out again.

But, rather uncharacteristically, Mingyen didn't feel like reading either. It's all brainwash anyway. Brainwash papers. Brainwash books. What else was there to read these days?

Mingyen tried to recite in his mind some Bible verses from memory. This was his habit when he went to sleep at night. Who would have thought he'd have need of this skill he so laboriously taught in his travels to the illiterate peasants in Zhejiang and Jiangsu? He had devoted hours and hours to helping them memorize the scriptures, and he didn't realize all the while he was embedding them into his own brain too. He just assumed it was only useful for those who couldn't read. But in the last eleven years it had become his lifeline, for he hadn't seen a Bible since the day he was last arrested.

Tonight, however, he found he didn't really have the heart to speak God's words back to him. He sat up and looked around the room. They had moved into newly constructed sleeping quarters last year. No more thatched roof; it was now tile. No more crudely made mud bricks either; they were now factory-produced. The longish room was subdivided by partial walls into three sections. The *kangs* were shorter, sleeping six men on each, two *kangs* per subsection. A few men were playing a card game at the far end of the room, a couple others were reading. But that was the extent of the action inside tonight.

Mingyen laid back down again. What can I do, God? I've got to talk to her. Please.

Morning came, the dawn of a new day. It had been a fitful night for Mingyen and he had not slept much. As usual, after breakfast, he made his way to the cesspools. A series of pits roughly two meters wide by two meters long were laid out behind the lot that housed a group. The human waste from the brigade was dumped here, where the solids, over time, were "digested" or reduced. Eventually what remained was sun baked into a kind of compost to be used as fertilizer for the crops.

The smell was toxic, unbearable, and the risk of catching disease hazardous. It was by far the lowest job a laborer could be assigned to in the labor camp. Very few people would socialize with the cesspool man because the odor was virtually impossible to wash off your clothes and person, no matter how hard you tried.

About the only positive aspect of this job was that it ensured privacy. No guard or inmate in his right mind wanted to watch over the cesspool man or carry a message to him. It wasn't just the fact that it reeked; it was quite likely an accident could happen. The pools were so deep the laborer couldn't always see or hear when someone was approaching while shoveling the manure out. And if you happened to be standing in the wrong place at the right time . . .

The relaxed watch on the cesspool man also meant that no false or negative reports were made to the camp authorities. But then how much worse could your position possibly get?

When a pool had been through the 'digesting' stage, its contents had to be shoveled out. Each shovel-full turned out became a little "cake", and these were distributed around the pool area. After a couple of days the cakes would be hardened and then they were ready to be used on the crops. At two meters deep, however, the filth in the pits came way over the heads of most laborers. He could only scoop excrement standing on the edge for so long. At some point, he had to get in.

Obviously Mingyen tried to put that off as long as possible. He tucked his trousers into his socks, always trying to avoid as much direct contact with his skin as possible. When the excrement became too far for him to reach while standing on the edge, which always happened too soon, he would lie down on his stomach and begin to carve steps into the inner wall of the pit. Using the steps as a foothold or handgrip as needed, he would shovel with one hand without actually immersing himself into the mess. The steps were gradually carved deeper and deeper into the pit, as the surface level dropped. He usually managed to keep himself out of the mess until it was about knee deep, and he successfully emptied a pit a day.

This day Mingyen was doubly thankful for the privacy. It meant he could lament aloud. "God, how could you let this happen?" he asked, still thinking of the letter from Chi's company. "Nothing's going as it should. What am I doing here?" In this way he bemoaned his fate.

A passage came to mind. He recited Jeremiah 29:11 aloud, "For I know the plans I have for you . . . plans to give you hope and a future." Mingyen stopped. He realized what his problem was. He had lost sight of his hope in the last twenty-four hours. He had allowed himself to become overwhelmed by his misfortunes, to wallow in self-pity. I must maintain focus, he told himself. I must remember where my help and hope come from. He decided to sing. That always cheered him up.

> *I come to the garden alone*
> *While the dew is still on the roses*
> *And the voice I hear, falling on my ears*
> *The Son of God discloses*
> *And He walks with me, and He talks with me*
> *And He tells me I am His own*
> *And the joy we share as we tarry there*
> *None other has ever known*

Tears came into Mingyen's eyes as he sang the old English hymn. All of a sudden he felt the closeness of God come to him, just like the song described. And what a garden he was in!

"God," he said, "I know I've been feeling sorry for myself. Please forgive me. Please help me remember, no matter how much pain I feel, my hope lies in you alone. You are the reason I live."

Mingyen didn't understand it. Absolutely everything was revolting about the cesspools, but it was here he always felt closest to God. It was here he had the most intimate, real moments with him. Why was it here he felt God was revealed the most? The only thing he could think of was that God sure had a sense of humor. What a garden indeed.

A few weeks passed. Mingyen was called into Comrade Pei's office.

"Well, Mingyen Chen. You've been doing a pretty good job in the cesspools."

Mingyen remained silent.

"Not one word of complaint all these years. I believe, actually, you're one of the fastest we've ever had at clearing the pits."

Still Mingyen didn't say a word.

"You're awfully quiet. Don't you have anything to say for yourself?"

What could he say? Mingyen felt like all this guy ever wanted to do was put him down.

"Well, enough small talk, I suppose," Pei resumed. "It seems we've a bit of a problem here. Brigade chief wants to purchase a television set but he's never done anything like that before. None of us have, actually. You're from Shanghai and know how the city works. You're also from a rich family so you'd have more experience buying these kinds of expensive things. So he wants you to go and choose one for him."

Was this for real? Mingyen couldn't believe his ears.

"Well, don't you have anything to say?"

"Uh, all right, Sir. When do I go?"

Mingyen stood across the street, behind a tree, outside the apartment block. He'd been here for half an hour already, debating within himself the best way to broach the subject. In his mind he ran back and forth between different ideas. Unable to come to any conclusion, he finally firmed himself. He would go, knock, and just move with what happened. He strode across the street, up the flight of stairs and rapped on the door. It opened.

"Mingyen!"

"Chi."

"How? What are you doing here?"

"I came to see you, Chi. Will you let me in?"

"Of course." The startled woman opened wide the door. She had moved back to her parents' place.

"Where's Tai?" asked Mingyen, looking around hopefully.

"He's out with his grandparents." Chi made a conscious effort to remain calm. "Won't you sit down?"

Mingyen sat on the sofa, disappointed he wasn't able to see how much his son had grown. Chi chose the armchair. There began an awkward silence.

Then, "Why did you come, Mingyen?"

"Why did I come?!" Everything seemed to boil over inside him at once. "You divorced me, Chi! Did you forget? You didn't even have the guts to tell me yourself! How could you do that?"

"You don't know what it's been like here," she was quick to defend, "how hard it's been, how, how crazy everything is! They were going to fire me, Mingyen! Our boy would have been stigmatized for life! I did what was best for him!"

"And now he won't have a father."

"He doesn't have a father anyway. You aren't here! And who knows when you will be? Ten years!" She spat out those last two words disdainfully.

Mingyen got up and walked over to the window. He feigned an interest in pulling back the sheer curtain and peering out into the street. Inwardly he felt as if a knife had stabbed him in the heart through her last response. He needed time to compose himself.

"So," Chi asked somewhat hesitatingly, "are you out

now, Mingyen?"

"No."

"Then why are you in Shanghai?"

"I was sent here to do something for the prison officials. And I came to ask you to reconsider." He turned to face her again.

"Oh." She didn't know what else to say, her eyes falling to the floor.

Then, gently, "Do you think it would be possible? We could get back together? Please?"

Chi began wringing her hands. "No . . . I don't know . . . No. I don't think so."

Mingyen looked down on the floor. He tried not to lose his hope. "And what about God, Chi? Doesn't he mean anything to you anymore?"

"God! Where is he? There's been nothing but chaos going on around here. Those Red Guards are nothing but a nightmare . . . Oh, but how could you know?" She sniffled and wiped some tears from her eyes. Then, "I don't believe in God anymore, Mingyen."

The knife felt like it just plunged in deeper. He put his hand to his chest as if to stop the bleeding. "So this is it then?" He could barely form the words.

"This is it."

LILI TANG

1989. If I'm going to be executed, Lili decided, I'd rather it be because I'm a follower of Christ and not the student democracy movement! That was the clincher. That was what prompted to her reveal her true identity to the prison authorities. Two weeks later, after verifying the names and addresses she had given them, and after satisfying themselves that the solar battery chargers were not weapons to be used in a coup d'état, the authorities moved Lili to a prison outside of the provincial capital.

The door locked behind her again. The new cell was similar in layout to the city jail, only marginally smaller in size, and there was no glass ceiling or observation gallery this time. All of her new inmates, five other women, were strangers to Shanxi province.

For the first four months Lili was kept in total confinement. Other than for interrogation, she was not allowed out of her cell. She was not permitted the daily trips to the communal basin, the only access prisoners had to fresh water, to brush her teeth, bathe herself or clean her clothes. She was not allotted the twice daily, twenty minute, exercise trips outside in the yard either. Finally, there were no outside visits allowed to her.

It was common practice for prisoners to purchase their own toilet paper, toothpaste, feminine hygiene products and other basic necessities from the prison store. Sometimes too, family members or friends would deliver such amenities. They would also bring items of clothes, especially for seasonal changes.

Things were critical for Lili though. Autumn had passed and winter was here. With her arrest at the end of summer, she was still attired in her thin cotton trousers, blouse, vest and light jacket. She was ill prepared to face the bitter, dry cold of the unheated concrete cell. Temperatures plunged below freezing, and she began to be wracked with worry: Why hadn't anyone in her church or family dropped anything off yet? She thought by now they should have brought something—anything—even if they didn't know where she was. All they'd have to do is knock on the prison door and ask if she was an inmate. There were only so many jails in the county. She hadn't even been able to purchase toilet paper because she had no money.

Further exasperating her troubles was the fact that none of her roommates had much themselves either. After seeing her degrading condition, they could not help but sympathize with her plight. They would have shared something with her if they could, but, as out-of-province prisoners, they had no families nearby who could supply them with useful items.

It was a wretched, miserable time. The less-than-ideal physical conditions played on Lili's mind, at first toying with her self-esteem. You're filthy! You stink! You haven't taken a bath in ages! And what to do about toilet paper? Menstruation? Lili had no other choice. She sacrificed the vest she was wearing and tore it apart into scraps. These scraps would be used and reused again and again over those few months to take care of business. She thanked God for the mercy of her fellow inmates, who would occasionally bring back a bowl of fresh water for her from the communal basin, enabling her to clean herself a little. It also provided the means for her to wash and reuse her vest scraps.

And now the real investigation had begun. The

confession that landed her in this county jail only convinced the authorities that she wasn't a student leader. Now they were working to compile the evidence with which to determine the length of sentence she should receive as a leader of the underground church. That meant intense interrogation. Thus began an even greater mental battle for Lili.

The PSB applied to the prison authorities to release Lili to them for interrogation an average of four days out of seven in those first four months.

"You've been plotting to undermine government institutions. Admit it," her inquisitor pressed.

"I don't know what you mean." It was all an enervated Lili could muster in answer. Yet she could not give in. She knew she must protect the church. The session was extending into its seventh hour and she hadn't been able to sit down once. The interrogator also made her hold her arms straight up in the air for much of the time. If she lowered them ever so slightly, she'd be whacked on the back of the legs with a wooden club.

"You tell people the Three Self Church is evil."

"I teach people to be true Christians and good Chinese citizens, to be kind to others, to help those in need. What's so bad about that?"

Whack! "Trying to show attitude? I think not!"

Lili bit her lip to suppress the scream she wanted to make. She didn't know how much more she could take. Her legs were already beaten to a pulp. Give me strength, God! she cried inside.

"Have you seen yourself in the mirror lately?" he sneered. "A lot of good your teaching has done! We're in the middle of the coldest winter in ten years and none of your followers have even brought you a coat! So what do you think you mean to them? I'd say it adds up to zilch. Zero. Zip." He chucked out the last three words, his free hand indicating a slicing motion at his neck.

Lili remained silent. But she felt that slash in her heart. It was true. They hadn't come. Not even one.

"What's your connection with Hong Kong?" he continued.

Help me not to betray my brothers and sisters, Lord. "What do you mean? I've never been there before."

"How'd you get the VCRs then? The solar panels? The panels aren't exactly the kinds of things you'd see in stores around here."

"I bought them. On a street in Guangzhou. I didn't know they were from Hong Kong. The person I got them from didn't say anything about that."

"This person. What's his name? How'd you find him? Where?"

"You know what it's like—people sell anything anywhere down there. He was just one of those guys. I don't know his name. Like I said, I was just walking down the street and there he was."

"So where'd you find him?"

"I don't remember exactly."

"Try." The interrogator said this with a considerable edge in his voice, while lightly tapping the club in his hand.

Lili searched frantically in her mind for an answer. "Maybe it was somewhere in the old part of the city, maybe around Qingping market. There might have been some water too. But I can't say for sure—have you ever been there? The streets are all a maze in that area."

The interrogator sniffed with a haughty air. Women are always so terrible at navigating directions. "We've been talking to some of your friends, Lili Tang. They tell us you've been speaking at many secret meetings. Don't you know you should be registering with the Three Self Church if you want to preach?"

"We're just friends visiting other friends. I didn't know that was illegal."

"But you're preaching."

"I talk a lot. I can't help it if I'm a chatterbox. I've always been like this. Ask my parents. If that's what they call preaching, then it was unintentional."

Yes, I can see you're quite the talker, the interrogator thought to himself. Almost four months now and she was still saying nothing. Inwardly he sighed. He was tired. She was one tough nut to crack. The interrogator waved his hand in the direction of the door. The guard standing there came and took Lili back to her cell.

Thank God! Lili thought as soon as she got back. She collapsed on the stone slab and laid out flat, arms stretched wide. Seven and a half hours today. At least it was better than the twelve the other day. Lord, have mercy on me!

The collective scramble of her fellow cellmates told her the food trolley was nearby. They all reached for their bowls.

I've got to keep up my strength, Lili told herself. Even though she desperately wanted to sleep, she dragged herself up. She trudged to the far side of the slab and grabbed her sole possession, a slightly cracked plastic bowl, given to her out of pity by one of her cellmates.

The cart arrived. Three skimpy noodles were ladled out along with some murky tasteless soup, and the prisoners sat down to eat. The usual mealtime conversation ensued.

"I'm imagining mine is rich, thick congee with thousand-year-old egg and lean pork," said one of the prisoners.

"Mine is fish cake," said another.

"I wonder what we're going to get for breakfast tomorrow," said a third.

Lili sat there drinking her lukewarm soup. Inwardly she rolled her eyes. She couldn't afford the luxury of thinking about food in any way, shape or form. She focused her mind on reviewing the day's interrogation session. What questions did he ask today? How did I respond? Was there anything that could have exposed the brothers and sisters? He seemed to put a lot of emphasis on the Three Self Church today. That means he'll probably push harder in that area next time, to follow up . . . Don't forget a thing . . . Lord, give me wisdom to know what to say . . . I don't know how much more of this I can take. My legs—God, I want to scream!— it's sheer agony . . . Lili's legs, constantly aching, had massive, severe bruises, and every step she took further accentuated the pain she felt . . . My body is constantly numb with cold. I'm sorry if I sound like I'm complaining, Lord. I don't mean to . . . Come on, girl, think of something positive, something praiseworthy . . . Thank you, Lord, that I haven't been sick in these past few months, that things aren't any worse than they are . . . But how much worse could they get? Sorry, Lord.

There was no interrogation the next day. Lili was made to sit in her cell along with everyone else, as was their daily routine. They sat at the end of the stone slab, silent, no conversation allowed, staring straight ahead. They weren't permitted to move from that position until exercise or lunch, after which they would have to resume the position. Of course, Lili had no exercise session, so she had to remain there without a break.

Lili felt this couldn't be healthy, to stare at a colorless wall just an arm's length away for hours upon hours. She felt like she was beginning to go cross-eyed. At the moment, however, it was the least of her worries. She used the time to prepare herself for the next interrogation, going over in her mind what she should and should not say, trying to anticipate what could be asked and preparing appropriate responses. She must protect the church.

That night, after another lukewarm bowl of flavorless soup, she went through her evening routine of trying to get the circulation in her body going. She jumped up and down on the floor and ran on the spot, trying to stamp life into her frozen feet. When she got too tired running, which didn't take long these days, she vigorously rubbed her arms and legs, where they weren't bruised, and blew on her hands in an effort to thaw them. As she lay down for the night, she held tight the collar of her feather-light summer jacket and tried to keep what little body heat she had from escaping.

As she lay there shivering in a huddle on the glacial slab, the words of the interrogator yesterday came back to haunt her. God, she asked, why hasn't anyone from the church come? When they were in prison, I visited them, even if they were far away. I rode my bike across the province to see them, caught a bus . . . Where are they now? . . . And even if they weren't allowed visitors, at least I brought them things that would be of use in prison. Lili bit her lip here, to stop herself from crying. It didn't work. God, she resumed, I don't think I want to be a full time church worker anymore. When I leave this place, I'll still be a Christian, but I'll just work a normal job. I just can't handle this anymore . . .

And then she was handed a bunch of keys. Wow, she thought, I can open doors with these! Then the first door appeared. She inserted a key and it opened. Next came the second. She was through with no problem. Then she saw the third door. But before she could open it, she woke up.

Oh why?! she thought. Why did I have to wake up? I never got to see the end of the dream! It was so exciting, too, to open up all those doors. What could it mean? she pondered over breakfast. But her thoughts were soon dispelled, for she was summoned to yet another interrogation session.

Immediately the dread came upon her again, the feeling of mental weariness, of constant oppression. I don't want to go! she screamed inside. Oh, let them kill me if they want! She took a deep breath. Don't be silly, girl. You're a Christian. Pull yourself together. You've got to be a good witness. Give a good testimony.

Lili rose to meet the guard. He led her down the corridor, where the chill always seemed to penetrate the deepest. The upper windows were kept open day and night, and this morning the bite of the icy wind seemed especially potent as it gusted down on her like tiny darts. She wanted to cry but she dared not; she felt it would be showing a sign of weakness to the authorities and she didn't want to do that. Her teeth were already chattering. That was enough for them; that was all she would let them see. She would have liked to blow on her fingers but her hands were cuffed behind her back. Finally she was led into the room.

The cuffs were removed and Lili was left standing in the center, the guard retreating to his post by the door. The interrogator was seated at the table at the head of the room.

"So, how are you today, Lili Tang?" he asked, smiling like a wolf drooling over a helpless lamb. "Did you sleep all right?"

Lili made no answer. She didn't even look at the guy.

"Come now!" he taunted. "Don't tell me you're going to show me your temper this morning. That wouldn't be very Christian-like, would it?"

Still Lili didn't respond.

"In a mood, are we?" he asked, as if he were talking to a child. He snorted.

"Are you even human?" Lili exclaimed.

The interrogator was startled. "What kind of a question is that? Of course I am! I eat, I work, I sleep with my wife! What do you mean, am I human?"

"Look at you!" said Lili, her arm pointing at him, her hand wide open. "Look at what you're wearing! Look at what the guard's wearing! Now look at me!"

Wah! he thought to himself, this woman has spirit! He got up from his chair and began to laugh. "Oh, I'm sorry! I'm so sorry!" He kept chuckling as he walked over to a closet in the corner. He opened the door and pulled out a down jacket and a pair of wool trousers. "Here. The prison should have given these to you sooner."

Lili received them, stunned. Was this the first door?

Lili was returned to her cell. There was great relief—relief to have the warmer clothes and relief that the interrogation session was so short today. It had never been that brief before. Normally they averaged about three hours in length, but they could go on for greater stretches, the longest to date having been thirteen hours. For the first time since she had arrived there though, Lili felt like she could breathe a bit easier.

In the afternoon the prison announced a contest. A book of the facility's rules and regulations was to be studied by each prisoner and in two weeks they would be tested.

There would be prizes awarded for first, second and third places, for the inmates who answered the most questions. Every person was given their own copy of the book.

While her cellmates busied themselves reading and memorizing over the next two weeks, Lili would be preparing for her next interrogation. She may have been given a couple of pieces of winter clothing, but she wasn't off the hook and she knew it. She would review the previous session and anticipate the next one, praying desperately for God to give her the words to say each time. A couple of times she flipped to the odd page here and there in the book, to give herself a break from the strain of concentrating on the interrogations but the truth was, she couldn't really care less about the contest. She had much more pressing matters on her mind.

The day of the contest came. All the prisoners were assembled in the auditorium, about eight hundred of them, standing row upon row. The test would be conducted verbally. One by one the examiner would call out each prisoner and ask them a question.

It was tedious, to say the least, to be kept standing there, waiting your turn. It was more than four hours before Lili was called out by the examiner. She was standing two people from the end.

Lili stepped out into the aisle, not expecting anything for herself. She had seen how it had all gone. Not a single person in the whole place had been able to answer a question correctly. Not one. As if she would do any better, she who could count on one hand the number of times she actually opened her book.

"Okay," the examiner began, not much more hopeful than Lili, it might be added—the whole lot so far were totally clueless! "Regulation number twenty-seven, section three.

What does it say?"

Lili was astonished. She recognized the number. "Prisoners are not permitted to receive gifts of food or books from outside visitors."

"Correct!" the examiner said excitedly. Finally! Finally someone knows something in this place!

In fact, everyone in the hall was so surprised they all applauded, including the officials seated on the stage.

"That was very good," the examiner said when the applause died down. "Shall we try another one? Okay. Regulation number sixty-two, section four. What does it say?"

Again Lili was shocked. She knew this one too. "Prisoners are permitted to use a pair of scissors only under the supervision of a guard or prison official."

"Correct!"

A burst of applause filled the hall once more. Prisoners began turning around, trying to spot the genius. Who is she? Where is she? The straight lines of people fell into tangles, and the room went into disarray.

"Order! Order!" the examiner yelled. "Guards! Restore order!"

When calm had been restored, the examiner asked Lili a third question. Again she answered correctly to the delight and wonder of everyone in the room. Then he moved on to the final two people. Lili was glad of that because she couldn't have recalled anymore. The last two contestants failed to give any response.

Needless to say, Lili was awarded all three prizes. She was ecstatic! Three questions, three open doors! She now had in her possession hampers which contained toilet paper, soap, towels, fruit, candies and more. There was so much toilet paper, in fact, three of her cellmates had to help her carry it back. God was so amazing! To think that he had so perfectly guided her questions to be things that she knew. She gave him thanks from the bottom of her heart.

SAIMEN LIANG

1990. The air was musty and somewhat stuffy in the second floor room where they gathered. Nobody seemed to notice though. Everyone was engrossed in the words of the teacher at the front. It wasn't often they were able to hear one of the leaders of their house church movement speak. He managed to make his circuit to Hubei province once, maybe twice a year if they were lucky.

The meeting was held in Dinghu county, virtually on the border with Henan, above a teahouse owned by a Christian widow. While conducting her business, the owner also acted as guard for the meeting above, sending her daughter upstairs for "more flour for the dumplings" if she suspected trouble with the PSB or anyone else.

Saimen began to expound on a verse in the book of Acts. "But," he said, "you will receive power when the Holy Spirit comes on you; and you will be my witnesses in Jerusalem, and in all Judea and Samaria . . ." He put the Bible down on the table and looked out at the forty or so workers from the province's branch churches. They were seated mostly on the floor. "When I was a young man, an old lady taught me that 'Jerusalem' was 'shaking the basket, planting the seed'[12] and 'Samaria' was the 'fire burns Mary,'"[13] he said with a chuckle, which sparked a few quiet giggles and smiles around in the room. "Needless to say, her mispronunciations caused me

---

[12] If spoken slightly off tone in Mandarin the word "Jerusalem" sounds like "shaking the basket, planting the seed".
[13] If spoken slightly off tone in Mandarin the Word "Samaria" sounds like "fire burns Mary".

some confusion. After all, how could the woman who bore the Son of God be burned? How could someone who was chosen for her purity to serve God in this way burn in a fire like hell?" More silent laughter sprang out in the room. The workers were conscious of making too much noise, lest they attract the attention of the customers dining below or pedestrians in the street.

Saimen waited for the group to compose itself. Then he went on. "When I got my first whole New Testament in 1981, I searched everywhere to find out what became of Mary. But of course that never happened to her." There were smiles on every face. "But the principle of the mispronounced 'Jerusalem' still remains with me. We need to keep planting the Word of God everywhere we go. We can't stop. There are so many people who haven't heard, so many who *will* burn in hell if we don't do it. We must always be willing to share what he means to us, and we can with the help of the good fire, the useful fire. That's the fire of the Holy Spirit . . ."

In the ten years since Saimen had been released from the Huining labor camp, he had seen his little Kaiyang county church grow and his own responsibilities and influence as a minister reach beyond the borders of his home province. It was an invigorating time for him, traveling to the various churches in the provinces surrounding his own, and yet lately it felt like it was all getting out of control. Who would have thought the number of believers would have exploded like this? And how could he and his team possibly reach them all, teach them all, help them all sort out their problems? That's all they seemed to do these days, troubleshoot. Who was he, for example, to say which was the best Bible scripture to put on the red banners that were pasted over and down the sides of the front door of someone's house? And did it really matter if a believer didn't have one over his door? Or, for that matter, if a nonbeliever chose to put one up because he wanted God's blessing anyway? And why should he stop a notorious robber from telling people that Jesus saved him? Some church workers thought he hadn't been a Christian long enough to be speaking publicly. How could they possibly move forward when they were stuck on niggly things like that?

Furthermore, since the outdoor meeting in the Lingan village square in 1980, the PSB had maintained a watch on him, despite releasing him, in and around his home province. They still suspected him and were waiting for him to slip up so they could secure a charge against him. As a result, Saimen had been forced to live his life on the run like a fugitive. It was the only way he could reduce the chances of exposing his fellow brothers and sisters and minimize the harassment of his own family.

He continued speaking for a couple of hours. The meeting drew to a close at dusk and he stepped out on to the street below. He took in a couple of deep breaths of the summer air, then began walking. Storekeepers along the street periodically came outside to check their wares, adjusting crates and bowls of goods ranging from t-shirts to fried grasshoppers to plastic stools. Strolling pedestrians paused in front of one store, inspected some items, then moved on to the next place that caught their eye. Motorbikes zoomed by, not uncommonly with father as driver and mother on the back carrying baby and several bags of purchases; or a couple of workmen delivering, say, a large sheet of glass to a construction site. The lack of helmets and the fact that one held heavy glass with bare hands were not matters for concern. As long as one got from Point A to B as quickly as possible. That was the important thing.

A few blocks later Saimen came to the fringes of the neighborhood wet market. He would find a noodle stall in there for his dinner tonight. The thought of food made him realize he was famished. He hadn't eaten anything since breakfast, and that was only a bowl of congee. He looked both ways before crossing the street. It was clear. Then, just as he was about to cross the street to enter the market, a black Mitsubishi Pajero turned a corner and drove up alongside him. It stopped, blocking his way. Saimen recognized it as the standard vehicle of the PSB.

The officer in the front passenger seat got out and stood in front of Saimen. "Liang," he said with a menacing grin on his face, "we were wondering when you'd show up."

What could the preacher do? He had nowhere to run and no resistance to offer. Perhaps this would only be one of those times the local authorities just wanted to "chat". He was cuffed and seated in the back seat of the jeep. As far as he was concerned, better he alone be caught than the church workers who were waiting to disperse themselves discreetly from the teahouse when night fell.

Upon entering the local PSB precinct, Saimen happened to notice the calendar hanging on the wall. Of course, he thought to himself, my son turns eighteen this month. Immediately he recalled his prayer to God when he left the labor camp in 1980. He also couldn't help remembering the last conversation he had had with Ren. It was only last week.

"So what do you think, Dad?" the son had asked.

"Are you sure about this?"

"Yeah."

"Really?"

"Yeah." The youth sounded a little exasperated. "I've

thought about it. I've prayed about it. I'm sure about it.
Now, what do you think?"

The father hesitated for a moment. Then, "Did you ask
your mother? Why don't you ask her for her permission?"

"I did." More exasperation.

"What did she say?"

"She said if that's what I wanted to do and if that's what
God wanted me to do, then I should do it."

"You really want to be an evangelist?" Saimen couldn't
quite get around this in his mind.

"Yeah!" said the son for the umpteenth time.

"It's a hard life, you know. You see how I live."

"I know, but God is worth it."

The father didn't have anything to say to that. It was
true.

"You still haven't told me what you think though," the
son reiterated.

How could he say? He didn't know. Inside his thoughts
and emotions were extremely contorted. His son loved God
of his own accord, not because of his parents. Imagine that!
Saimen felt joy at the thought, immense satisfaction. And
yet, how was it possible? The father instantly felt a sharp
pang of guilt that he hadn't been around enough to be a
proper parent to the boy. Then he was proud—proud of his
son. Ren wanted to follow in his footsteps! He must have
done something right.

But look at me now, thought Saimen, as he sat waiting
in the interview room, hands cuffed behind his back. There
was no question: It's a hard life indeed.

Saimen was transferred back to Kaiyang county in Henan,
where he had to endure the formal investigation period of

his case over the next six months. This, of course, meant interrogation. Those terrible sessions, he thought with a sigh. They occurred three or four times a week over the next half year.

During the first couple of days, the guards punched him repeatedly, brutally stamped on his legs in their heavy army boots and grabbed his head by the hair, slamming it into the wall. He was seated on the floor with his legs straight together out in front of him and hands cuffed behind his back. The ruthless treatment left Saimen in an outrage. "If you keep hitting me," he said, "I won't talk to you anymore."

This only incensed the interrogator, who turned out to be none other than Secretary Wei. He was not as handsome as when Saimen had first encountered him; he seemed somehow haggard. However, his hair was still thick, although it hadn't been gelled back with its usual care, and it lacked its normal lustre. The top and sides kept slipping forward every time he bent over, further adding to the annoyance he felt with the uncooperative attitude of the prisoner. But how he had longed for this opportunity, to question Liang once again. Since the incident in Lingan, in fact. It had been of the utmost curiosity to him how a simple peasant could command the attention of eight hundred people for so long and, in the process, hold at bay a whole PSB village precinct. So he had asked for the Liang case and had been personally overseeing it for the past decade.

Wei ordered the guards to continue the beating. Saimen kept his mouth firmly shut. The leg stamping grew in intensity, sending a sharp shot of pain throughout the prisoner's body with each violent jolt. But still Saimen remained obstinately silent, and, after what felt like an hour, Wei gave up.

This is one pig-headed man, he grumbled to himself. He's not so simple as he appears. He signaled the guards to desist from beating for a while. All right, Liang, we'll play it your way for a while. "So, tell me where you were coming from," he barked in the mildest way he could.

Saimen saw the change in manner and understood. He took a moment to gather his breath. "I told you," he replied, "I just finished having tea." Thank goodness they don't seem to be aware of our meeting, he thought.

"That's not what I was asking. What were you doing in Hubei? Why aren't you at home in Kaiyang working, living with your family?"

"I was on a trip. I came to help some brothers and sisters."

"Help them do what?"

I must not implicate them, Saimen reminded himself. I must not. "I teach them. I help them understand the Bible better."

Saimen's inquisitor scoffed with disdain, "You and your Bible." He circled the prisoner, who remained in his position on the floor. "So what route did you travel to Dinghu? Where did you stay along the way?"

"I slept under bridges or trees beside the road. I didn't stay in any inns. I don't have enough money for that."

"Ha! You have no money!" he spit out. "No wonder! You don't work at anything useful."

Saimen remained silent.

Wei wasn't satisfied. He signaled the guards to resume the physical punishment. This was accompanied by another round of obdurate silence from the prisoner, which eventually led to another grudging abatement of abuse. And so the cycle continued.

Saimen endured interrogation sessions such as these

over the course of the next half year. Whether they were a couple of hours or as long as half the day, he knew that he just had to persevere and get through them, that by so doing God would somehow be glorified. That was what he focused on. That and the need to protect the church.

At the end of that time, Wei presented a summary of Saimen's case to his superiors for their approval. Gaining this was necessary before submitting it to the judges of the court. He had waited for this day for so long. He had, to some extent, staked his career on the case, turning down minor promotions because of the yearning in him to find the source of Liang's power. He was stymied, therefore, when his junior officer returned so quickly with their response.

"What?!" Wei blew up and let loose a long string of expletives. "He can't be charged?! After we finally catch him after all these years?" He was absolutely incredulous. "Crap! Is that what you're tellin' me?"

In its ever continuous drive to modernize, it turned out, China had recently modified its laws. The "anti-revolutionary" charge could no longer be applied against people of religious faith or occupation.

"Yes, Sir," came the meek reply from the reporting officer. The outburst from his boss somewhat overawed him.

"Crap!" Wei exploded into another round of profanity, venting his frustration. He thought of all those wasted journeys up that blasted mountain to raid that blasted Liang home too. At least fifty times he had sent men since 1981, all of whom came back cursing and complaining about the strenuous hike up. He knew it well himself. After the one time he accompanied his own men, when he happened to be visiting Kaiyang county, he never went again himself. "So what do the legal advisers suggest then?" He continued grumbling to himself as he asked this, swearing he wouldn't let the guy go no matter what.

"Well, Sir, they suggest you file charges for disrupting the community peace and order."

"That's it?!" Wei stood there with a look of utter disbelief on his face, his cigarette falling out of the corner of his mouth. He had been hoping for more. A lot more. "You can't be serious."

"I'm afraid I am, Sir. That's all they had to say."

So Saimen was charged with disrupting the community peace and order and was detained another eight months in the county prison.

Saimen sat in his cell. There were ten other inmates but he was bored. They were all bored because, as usual in a county jail, they weren't allowed to talk or move. Two things regularly went through his mind. First, he thought, I didn't really disrupt the community peace or social order. I was just in a home meeting. How can they say that? He sighed as he closed his eyes. He had a slight headache. The monotony of staring at the bland prison walls was getting to him. He resisted the urge to get up and walk around. If a guard caught him, it would mean a beating. A few seconds later he decided he couldn't stand it anymore. He got up and feigned the need to go to the toilet. He walked over to the corner of the cell.

When he was done he returned to his spot. As he sat down he thought about the second thing that went through his mind—the church. How are they getting on? How would they manage? What else needs to be done?

At least sentencing is over though, he thought to himself. That's the worst: not knowing what will happen, being in limbo. At least there's a release date to look forward to now.

Yes, Saimen thought again, it's definitely worse not knowing what's going to happen. The year was now 1999 and he found himself stuck once more in a Henan county prison. He thought back to the fourteen months he was detained in 1990, and then to the month he had been held in 1994. He was familiar with the pattern by now, knowing full well what to expect—investigation by interrogation and physical abuse—but it didn't make it any easier to go through. He took a deep breath to gear himself up for the battle that lay ahead. At least in '94, after being caught in a raid on a meeting, it wasn't that long because of appeals from the international community, he thought. But something told him this time he wouldn't be let off so easy.

As he sat there reflecting, he found he wasn't afraid of imprisonment anymore. It was, he decided, more an inconvenience than anything else. Sure, there was the investigation period—that was tough and you just had to hunker down and get through it—but afterwards it wasn't so bad. At least you got a break from looking over your shoulder all the time. Apart from that, it didn't really change anything else. You got moved from the county jail to a labor camp, where at least you could walk around and do something with your hands. Furthermore, when you were there, it was pretty easy to resume the task of evangelizing and encouraging fellow believers. It wasn't like a county jail where strict silence was maintained. In fact, it turned out to be no different than when you were free. There was still work to be done for God.

However, the biggest concern for him tended to be the church outside. He didn't have an exact figure, but he estimated that, as a result of the efforts of his little church over the past fifteen years or so, they must have somewhere in the neighborhood of 10 million believers nationwide now. They did, after all, have meeting points established in every province. He worried, momentarily, that operations would be interrupted, but then he realized that there was a whole team of people who worked alongside him and they would manage. It was, admittedly, somewhat of a cumbersome team to pull together at times—there were 100,000 full time workers and at least a million part-timers—but he felt sure that they would get along somehow. God would manage them.

The cell door opened. A guard called out, "Liang!"

This is it, thought Saimen. He got up and made his way over to the door. Handcuffs were slipped around his wrists in the corridor and he was led away for questioning.

He entered a smaller room than he was used to for interrogation. The cuffs were temporarily unlocked, his shirt removed. A low bench was then shoved under his knees and he was forced to sit in the middle of the room. His arms were spread out at full length as on a cross, and a second pair of cuffs was produced so that his wrists were locked to pipes running down on either side of the room. With his body leaning slightly forward, he prayed, Lord help me.

The next seventy-eight hours proved to be the longest of his life. It was the worst he had suffered physically at the hands of the PSB. In addition to being beaten with a wooden club, he was electrocuted, punched repeatedly in the head and torso, and allowed no sleep, being bombarded with noise from a TV when the interrogator was out of the room.

"So where is your church office?" asked the interrogator after another brutal electrical shock in the back.

"We don't have it anymore," a severely weakened Saimen gasped. The area around his left eye was swollen from a series of punches inflicted earlier. Blood from his nose was beginning to dry in patches on his face.

"We found your old location on Proletariat Street in Jinping."

"That used to be the office. We gave it up."

The inquisitor straddled across one of Saimen's arms and bent down to stare the prisoner in the face. "So where have you moved now?"

"Nowhere. We gave it up because we didn't need it."

"You lie." He signaled the electrician to give the prisoner another shock.

Saimen screamed in agony. Lord, give me strength, he prayed.

"You've been speaking to foreigners. Tell us who your connections are."

"I don't have foreign connections." Saimen fought to keep conscious of what he was saying.

"Then why all that noise from the human rights organizations last time?" The interrogator held the wooden club under Saimen's chin as he said this, propping his otherwise drooping head up.

"You know how they are. They hear things, they take up a cause. I have no control over what they hear or do."

The interrogator stepped away from the prisoner, and Saimen's weary head flopped down on his chest. Blast, he thought to himself. "I don't believe you. Let's try this again. Who are your foreign connections?"

"I don't have any."

There was another nod to the electrician and another shock.

Another harrowing scream came from Saimen. Then he passed out.

MINGYEN CHEN

1971. It was three degrees Celsius this morning. How the winter wind nipped at his face as Mingyen walked over to the cesspools after breakfast. He arrived and his nostrils were immediately filled with the rude smell. He would concede, however, that it was relatively milder at this time of year compared to the summer. And the number of irritating flying insects was certainly less. He hardly seemed to notice these days though. His heart still ached from the disappointment of his meeting with Chi almost six months ago. Would it ever recover? He wished the cold temperature would numb his mental anguish for a while.

His one solace since his return from Shanghai was the ever present realization of God "walking" and "talking" with him in his "garden". He could sing and call to him at the top of his lungs and no one would complain. It was a great release for him and the only time now he could forget himself and his troubles. It was the only time he knew true peace of mind.

He got down on his stomach to dig the first step in the pit. The ground was harder now. With one hand bracing the wall of the pit for support and his spade in the other, Mingyen had to jab at it several more times than usual to loosen it. He inhaled and stabbed hard at the inner wall. The tip of the spade slid off a concealed rock and nicked the index finger on his left hand. Ouch! He resisted the urge to suck his filthy finger. A small stream of blood poured out and he got up and pulled a rag out of his pocket to staunch it.

As he was about to cover it, he noticed the vividness of the red fluid, the warmth of its color, which seemed to stand out in stark contrast to the cold bleakness of the season and the day. The life is in the blood, he thought to himself; the blood is the life. He closed his eyes as he was reminded that Jesus himself had bled. Jesus had bled for him.

He carefully wrapped his finger up, then sat there with it cradled in his other hand, waiting for the bleeding to stop. Lord, I don't want to complain, he said inwardly; I'm just wondering. Where is my life going? And, as he scanned the series of cesspools, when will this all end?

By the middle of the afternoon he had worked himself nearly three-quarters of the way down into the pool, when he heard a shout.

"Chen! Stop shoveling! Chen! Stop!"

Mingyen popped his head out of the pit and saw Comrade Man standing there with his arms shielding his head in case a shovel-load of excrement hit him by accident.

"What is it, Comrade?" he asked, climbing his way out.

"Comrade Pei sent me to take you to the infirmary," he said, visibly relaxing now that Mingyen was no longer blindly flinging the contents of his shovel.

"Why?" asked Mingyen. "I'm not sick."

"Seems the Chinese herbal pharmacy is short of help. There's some sort of virus and there's no one to fill the prescriptions or something like that."

"When do we go?"

"Immediately, Chen. They need someone now."

"What about this?" he asked, pointing to the cesspools.

"Leave it."

That's fine with me, Mingyen thought. He dropped his spade and followed Comrade Man to the infirmary.

"Here's the man, Dr. Wen," said Man when the two of

them had entered the medical building.

"Aiyah, Comrade!" shrieked the doctor, "Clean him up, for heaven's sake! This is a hospital!"

Man led Mingyen to the staff washrooms. For the first time in all his years in the camp, Mingyen had a hot bath. He reveled in the luxurious warmth and the abundance of soap, as compared to the regular barracks. He lathered his hair until it was thick enough to stand upright. He squished the bubbles through his fingers and basked in the knowledge that he was going to be clean once more. It ended all too soon. Man managed to find Mingyen some clean clothes and came back to hurry him up.

Dr. Wen, it turned out, was the head doctor of the infirmary, trained in western medicine himself. He directed Mingyen to the Chinese pharmacy. It appeared the two regular herbal practitioners had caught some kind of virus and were out of commission for at least the rest of the week. Mingyen would also have to treat the patients who required Chinese medicine.

It was strange to be among things in a clean environment again. It was a welcome change, of course, just something he hadn't been accustomed to in a long while. Mingyen felt the crispness of the white sheets on the beds as he walked by. There was an actual mattress, albeit thin, and not just a brick-hard *kang*. He inhaled the smell of disinfectant in the halls and fingered utensils that were not laden in layers of muck. He tried not to enjoy it too much though. He knew it was only temporary. There was no way Pei would allow him to remain once the emergency was over. The only reason the team captain would have acquiesced to the idea of his cesspool man working in the infirmary now is because someone higher up must have ordered it.

The next morning the brigade chief came in. The cold

weather and chronic rheumatism made the chief a regular visitor this time of year. Upon seeing the sixty-seven-year-old man enter the premises, Dr. Wen immediately forgot the lowly prisoner he was examining and went over to him. "Chief! Let me help you!"

"No! Get away from me!" the grumpy chief shouted.

"But Sir, I'll need to examine you." Wen tried to move in closer to the man.

"Stay away from me! Get me someone else!" The old man pointed his cane at Wen as he said this. "I don't want anymore of your western medicine! All it does is block me up!" He pulled his hat off and slowly shuffled his way to the nearest bed in the ward. "Can't a person get a good old Chinese remedy around here anymore?"

Dr. Wen signaled a nurse to get Mingyen from the Chinese dispensary, and flagged another to help the crusty old man climb up on the bed.

"What seems to be the problem, Sir?" asked Mingyen when he arrived.

"I'm getting old!" complained the chief. "What can you give me for my rheumatism? It always flares up when the temperatures drop like this."

"Well, ideally, you'd want to try some ginseng boiled with sliced deer antler," said Mingyen as he felt the old man's pulse, "but the camp pharmacy doesn't have any of that in stock. So we'll have to recommend something else. Could you please open your mouth, Sir?"

The brigade chief complied with the polite request.

Mingyen poked in a flat stick to have a look. Hm, he thought, his tongue is pretty white. "Are you experiencing any fever, Sir?"

"No."

"Any other problems besides the rheumatism?"

"I'm all blocked up!" The chief shot a glaring look across the ward to Dr. Wen, who was busy checking on another patient. It did not go unnoticed by Mingyen.

"Have you ever tried ginger double boiled with chicken, peony and cinnamon bark?"

"No."

"Well, why don't I give you some of those herbs? I'll give you a bit of angelica too, to help unblock you." Mingyen began to write down his notes and prescription. "It will take several hours to boil the soup though, I'm afraid. But I'll give you some tienchi flower tea, to give you a little relief in the meantime."

The old man was soothed by Mingyen's gentle bedside manner. He peered closer at the herbal practitioner. "I haven't seen you around here before. What's your name?"

"Chen, Sir. Mingyen Chen."

"Chen," the man muttered to himself. "Chen Mingyen . . . Hey! Aren't you the one who purchased my television set in Shanghai this summer?"

Mingyen was somewhat startled. He didn't know exactly who it had been for until now. "Oh, it was for you then . . . Yes, Sir."

"Well, it's a beauty! Thank you!"

"You're welcome, Sir. I'm glad you're pleased with it . . . Now, is there anything else that I can do for you today? Or would you like to see Dr. Wen?"

"No! Don't call that idiot! Everything he gives me always upsets my digestion."

Mingyen diplomatically remained silent, checking through the notes he had just written.

"So where have you been then, Chen, before you came here?"

"Do you mean in which part of the camp have I been

working, Sir?"

"Yeah."

"In the cesspools, Sir.   Actually, I'm only here temporarily, until the regular herbal doctors return."

"I see."

There was an awkward silence.   Chief An had had no idea his TV had been bought by the cesspool man.

"Now," said Mingyen, "let me just get the herbs from the dispensary. I'll be back in a few minutes."

Two days later, the Brigade Chief walked into the infirmary again.   "Chen!" he shouted vigorously in the normally quiet halls. "Mingyen Chen! Where are you?"

Mingyen waved a hand out the window of the Chinese pharmacy down the hall.

"Hey, Chen! I've brought my mother-in-law to see you. She'll be here in a minute—my daughter's helping her in."

"Thank you, Sir. Do you know what her ailment is?"

"Oh I don't know—that woman's always moaning about something . . . Anyway, I wanted to say thank you for your prescription the other day. I felt much better yesterday and today."

"It's my pleasure, Sir. If you need anything more, just let me know."

"I will. I also wanted to let you know I've arranged for your work station to be permanently transferred here. You're not returning to the cesspools."

"Thank you, Sir!" said a grateful Mingyen. And thank you, God!

After he treated the chief's mother-in-law, Mingyen turned to the task of writing up his daily reports. He began by jotting down the date, December 25, 1971. It's Christmas

Day, he realized. His mind became filled with the memory of the first time he learned of the gift-giving holiday. It was at St. Francis Xavier College, his elementary school. He remembered thinking, as a nine-year-old boy, how strange that a holiday was celebrated in his school but not in his home. And who would have imagined? Years later he would receive a present on this of all days. Thank you, Lord.

Many cadres and their family members came to Mingyen when they wanted Chinese herbal remedies. He also treated prisoners. Dr. Chen was known to be a kind yet fair practitioner, not predisposed to favor one patient over another, regardless of status. He soon established a good reputation in the labor camp and it continued to grow. In 1972 he was promoted. He became the head doctor of Chinese medicine in the infirmary, which included overseeing the herbal pharmacy. Mingyen gave thanks to God for his recent good fortune and for every time a patient was successfully treated.

In 1973 the camp moved premises. From Susong county the prisoners were transported in army trucks to a site in Lujiang county, south of Chao Lake, nearer to the center of Anhui. The government had reclaimed the Susong camp to be used as a national farm to accommodate a new policy. This policy required urban students who wanted to attend post-secondary schools to spend a year working in the countryside with the peasants before commencing studies.

Mingyen was busy supervising the re-organizing of the herbal dispensary in Lujiang when he was called in to a ward to diagnose a patient.

After examining and discussing the medical problem, Mingyen asked the younger man, "So, where are you from? Your accent doesn't sound Anhuian."

"Where do you think I'm from?" said Lan, the twenty-seven-old prisoner.

"To me, you sound east coast, maybe Jiangsu?" With raised eyebrows, Mingyen looked up from his clipboard, where he was scribbling down some notes, to see if he was right.

"The doc knows his stuff! Are you from there too?"

"Actually I'm from Shanghai. But I spent time in Jiangsu, in the mid-'50s. I used to travel there quite often, also in Zhejiang."

"What for?"

"I was building churches. I'm a Christian. That's why I'm here." He waved his right hand to indicate the labor camp.

"What? Why would you be constructing religious buildings? The party says there's no God—what's the point?"

Mingyen chuckled silently. In a friendly manner, he replied, "No, not buildings. People. I was a pastor and I taught people about God."

"Oh."

"So why are you here?" Mingyen couldn't explain why, but he felt a deeper compassion for the young man, more so than with his average patient.

"I'd rather not say." Lan turned his head to look over to the opposite side of the room as he laid on the bed.

"I've been in prison for thirteen years now. There's not much that I haven't heard."

"It just seems so awful compared to you . . . but I'll tell you anyway. You seem like an all right guy." He paused to lick his lips. "I killed someone."

"Mm."

"It was my fiancé. And then I ran away. That's why I'm here." His eyes rolled from left to right, spanning the room.

There was a moment of silence.

Remorse overcame the young man and he turned his gaze back to the door across the room. "I regret doing it, doc. I really do." Lan licked his lips again. "If I could change what happened I would, but I can't." He kept his eyes fixed on the door.

Mingyen was moved by the honesty of the young man. "Well," he said, giving the patient a pat on the arm, "there is forgiveness. You only have to ask God. I'll go and make up your compress now."

LILI TANG

1990. Lili rode the prison bus to the southwest corner of Shanxi province in early May. She was on her way to the *laojiao*, the reeducation through labor camp. The interrogation sessions for her case had been maintained at the same rate after the rules and regulations contest, about four days out of seven, for a further four months. Then, after being charged for conducting illegal religious meetings and activities, she was sentenced to three years confinement in the *laojiao*. In total, Lili had been incarcerated in the county jail for just over eight months. The authorities had taken two months longer than the law permitted to investigate and try her case.

As she watched the heavily eroded Luliang mountain range pass by, Lili reflected on the one visit she had received in those eight months, only the day before. Her sister, Yangzi and Lingmei had come, bringing with them a supply of clothes for the upcoming summer. When Lili saw them approaching from the far side of the room, the feelings of frustration, anger and despair borne in those first four months were stirred up all at once. She didn't want to see them. And yet the sight of long lost loved ones moved her to tears.

She tried to maintain her anger at them. "You know, I don't know why you guys even bothered to come. The prison already gave me clothes, since no one else would."

"What are you talking about?" Meimei asked. "Mama and I brought you clothes and food several times. Didn't you get any of it?"

"My mom made you extra thick cotton shoes," Yangzi said. "I told her to, because I know how much you can't stand the cold."

"And I knit you wool socks and gloves," Lingmei added. "Do you mean to say you didn't get those either?"

Lili looked at each one of them, at a loss for words. "You, you all brought stuff?"

"Yeah!" all three exclaimed in unison.

"Really?"

"Yeah!"

Lili wept as the yellow earth of the tableland area began to dominate the scenery. How could she have doubted them? How could she have thought they didn't care? God, she prayed inwardly, please forgive me, and please help me to cope better at the labor camp.

The labor camp was an all-woman facility divided into four groups of up to 160 prisoners each. Lili was initially assigned to work in the kitchen. The time there proved to be more than tolerable to her, even refreshing, as there were three other believers in the small crew that she shared fellowship with.

At the end of five weeks though, she was called into the camp's headquarters.

"We've been reviewing your file, Tang," said Comrade Tei, a group warden. He was a man of medium build and height, and generally quite good natured. "A leader in your church, a teacher, preacher . . . It appears you have some good people and organizational skills." He looked up at Lili to see how she was receiving this assessment.

Lili looked blank. She couldn't figure out what the

warden was leading up to.

"What do you say to being Group Leader of Unit Four?"

Lili's heart sank. That was the last thing she wanted. Who would want to be responsible for motivating a bunch of hardened criminals who had no incentive to work or obey orders? And if group members didn't work, who would be blamed? If a group failed to meet targets or complete tasks, it would be the leader who was punished. That was stress she could live without. "Oh no! No!" she cried out. "I couldn't do it. Really. I couldn't handle it at all!"

"Why do you say that? You're obviously comfortable directing large numbers of people in your church. What would be the difference here?"

"Please, Sir, please don't make me do it!" Lili scrambled in her mind for a way to plead her case. "You, you can make me do anything else! I'll clean the toilets, the drains— anything. Just—please, not this."

"Why? What are you afraid of?" Tei was rather surprised at how opposed to the idea she was. He was offering her a position of honor, not of shame.

"I can't take care of them. I can't scold them, hit them. I would be terrible at the job!"

"You don't need to hit someone, you know. There are other ways to manage a team. You'll be able to find them. I'm sure of it."

"Oh, Sir, please don't ask me to do this!"

"Look," said the warden, losing patience, "who's giving who a command here?" He stood to his fullest height, chest out. "Are you the one in charge here or me?"

Lili became sheepish. "You, Sir."

"Good. You are the new leader of Unit Four."

The No. 2 Provincial Reeducation Camp for Women had several factories which manufactured goods for export—hand embroidered table cloths, lace and beaded gloves, wigs, dresses and other apparel. A smaller amount of output was designated for domestic use, like army boots and blankets. These latter items were the responsibility of Unit Four, which was notorious for getting all the "leftovers", the girls who had no useful skills or talents. This included the elderly, chronically sick, prostitutes, drug addicts, thieves and murderers—the most haphazard and eclectic collection of women in the whole camp.

And it was an unenviable first assignment that Lili had as Group Leader for Unit Four: Make them into the model *laojiao* group in China. The officials announced the camp-wide competition which would take place in thirty days from now. The four units would be tested in their marching drills, ability to follow orders and to maintain discipline as a whole. The winning group would receive prizes and, most importantly, be distinguished with the "model" label as a pattern for other camps to follow.

Lili looked at her group. They were the most non-uniform in physical appearance of all the units in the labor camp. There were old women with hunched backs; young, buxom women with absolutely no interest in anything at all but themselves; tall, short, skinny, fat. Even if she could get them to move as one unit, they wouldn't look as if they belonged together anyway—unlike, say, the embroidery unit, who all had good eyes and were of similar age, height and health.

Over the next few weeks, after Comrade Tei and his team of cadres taught Unit Four their marching drills, Lili was left to ensure the group practiced and understood the commands. She did her best to encourage each woman.

But still the older and weaker women had problems keeping pace with the others; and some of the younger women became nonchalant and lax as soon as the officials left. God, we're such a mess! You've got to help us! Please! You're our only hope.

Lili went into the comrade's office to make her report of the last practice.

"Well, Tang? How's the group looking? Tomorrow's the big day, you know!" said Comrade Tei.

Lili didn't know what to say. In truth, she thought the group looked horrible. They were nowhere near together. Still, she couldn't very well say this to the comrade. "Sir, I think they're just fine."

Tei chuckled. "You think so, eh? Even I have to admit they look like slow learners to me. Maybe you should pray to your God for a miracle."

"I have, Sir." The words came out before she could stop them. Even she was surprised at how bold and confident they sounded, although an observer of the scene couldn't tell by her body language.

Tei was flabbergasted.

"You just watch, Sir," said Lili, her smile beginning to widen. Something inside her was telling her her faith was not in vain. "My God will help us tomorrow. In fact, you better have a couple of drivers ready to pick up our prizes!"

The big day arrived. The four group leaders were called forward to draw lots to decide which order they would go through their drills. Lili drew third spot for Unit Four. She went back to her group.

"All right, comrades," said a perky Lili. "You know one of the prizes is a one month reduction in your prison sentence. What are you going to do with that extra month outside?"

"I'm going to take a long, hot bath!" shouted one of the girls.

"I'm going to eat *jiaozi*!" said a second.

"Go shopping in the city!"

One by one the girls called out their answers and soon Unit Four was rallied into a frenzy of excitement. Suddenly the prospect of a lesser sentence became so much more real and within their grasp than ever before. Lili calmed them down and they watched the first unit go through their drills.

Lili's heart sank. They were so good. Those embroidery girls had the advantage of looking so tidy and uniform. As they marched off the field to end their routine, a girl hastily grabbed for the back of her skirt, breaking the uniformity of their ranks. In a split second panic, she feared her skirt had become unclasped and didn't want it to fall. The embroidery unit saw a drop in their final score to 9.6 points out of ten.

The wigmakers were next up. Lili thought these ladies always had such flair in their conduct. She watched them with anticipation. They were good too—until near the end, that is. Again, the unit had a problem. One of the girls stepped on the heel of the woman in front of her, causing the two of them to stumble over each other on their way off the field. Seven points out of ten.

Unit Four stepped up. The drill sergeant called out the commands.

"Forward march!" Unit Four marched for a dozen paces. "Turn left!" They obeyed like clockwork. "Turn right!" The unevenly-sized unit continued through their paces in order, with no mistakes, over the twenty minute routine. And then they waited for their score. Lili thought it would never come.

Finally—9.7! It was the highest score so far! The girls in Unit Four squealed with delight.

Finally it was the dressmakers' turn. Lili and Unit Four waited anxiously as the last group went through its drills. Biting their fingernails, they hoped and prayed they would remain on top. When the last routine was over, the wait for the final score seemed to be exceptionally long. And then eight points flashed up in the cards.

Unit Four screamed victoriously! They had done it! Comrade Tei and his team of cadres were praised for their excellent teambuilding skills.

"See, Comrade?" said Lili, "Didn't I tell you my God would help us?"

"Ha! Ha! Ha! And didn't I tell you you'd make a good group leader?"

The respect for Lili grew within Unit Four after the competition.

"You're one of the nicest group leaders we've ever had," said Grandma Liou.

"Yeah. You're all right, Tang," said Laifa, a convicted swindler. "At least you don't punch us in the head like our previous leader."

Lili's clout also rose with Comrade Tei. She went to see him one day.

"Comrade Tei," she began, "I've come to ask you to give me authority to apply the five day rule[14] for good behavior."

"Why should I give that to you?" the warden asked, amused at the audacity of the woman. One minute she was whining to get out of the job; now she was so bold in it.

---

[14] In China *laojiao* sentences are counted by the month, not year. If a prisoner, for example, is rewarded a five day deduction from his sentence six times in one calendar year, that would amount to a total of thirty days less in his/her overall sentence.

"If you are serious about me leading these women, I'll need it." Since being assigned to Unit Four, the flagrantly bared bodies of some of the women in her charge was an outrage to Lili, who had, until then, been pretty much sheltered in the kitchen. Unabashedly, these women walked around topless in the summer heat and profanity was liberally sprinkled into their conversation. Lili sincerely wanted to see these women transformed. "If you give me that authority," she continued, "I promise you will see a change in their behavior."

Tei scrutinized his group leader. The woman was in earnest. He considered the request for a moment. "All right," he said standing up from his chair. "You can have it."

Lili went hard at the job. She organized her group into "cells", mini groups, wherein each one had its own leader who would report back to her. That way she didn't have to watch over 160 women herself. The cell members supported, helped, warned and encouraged each other, knowing they could be rewarded for good behavior and good work. With the potential of shortened sentences a real motivating factor, Unit Four became the most disciplined and well ordered group of the camp, winning further accolades for Comrade Tei and his team of cadres.

So successful had the turnaround been, the camp authorities had inquired as to Tei's managing techniques so that they in turn could be implemented throughout the rest of No. 2 and in other penal facilities around the province. Naturally Lili rose even higher in the esteem of Comrade Tei and his crew of cadres. They began to invite her to their headquarters in the evenings, to share their tea, fruit and other food they brought from home; to chat; and very soon they developed into mutual friends.

"Well, Lili," said Tei to her one evening, "we were just

discussing your Jesus just before you got here."

"Yeah," said Comrade Long, Tei's second in command. She handed Lili a bowl of soup. "My mother-in-law made this specially for you. It's supposed to help you have more iron. Drink it while it's hot."

"Thank you, Yinling," replied Lili to the cadre. She was used to spending time with the cadres in their office now.

"I've been thinking about the things you said the other night," Tei resumed, "but I don't understand why he had to die. Why couldn't he just have called his angels down to rescue him from the cross? Surely that would have been a powerful display that he was the son of God."

Lili took a sip of soup. "If Jesus didn't die, our sins couldn't be forgiven. It's as simple as that. What's the point in a sacrifice if it's still alive? It wouldn't be a sacrifice then, would it? But that is exactly what his death was meant to be for us."

"You sound like my mother. She always talks like that," said Tei.

"You should listen to her," said Lili sternly after swallowing some more soup. "You tell me she's been praying for you all these years. Her praying alone isn't going to save you, you know. You have to make the decision for yourself."

"You make it sound so real," said Long, piling a bowl of rice with steamed chicken and preserved vegetables.

"It is real, Yinling . . . Thanks." Lili received the food from the cadre, quickly finished drinking the broth and handed her the empty bowl. "Do you think it's a small decision to die for the world, to spill your blood? Just think of it—he *bled* for us. He allowed himself to be mocked, tormented, tortured at the hands of the Roman centurions. What he undertook for us—he was more serious that we could imagine!"

Long handed her a pair of chopsticks. "But couldn't there have been another way?"

Lili took the eating utensil. "You know," she said, "the way he did it meant that he could identify with our humanness. He knows how real it is to feel pain, to hurt, laugh, cry—everything that we feel. He knows the reality too well." She looked at the cadres earnestly. Would they make the decision tonight?

"I don't know," said Yinling. "I'm going to have to think about it a bit more."

"Me too," said Tei, "although you do make it sound more logical than my mother."

"Well, don't take too long." Lili picked up a piece of chicken and popped it into her mouth.

Autumn 1991. Lili was ecstatic. So far over sixty women in her group had made commitments to Jesus. Moreover, Comrade Long and a couple other cadres had too. Life in the labor camp was turning out to be glorious! Who would ever have imagined that? she thought, as she made her way over to the group cadre office one morning.

"You wanted to see me, Sir?" she asked, popping her head into Comrade Tei's office.

"Yes, Tang," he said, closing the file he was looking at. "Come in. Sit down."

Lili sat down across from the warden.

"I've got a special assignment for your group, Tang," he began. "There's been severe flooding in Anhui. At least half a million homes were lost, you know."

"That's terrible, Sir."

"Yes. All around the country people are being asked to

contribute to the relief effort, and we, Unit Four, have been granted that honor here at No. 2." He looked pleased with himself as he said this.

Lili didn't make an immediate response to this. Something told her it wouldn't be a simple matter. "And what exactly are we to do, Sir?"

"The authorities are asking us to produce 10,000 blankets."

"You want Unit Four to make blankets? Why not Units One or Two? They have all the expert sewers."

"No, it's Unit Four's honor. You're the one that gets the results. Camp officials want us."

It figures. "And when will these blankets have to be made?"

"In one month, Tang. The Red Cross is expecting to receive them in one month."

"Is there anything else I need to know, Sir?"

"Uh, yeah." Tei's face spread into a foolish grin. "You have to make them in addition to your army boots."

"In addition to our army boots."

"Yeah, in the evening, overtime."

"Uh-huh."

"If you complete the task on time, each member of your group will receive two months off their sentences. If you don't, you will have six months added on."

Lili sat there doing some quick mental calculations. Overtime hours for the next thirty days wouldn't be enough for them to meet the target. A grim look came on her face. It wasn't as if you could say no to these "honors" from the government. "I see."

"I know it's difficult, Tang. Just pray to your God. He seems to have never failed you yet."

These women don't know how to sew! Lili thought as she left the office. The old ladies—bless them!—can hardly see to pick up their *mantou*[15], let alone handle a thread and needle! And to sew them at night, after having completed an already long, full day of work?!

Lili experienced greater stress than usual in the next few weeks. The pressure she felt to meet the deadline was tremendous. Every evening she would walk to the warehouse where the finished blankets were stored and would observe that very few blankets had been completed. How would they ever fill the place on time? She would return to her dorm and pace the floor all night in prayer. God, she pleaded in desperation, we need a miracle! Send your angels to sew some more! Please! Please do it for your glory! Otherwise people will say you can't hear us when we pray!

She would feel better the next day after she prayed. But then she would walk into the warehouse and see how barren it was, the reality of the situation completely overtaking her once more and robbing her of any peace that she had found. After a couple of weeks of this, she decided not to go to the warehouse anymore.

The time slipped by far too quickly. After tonight only four days would remain before the deadline. She had to check their status. She grit her teeth and went to the warehouse. Less than half the required blankets had been made! Lili was dispirited. Oh, God! What are we going to do? We need a miracle! She stayed up all night begging God to do something. Anything!

The next morning, tired from lack of sleep and worn out from her stress, Lili made her way over to the army boot

---

[15] Steamed buns.

plant as per usual.

Laifa came running out. "There's no electricity."

"No electricity? What's the problem?" asked Lili. Oh God, please don't let it be found that one of the prisoners vandalized the plant. I don't need that kind of trouble today. (The whole group would be punished for that.)

"I don't know. A technician's checking it out right now with Comrade Long."

About half an hour later, Comrade Long came out. "Well, looks like the main transformer's blown. We're going to have to order a new one."

Lili couldn't believe it. That would easily take days! Especially considering all the hoops they'd have to jump through to get it—explaining to authorities the problem, awaiting their permission to purchase, placing the order, then delivery, installation and so on . . . That would leave them free to work on the blankets! Her miracle had come!

On the fourth day, the army trucks arrived for the Red Cross. They picked up all 10,000 blankets and every woman in Unit Four was awarded two months off their sentences. Lili breathed a huge sigh of relief. You did it again, God.

Still: Moving Out

School's over. You've persevered, passed the exams and made it through to graduation. Or have you? Some people believe the true fulfillment of one's education is the implementation of lessons learned into "real life" situations. That is the ultimate test.

It's rather like a new recruit in the army. He is required to go through boot camp, training and drills before he is sent to the frontline. When going through exercises, in no way does the new recruit think he is on a real battlefield. He must first learn how to defend and, when necessary, to advance. The ultimate test follows.

Perhaps Lili herself put it to me best: "The Gospel is an action. It's not sitting in the church. It's not sitting in a room. It's an action, a step that we have to take. We have to take it in order to go and reach the world."

SAIMEN LIANG

2001. *R-R-RING!*

"Hello?"

"Shu?"

"Yeah. Is that you, Saimen?"

"Yeah."

"What's up?

"I'm just calling to let you know my new cell number. I had to dump the old phone. I think it was compromised."

The two men were in Baoting county, Henan.

"Compromised? How?" There was an audible tension in Shu's voice.

"I'm not really sure."

"How do you know then?"

"I managed to see Yanyan last night. She said the PSB have been keeping a watch around the house the last week or so. They're up to something, so I thought I should play it safe."

"Yeah," said Shu, understanding. "Well, do you have any idea who it could have been?"

Saimen paused for a second before he answered the question. "It might have been Yun. I don't think we should have appointed him caretaker of the office."

Shu was disenchanted. He had suspected as much. "It's my fault, Saimen. I was the one who felt sorry for him and urged you to give him the job. I'm sorry."

"I don't blame you, Shu. We made the decision collectively. But maybe you should just be careful of what you say if you run into him. Warn Ying too. But don't say anything to anyone else.

"Got it."

"So how much did it cost?" asked Shu, handing Saimen's new cellular phone back to him.

"Three hundred and fifty *yuan*," the owner replied, pocketing it again and then picking two pears out of a bag for the two of them to eat. "I bought it secondhand." They were sitting on the grass along the banks of the Hong River, enjoying a picnic lunch and a break from riding their bikes between villages. It was the next day.

"Three hundred and fifty!" exclaimed Shu. "Ying's gonna flip." Ying was the unofficial bookkeeper among the three of them. He was habitually on the lookout for the best deal and was where the buck stopped as far as their church finances were concerned.

"It was a good deal. It includes a hundred free minutes every month for a year."

"Oh," said Shu seemingly pacified. He bit into his pear. Then, with his mouth still full, "I suppose he'll say it's all right considering what could have happened if you were caught with the old phone."

"You think he's going to give me an earful about the price?" Saimen said this more as a statement than as a question.

"Well, you know how he is," replied Shu, waving his partially eaten pome. "Remember when we talked about buying the first two bikes for our church?" Shu chuckled as he thought of those days back in 1982. "They weren't even new! Together they only came to 100 *yuan* but what a dilemma! Should we, as Christian workers, indulge in the luxury of purchasing bicycles to cut down on our travel time between villages and counties, to help us use our time more efficiently?"

Both men fell back on the grass in laughter at the seemingly endless hours of discussion they had devoted to the topic. A few chunks of pear accidentally flew out of Shu's mouth.

"He was the one most opposed to buying them!" said Saimen, not noticing the mess his friend had made; he too was trying to keep fruit from spilling out of his own mouth.

"And to think we used to walk everywhere and endure all those blisters . . . Those were the good old days." Shu was nostalgic as he said this.

"They sure were."

The two men sat there for a moment in silence with smiles on their faces. All of a sudden Shu snickered.

"What?" asked Saimen, stopping mid chew.

"Oh, nothing," replied Shu, trying to stifle another snicker from coming forth.

Saimen looked at his friend, his left eyebrow raised. He swallowed his mouthful. "Really." There was an edge of mock sarcasm in his voice. He'd been friends with Shu long enough to know when "nothing" meant nothing and when it meant *something*.

"Really," Shu insisted with rather a silly grin on his face. He took a deep breath in an effort to compose himself. It worked—for about ten seconds—and then he burst into another series of giggles. The more he tried to control them, the more they gushed out.

"You're hopeless," said Saimen, turning to look the other away.

Shu took a couple more deep breaths. "Okay. I'm all right now." A few seconds later, he exploded into another fit of laughter.

"What's so funny? You can't say it's nothing now."

Shu let out a few more chuckles and then seemed to pull himself together. "All right. But you won't like it."

Saimen stared at him, beguiled. "Why do you say that? We've been friends for more than twenty years. We have a similar sense of humor."

"I just know. Anyway, don't say I didn't warn you . . ." Shu swallowed another bite of his pear. "It's about you. I was just remembering how long it took you to learn how to ride a bike! Six months!" He roared into hearty laughter, slapping his leg in the process. "I know we weren't spring chickens when we started learning but you were just so slow!"

Saimen sat there, not anywhere near as amused as his friend, who was ten years his senior. He was able to laugh at the fact that he himself had learned how to ride a bike at the relatively late age of thirty-one but he didn't think it was *that* funny!

"You were fine riding in an open field, but when you got on a road . . ." Shu howled again at the memory. "You were such a menace! Anytime you saw anyone on the road he automatically became a target for your bike!"

Saimen crossed his arms on his chest, in half mock indignation. That was quite enough. Really, the expression on his face and body seemed to say, couldn't we be a bit more mature around here? You've had your little joke. Now let's move on. He didn't appreciate being reminded of those days.

"And then that time—that time—" By now Shu was holding his gut and a passerby might not have been sure if the older man was in pain or hysterics. "You—you got given that bike—" It was all Shu could do to gasp air. "And you carried the bike home because you were too nervous to ride it in front of us!"

"It was a gift!" said Saimen defensively. "God was very gracious in allowing me to have it! I just wanted to treat it with honor . . ."

But it was to no avail. Shu was not in any condition to take heed. He was still struggling to breathe in between his laughs, almost hyperventilating.

"Yeah, yeah, yeah," said Saimen in response to his ailing friend, giving up the attempt to explain. He continued to hold his head up, trying to appear dignified and composed about the whole matter. "And I suppose next you'll bring up the ditch."

That brought another hoot from the older man. "Look! No hands!" Shu brought his arms down from above his head in a reenactment of that memory and was beside himself again. He continued to hold his side as he recalled the time Saimen, by then a more competent rider, had tried to cycle with no hands and wound up flying into a ditch, landing head first in the mud. He and Ying had had to pull him out by the legs.

"I told you you wouldn't like it!" said Shu, his sniggering just starting to ebb. Seeing his friend wasn't completely pacified, he continued, "Hey, but look at you now! You're great on the bike! You persevered and you overcame! That's all that matters!" He patted Saimen on the back.

The two friends settled into another moment of quiet.

"Hey," said Shu, "are you ready for tomorrow?"

"You mean the funeral?" asked Saimen, glad the subject had finally been changed.

"Yeah."

"I suppose so." Saimen took a last bite of his pear. As he did so, he chuckled. "Now *that's* a lady with a funny story."

"You talking about Grandma Lai?" asked Shu.

"Yeah."

Another attack of the giggles came on Shu.

"Remember how she used to say God 'over answered' her prayer about her husband?" said Saimen, whose chuckles were beginning to turn into a more hearty laughter.

"Help me cope with the persecution from my unbelieving husband, Lord!" Shu raised his arms again, this time in mock prayer, and the pitch of his voice as he recalled the testimony of the old lady.

"And then her husband dies!"

The two friends fell over in laughter again. After a few moments, calm set in again.

"She sure was a faithful prayer warrior though."

"She sure was," Saimen agreed. "Hey, are you going to help bring the body out?"

"If you want me to."

"Yeah, you do it."

"Okay."

The room was full to capacity. Grandma Lai, who had passed away only two short days ago, had been a well respected Christian, woman, mother, grandmother and great-grandmother. Her family and relatives were present among the hundred or so mourners. They sat in the front rows, their upper left arms bearing the black bands symbolizing the occasion. Two of her grandsons were official party members, employed in county-level government offices and Saimen knew they were not believers. In fact, most of the younger generation of Grandma Lai's family were not Christians.

Saimen stood up and walked to the front of the room. He positioned himself right of center and began to survey the people gathered. He was thankful to God for this opportunity to tell them about Jesus and that so many had actually attended. Lord, he prayed inside, give me the words to say today. Let those who don't know you, come to know you. It was Saimen's pride and joy to be able to share about how Grandma Lai lived and valued her faith. After all, it wasn't every day you could legally talk about such things publicly in China.

Saimen began the service by signaling to Shu. He was standing in the doorway of a small chamber off to the side, while another brother, Luo, was inside with the body of Grandma Lai. As was the local custom, the body had been laid flat on a door that had been removed from its hinges, and now the two men in the chamber respectfully lifted it off and carried it into the main room in front of everyone. They seated it on an empty fold-up chair in the center, standing on either side to hold it in place so it wouldn't flop to the floor. Shu delicately propped Grandma Lai's head up and held it in place as if it were looking out at the people gathered at this memorial.

"Grandma Lai was a beautiful Christian woman," Saimen began preaching to the crowd. "What you see here today is her old body, her sleeping body." He waved his right arm to the spot where it was seated to emphasize the fact. "She was not afraid to die," he continued. "She was as free in spirit and mind as you see her limbs moving now."

Shu and Luo began moving the body's arms and legs up and down, and around in circles to demonstrate the freedom Saimen was speaking of.

"She didn't fear death because she knew her Maker, because she knew she was going to Heaven." He continued his evangelistic message, telling people how they too could secure their own place in Heaven, how there was only one Way to get there, and that Way was Jesus. What better way than this, Saimen couldn't help thinking as he spoke, of helping people to see that death was real, and that the only One who could ever save them from it was literally knocking on the door of their hearts at this moment to let him come in? He wrapped up his talk an hour later, ending the service with a prayer.

People began filing out of the room. Some stayed behind in small clusters, catching up with old friends, while a few individuals came up to Saimen to thank him or comment on the service.

The last of these turned out to be a family member of the deceased woman, the black band on the man's arm alerting Saimen to the fact. Although he had slightly hunched shoulders, there was an officious air about him. He didn't seem to be a person who could take a joke. Not yet middle-aged, the man had a hairline that was beginning to recede which caused a rather large mole on his right temple to become more easily visible than in younger days, secretly annoying him, as he already had a couple on his chin and left cheek. "That was an interesting speech," he said in a rather gruff manner.

"Uh, thanks." Saimen wasn't quite sure how to respond to the comment. He extended his hand to shake the hand of the man in greeting. "I'm Liang. Saimen Liang. What's your name?"

"Lai," he answered abruptly, not offering anything more.

So this is one of her grandsons, Saimen figured, the moles being recognized from a family photo the grandma had shown him lately. He also remembered she told him that Lai was a party member. "Well, Comrade Lai, I hope you will seriously consider it. Your eternal destination is at stake."

"You seriously believe all that superstition?" Lai's skepticism was beginning to reveal itself now. There was even a hint of hostility in his tone. Vanity, arrogance and tiredness from forever trying to climb the party ladder all rolled into his bitter question. "And what do you mean she's 'sleeping'? She's dead. She's not waking up. All that moving around of her body isn't going to change that."

Saimen discerned Lai had somehow been disappointed in his life—if he had had to suffer, the comrade's attitude exuded, others should too. In his mind Saimen desperately asked God for wisdom on how to deal with this man. Then, "There is hope, you know," he began slowly, gently. "Difficult as it is to believe, it's true. Your grandma's life wasn't easy, as you know. She had her struggles like any of us, but she didn't complain. She was content, even in hard times, and now she has entered her rest."

"She was foolish," Lai spit out. "Her life was harder than it had to be. What's the point of her family's party connections if she won't take advantage of them?"

"Maybe that's not what she wanted in life."

"What else is there?" In his mind Lai couldn't conceive of anything else worth pursuing. Otherwise how else could you get ahead in China?

"Your grandmother wanted her family to be content, to know that contentment was possible. She saw how you work and work, but you don't have to strive always."

The word "strive" struck a chord inside Lai. He turned away from Saimen. It was true: He was always striving and, it seemed, always falling short. It was never enough. He kept thinking that if he just got this or that, or made it here or there, it would be all right. But he'd get there, and before he knew it a new discontent would soon prevail. When would the cycle ever end? Lai's hardness had begun to be softened by Saimen, but he didn't know what to do.

He walked past Saimen, up to the body of his skinny grandmother. Looking down on her, still seated in the chair between Shu and Luo, he reached out to touch her face with his finger. Gently he outlined the right side of her face. Then he stooped down to take a hold of the hands that had once held him as a child. He saw the age spots that dotted her skin, ran his thumb over them for a while, and then he peered back at her face. Was it possible? Or was he just imagining things? She did seem at peace now. She did look to be at rest. "Maybe," he said over his shoulder to Saimen, "maybe there's truth in what you say. Maybe not. I don't know. But maybe—" He paused. "Maybe if it's not too much trouble, you could pray for me sometimes."

"I will," said Saimen, relieved inside. "I will."

MINGYEN CHEN

1982. Mingyen looked at his watch. Ten to seven. The traffic in the hotel lobby was fairly steady. Tourists rushed in late from a full day's sightseeing in Beijing, and diners were already on the way out for their evening meal and entertainment. A few, like him, were seated on the sofas, waiting for dates, friends or business colleagues to arrive.

Mingyen was waiting for the latter. He wasn't, however, exactly sure what they looked like—those foreigners all looked the same to him. He only knew they were two men from Scandinavia. They would be searching for a forty-nine-year-old Chinese man with square glasses, a navy necktie, white shirt and an English newspaper in hand. They were twenty minutes late though. He hoped that nothing was wrong. He reopened his paper, shook out the corner that had fallen back in, and pretended to read.

A few minutes later, "Mr. Chen?"

He looked up. Two fair-haired, middle-aged gentlemen were standing there in chinos and polo shirts.

"Mr. Nilsson?"

"Yes. This is my friend, Mr. Larsson."

"It's nice to meet you both." Mingyen rose to his feet and the three men shook hands warmly.

"I'm sorry we're late," Mr. Nilsson resumed. "The traffic was so bad coming back from Badaling."

"No need to apologize," said Mingyen, straightening out his paper. "I'm just glad you're all right. Did you enjoy the Great Wall?"

"It was fantastic! What an amazing feat of engineering!" exclaimed an enthusiastic Nilsson.

Larsson nodded in agreement, a wide grin on his face.

Mingyen smiled politely. He'd been there several times. It wasn't that spectacular to him anymore—particularly the restored parts of the wall which were overrun with tourists. "Well, it's a pleasant evening. How about a stroll by the river before dinner?"

"Sounds good to me," replied Nilsson. "How about you?" He looked over to his friend.

Again Larsson nodded.

The three men walked out of the Kunlun Hotel and headed towards the Liangma River.

As they made their way under the leaves of the poplars, Nilsson remarked, "Your English is excellent, Mr. Chen." He hadn't expected to be able to find a local who would be so fluent.

A modest Mingyen brushed his hand in the air as if to wave off the comment. "Uh, thank you. I don't think so." It had taken him a while, he felt, to brush up on the language, having not used it for so long. It was just one language, but why did they all speak it so differently—the British, the Americans, these Scandinavians?

"Where did you learn English?" continued Nilsson.

"It used to be a standard part of the curriculum in the Shanghai education system when I was growing up. I started learning in school when I was eight years old."

"Well, I think it's wonderful," repeated the Scandinavian.

As they passed a street vendor packing up for the day, Mingyen decided it was time to move the conversation to business. "So have you brought them with you?"

"Yes. They're in our room," said Nilsson.

"How many?"

"A hundred and sixty. Will you take them away today?"

"No. I'll arrange for someone to pick them up later. How long are you here for?"

"Two more days. Then we fly to Guilin."

"Okay. I'll call you before you leave."

"Very good."

The illumination of the moon had just overtaken the final light of day. They passed a young couple on the bank, on their bikes. They were enjoying a few, brief moments of privacy after work.

"Mr. Chen," said Nilsson.

"Yes."

"We have more," he continued. "A team from our church will be coming in a couple of weeks."

"And you would like to arrange pick-up."

"Yes, please."

"I'll need their itinerary and a contact name. I'll get in touch when they're here to coordinate collection."

"Here," Nilsson dug out a piece of paper from his wallet and handed it to Mingyen. "It's all here."

Mingyen paused briefly under a street lamp to check it. "Good. If there's any change you can leave a message with my friends in Hong Kong. They'll know what to do."

"Mr. Chen," said Larsson, speaking for the first time.

"Yes, sir."

"These Bibles, they do all get to the rural underground church, don't they?" He asked this with a slight hesitation in his voice.

"Of course," said Mingyen. He stopped walking and turned to look at the visitors. What kind of question was that?

"I'm sorry," said Larsson. "I didn't mean to sound like I

doubted you. It's just, it's just we've sent a lot of Bibles in the last year. We don't actually know if any of them get to their destination."

Mingyen sighed, understanding. "Yes, they do," he said. He resumed his stroll. "If you only knew at what risk. People have been caught with the books in their possession, arrested and imprisoned. But the church here is so starved for the Word they'll pay any price, even if it means their freedom." He paused here, thinking of the dearth of knowledge and Bibles in the underground church he had just taught in a couple of days ago. The Christians there mistakenly believed for a time that the twelve tribes of Israel came about as a result of Abraham chopping up Isaac into twelve pieces. But what could you expect when the closest they had ever got to a Bible was a verbal description from the fading memory of an old person? He had heard wild tales like this time and again in the last three and a half years. "Do you know how the believers react when they're finally able to even just touch a Bible for the first time in their lives?" he continued. "They cry for joy. They kiss the book. They're so overwhelmed—it's actually there in their midst! They can hold it. They can put it to their cheek lovingly. They can read it for themselves. And they're so touched that people outside of China care enough to send it to them." He stopped walking again and turned to face the two visitors. "People like you, kind-hearted, who give so freely, you're an encouragement to us to press on."

Larsson and Nilsson stood there, humbled, their heads bowed. "Well, do you need more?" Larsson urged. "Is there anything else we can help you with?"

"The truth is, the shortage is still acute. I still get dozens of letters requesting me to find more. So if you can keep sending them, we can keep using them."

Mingyen arrived back at Teng's house, his accommodation in Beijing. Teng was a fellow believer.

"How'd your meeting go?" asked Teng. He stood at the sideboard pouring himself a cup of tea and pointed the thermos at Mingyen to see if he wanted some.

"Sure," acknowledged Mingyen, as he loosened his tie and sat down at the table. "The meeting went well enough. You'll have to arrange for someone to pick up some Bibles."

"No problem. Just say when and where."

"Hotel Kunlun. Tomorrow. Probably two guys—there's a hundred and sixty books." Mingyen kicked off his shoes as he said this. He received the cup of tea. "Thanks."

"When are you off to Hong Kong?"

"A couple of days. I catch the early train to Jiangsu tomorrow, pick up a few things and then I'm off."

Teng nodded. "We're sure going to miss you. You were perfect for the job, your ability to speak English, your understanding of Western ways—not just anyone can walk into those fancy hotels, you know."

Mingyen finished a sip and smiled. "Lots of good people are doing this work now, Teng. It's not like when I came out of the *laogai* in '78 and no one had a clue. You don't have to worry." He leaned forward in his chair. "My Hong Kong contacts are good. They'll handle everything. You won't have to change a thing."

"Well, me and the wife, we'll still miss you anyway."

"Thanks." He took some more sips of tea. "I'll be back one day though. I just don't know when. I have no idea how long it'll take to arrange things for my father and Wenyu." Wenyu was Mingyen's new wife. Chi had died of cancer the year he was released from the labor camp.

"So you're really going . . . Lucky dog." Teng leaned back in his chair, hands clasped behind his head.

"It's not luck," said Mingyen, putting his empty cup down. "It's a miracle. Who would have thought that after all these years my godmother still had my Hong Kong ID card from 1950? Our home in Shanghai was raided by the Red Guards. They took so much stuff, including Father's and Yichun's IDs. But for some reason she had mine with her when she moved to Hong Kong and kept it. God protected it through her."

Teng got up from his chair and grabbed a bag of preserved plums from the sideboard. He opened it, offered some to Mingyen, who declined, then pulled out a piece of the wrapped candy for himself.

"You're right," he said, after opening it and popping it into his mouth. "What made her remember it after twenty years, that she'd bring it to you? And who would have thought you'd be totally rehabilitated by the central government, and that that piece of paper would actually come in handy?"

Who would have thought indeed? Mingyen asked himself again as he laid down that night to sleep. Those last eight years in the labor camp, after his sentence had expired, had been such a struggle for him not to complain in his heart about the injustice of his case and the loss of his family. And yet, ultimately when he was released, he discovered that God had truly been working for his good. If he had been let out on time, he would have walked straight into the mayhem and atrocities of the Cultural Revolution. According to Maoist philosophy, he was the absolute worst of the worst in society—he came from a wealthy family; he was educated; and last but not least, he was a Christian pastor. Surely he would have been permanently maimed or even killed because of one or all of these strikes against him. In his heart he thanked God for his foresight and protection.

And then God had granted him favor with the local Jiangsu cadres. Mingyen had been allotted residency in a village in the province neighboring Shanghai, his old home, when he left the labor camp. It was the local cadres who brought his case to the attention of provincial officials which led, in 1981, to his total exoneration of all the charges that landed him in prison for eighteen years. He was even returned the 400 *yuan* (without interest, he thought with a wry grin) that was taken from his home when the police searched it in 1960.

In the silence of the night he thought of the future. What lay ahead for him now? Hong Kong was actually not his first choice, but it was the only way he and Wenyu could live together. As it stood at present, he was stuck in the countryside and she was in Shanghai. When the village cadres had asked what else they could do for him (after his rehabilitation) he had requested residency in Shanghai. It proved to be something beyond their jurisdiction. The best they could offer him was a move to Hong Kong.

His contacts in the British colony had assured him he would have no problem finding "work". But he wasn't sure about doing radio broadcasts into China. Oh, he could see how it would be helpful to the believers behind the bamboo curtain, and he'd certainly give it a shot. But he knew, from the bottom of his heart, his desire was to work alongside the poor in his native land. Well, he surmised, God had made things work for him before. He could certainly do it again.

1986. The two young ladies from Hong Kong waited in their hotel room in Shanghai. Kathy, in her early thirties, flicked through the channels on the TV, used to the fact that things could take time inside China. Winnie, in her early twenties, paced the room nervously. This was her first "covert" trip to the Mainland.

"What do you think is keeping him?" asked Winnie.

"It's only half an hour. Don't worry," replied Kathy. "It's probably just some cadre being longwinded. You know how it is."

Winnie sighed as she sat down at the desk. She picked up a hotel magazine and began flipping through it. "He's from here, isn't he?"

"Yeah," replied Kathy absently.

"I don't know how he does it, coming back here like nothing happened."

"He's pretty amazing, isn't he?" She turned her attention momentarily away from the TV and stared at the far wall. "He used to walk miles and miles, you know, between villages."

"So I've heard." Winnie was still flipping through the magazine, though she wasn't really mindful of its contents. "How did he do it?"

"He'd spend one or two days in a village, working in the fields with the locals and treating them for simple medical problems, then evangelize at night." Kathy fell back on the bed as she said this.

"So short?" Winnie dropped the publication back on the desk. "How could he build relationships?"

"He'd do a circuit, then repeat it. He was wary of staying in one place for too long. Otherwise the people would come from other villages and there'd be a crowd. That was the last thing he wanted because then it would draw the attention of the PSB." Kathy rolled over on to her stomach and propped her chin up on her hands.

"He always thinks about those things, doesn't he?"

"He sure does. It's well worth following any advice he gives you."

There was a knock on their door. Winnie sprang to answer it.

"Pastor Chen!" she greeted him with relief.

"Winnie," he nodded to her as he entered the room. "Kathy. Sorry I'm late." The girl respectfully scrambled to sit up on the edge of her bed. "Those cadres sure can talk." He took off his suit jacket and sat down on a chair.

Kathy raised her eyebrows here, passing the "I told you so" look over to her younger colleague.

"But at least we got approval to install a new water pump," he continued. "By the way, he's invited all of us to dinner tonight—at his house."

"Wow." Kathy knew how rare that was. "What time?"

Mingyen looked at his watch as he loosened his tie. His eyes opened wide in surprise. "Oh, in a couple of hours. We should probably leave in an hour because he lives on the other side of the city. Winnie, make sure you buy some fruit before we go, okay?"

Winnie nodded.

"So what have you two girls accomplished today?"

"We met with two different contacts, Pastor," Kathy reported. "We told them where to collect their Bibles from and they told us how many more they need."

Mingyen nodded. "Did you arrange the next drop off then?"

"Yes. One of them asked too, if you could come and do some teaching for his leaders specifically."

"All right. Did he indicate when and what topic he had

in mind?"

"He was hoping the sooner the better but he's open to what works for you."

"We'll check the schedule when we get back to Hong Kong. What about the topic?"

"Qualities of a good leader."

Mingyen nodded again. "Say," he said, as if just remembering something he wanted to say, "is that what you two wore to meet the contacts?"

The two girls nodded with smiles on their faces. They were proud of their "disguises", that they blended in so well with the proletariat with their loose-fitting pants and Mandarin-collared tops and jackets.

"In future, I think you should drop the Mao clothes," he said rather bluntly. "Haven't you noticed people in the cities are fashion-conscious now? They're well dressed in Western styles. Leave the peasant garb for the rice paddy fields!"

LILI TANG

1993.

"You know, I'm just not going to be able to choose. You'll have to do it."

"Me? I can't—this concerns *you*!"

"I don't mean you alone—you and the others. You decide with them."

"How can you say that?! This is *your* life, *your* future! *You* have to make the choice!"

"Look. I've prayed and prayed and I've thought about it for so long, but I can't make up my mind. This was all your idea in the first place. You guys decide. I'm going for a walk. Tell me your final decision when I return. I'll abide by it." And Lili walked out of the farm house.

Once again they were in the backwater of Shanxi province.

Kuan was left behind, dumbfounded. How are we supposed to decide? It's not as if we're picking out a bicycle to buy here! He went to the front door. Immediately the "others" swarmed around him, the three other church elders who rounded out their team of five.

"What did she say?"

"Did she choose?"

"Why did she just walk away like that?"

Kuan took a deep breath. "Look, she hasn't made a decision."

"What?!" the three exclaimed in unison.

"She says she can't. We've got to do it for her."

"*We've* got to! That's preposterous!" Sheng shrieked, "Doesn't she realize she's choosing a husband and not a bike?!" Her lower lip began to quiver in her heightened state of emotion.

"Now, Sheng, relax," Kuan responded, taking another long, deep breath in the process. He was mired in internal conflict at that moment—on the one hand he assumed his accustomed role of big brother, trying to help calm the woman down; on the other, however, he was suppressing his own desire to express the exact same sentiment she had. "I know you've always regarded Lili as a younger sister, but don't be so hard on her."

"But how can she expect us to choose her husband?" asked Bai incredulously. "We already gave her some recommendations. She only has to choose from three. How hard can that be?"

"Yeah. How hard?" echoed Wan. Bai and Wan, both farmers with gray hair, were the two oldest in the group and tended, perhaps at their stage in life, to have a very pragmatic outlook on life. Wan continued, "For most people, getting married's just a normal part of life. Look at us! We're all married with children and we still serve in the church."

"You know Lili's not your average girl," replied Kuan, ever the pacifier in the group. It seemed, he thought somewhat resignedly, his lot in life was to be forever tried by the task of balancing this team of leaders. If it wasn't the naïve idealism of youth that was maddening him, it was the stubborn notions of the middle-aged. "She's always done things differently—how many people do you know who would try half the things she does? And even though she's been a part of our eldership for as long as we can remember, don't forget she's still nearly twenty years younger than us.

Have some patience with her."

"Patience! We've been hinting to her about marriage for the last five years!" With his eyes nearly popping out of his head, Wan lifted his arms in exasperation. "You've been talking directly about it with her the past few months! She says she agrees with us. But then what does she do? She goes traipsing off around the country and doesn't bother looking out for herself. She's always 'too busy training the workers.'" Wan raised the tone of his voice here in a rather poor attempt to imitate Lili as she spoke. "But she's so engrossed she doesn't see her work brings her into contact with hundreds of potential husbands every week! Can her eyes really see?"

"Yeah," Bai piped in. He butted his shoulder in closer to the group, as if to emphasize his indignation at the girl's lack of responsibility in this area.

"Then," Wan resumed, "we help her by pointing out a few suitable candidates and now all she's got to do is pick one—but she can't even do that?! How much more patient can we be?" By this time the farmer had worked himself up into such a frenzy the veins in his neck could be seen jutting out.

"M-, maybe she's getting cold feet. I-, is she backing out?" Sheng asked, her voice trembling. She was gripping her handbag to her chest, so tightly, in fact, the cotton fabric had been scrunched up into a bunch.

"She's not backing out," Kuan said definitively. "Look, she said she'd go along with our decision. She just can't make it herself."

"I can't believe you let her walk out like that," Sheng continued in her state of agitation, "I should have talked to her myself instead of letting you." She crossed her arms and turned her back on Kuan, her lower lip protruding in a pout.

"Look—you're the one who said she listens to me more than you," Kuan rebutted. He could hardly believe her about-face. Women! he thought as he turned his back on her too.

"All right! All right!" Bai interjected waving his arms. "It's no one's fault here. Let's all just calm down." He looked at the group to see if they would turn around and face each other again. They did. "Good," he said pleased. "This isn't exactly an easy time for Lili either, having just got out of prison a few months ago. She's still adjusting back to normal life. Let's just think about this calmly and sensibly."

"Well, I don't think it would be right for us to make the final choice for her," Kuan said.

"I think I agree with you there," Bai replied. The four of them sat down inside the house. Silence ensued for several moments, while each one was trying to find a solution. Then, gingerly, "What do you think about drawing lots? That's how they made decisions in the Bible."

"Yeah, get her to draw lots," Wan agreed.

"Sounds good to me," said Kuan.

The three men turned to Sheng. "Okay. I'll go along with that."

Lili walked through the open field. It was a cool, overcast day in early spring. There were still pockets of hardened snow on the ground. Lili felt it crunch under her feet in places. Maybe it is time. *Crunch*. I'm thirty-two years old and Mother and Father do worry about me, that I'll grow old and have no one to look after me. *Crunch*. And it's true. *Crunch*. There are so many unmarried sisters in our church and it's dangerous for them, traveling around so much with no one to protect them. *Crunch*. I guess it's time. *Crunch*.

It *is* time. *Crunch.* But I really don't know how I can do it—what on earth will I do with a husband? *Crunch.* All I ever wanted is to love Jesus and have the freedom to express that love . . . *Crunch.*

Lili stopped in her tracks to watch a young man in the distance help his elderly mother walk down the country lane. They had just alighted from a bus. That could be me one day. An old lady struggling to walk but with no one to help support me . . . What a good son . . . His build is like that of Fei, she thought, strong and able. It's funny, really, how that all turned out. His mother and sisters ended up becoming believers and he—well, I don't know what he's up to today. It's been so long now since I've seen him . . .

The memories flooded Lili's mind as she resumed walking. It was 1979 and her father had come in from the courtyard one morning and said, "We're having special guests for dinner tonight. Make sure you're home on time." She dared not ignore that tone of voice.

And there he was, Feizhi, sitting with his parents at the Tang dinner table that night. The match had been arranged by mutual friends of both sets of parents. The mutual friends happened to be uncles of the families and it was impossible *not* to be there, *not* to meet this guy. I don't need a boyfriend, Lili said to herself. I don't even want to get married—how could I be free to go around and tell people about Jesus then? I'd be stuck at home. I'd have to mind a house, a farm and kids . . . Yeesh . . . But if I don't try to be friends with him, Father will lose face—and he's the village party cadre—people really respect him. That wouldn't be good. And things aren't exactly easy between us these days . . . At least I won't be expected to talk tonight . . .

"Ha! Ha! That's Uncle Chun all right! He's always doing stuff like that!" roared Mr. Tang. "Anlin!" he called out, "Warm up some more rice wine! We're running low here!"

"Mmm! This duck is delicious!" Feizhi's mother said. "What did you season it with?" she asked Mrs. Tang as she came back into the room, having already anticipated the call for more alcohol.

"Oh, it's just an old recipe my mother taught me," replied the modest hostess.

"Two sons! You are lucky, Mr. Tang!" Mr. Peng remarked as he looked around the table. "Lots of helping hands for you on the farm! And such a pretty daughter! Don't you think so, Feizhi?" He winked at his son as he said this. Feizhi tipped his head slightly in silent agreement. Lili glued her eyes on the dish of deep fried tofu she was placing on the table, her black waist-long hair mercifully falling forward to cover part of her face.

"Well, what do you think?" Mr. Tang asked Lili after the Pengs had left. "Do you have anything to criticize about him? He comes from a good family, you know, and Uncle Chun and his uncle have been friends since they were school boys." He paused to let the fact of good family connections and filial duty sink into his daughter's mind. "You don't have to decide right away though—take some time to get to know him yourself. You know, go out with him for a while. I don't mind telling you, but I think it'd be a good match."

What could Lili say? "Well, no, I've got nothing. If you think he's good, Father, then that's fine. I'll try and get to know him."

Lili walked across the field. Following close in her wake was Feizhi.

"So Lil, I heard your friend Shan got married last week."

"Mm-hm."

"Did you go to her wedding?"

"Of course. She's from our village and we went to school together."

"Well, what'd you think?"

"About the wedding?"

"What else?"

"Oh, it was all right."

"That's all?"

"What do you want me to say? I've been to weddings before. You know my father's position—we get invited to them."

"It's not like weddings happen every day, you know—people normally like to talk about them."

"Well . . . I suppose, if you want to talk about it, it was one of the nicer ones I've been to. Shan made a beautiful bride, and the food at the banquet was great."

"Father said the dowry was quite high."

"Well, I wouldn't know."

"She's your friend—didn't you ask her?"

"Actually, I've been so busy lately with the farm in the day and the meetings at night, I haven't seen her much in the run-up to the wedding. Besides, girls don't talk about things like that—that's the fathers' job."

The two walked on in silence for a few minutes.

"Well, what do you say, Lil? We've known each other for more than a year now. What say we get married?"

"You're sweet, Fei, but you already know where I stand: I won't marry a man who doesn't believe in Jesus."

"But I do believe in Jesus—I've been to so many of your meetings. You've seen that."

"It's not enough just to go to the meetings, Feizhi. You've got to confess your sins to him. You've got to give your whole life to him."

"Is that your secret then? Is that how you make all those miracles happen? All those people who get healed—you still haven't told me how you do *that*."

"Look, I told you before—I have no secret!"

"Yeah, and blind people can just all of a sudden see, and the dumb just start talking. How do you do it? Do you hypnotize them without them realizing it? Put them under some kind of spell?" Caught up in his excitement at remembering the incredible things he had witnessed, Feizhi swore.

Lili shot a disapproving eye over his way.

"Oops—sorry! . . . I didn't mean that . . . But that man last week! Did you see the tumor on his neck—the size of a plum! It was painful just looking at it! And then—whoosh! It's all gone! And that lady with the bent back—she just wouldn't stop running around the courtyard. Wasn't that funny? She was so excited she could stand up straight for the first time in her life! Things like that don't just happen, Lil. You have some kind of special gift. Come on, what is it? What's your secret weapon?"

"Get it in your head, Fei: I have no magic wand! When we have meetings, when we come together, you know, it's, it's him, it's Jesus who does it. It's not me or anyone else. *He's* the one who performs the miracles and healings."

"Well, as far as I'm concerned, I have no objections to your Jesus. After we're married you can keep going and preaching at however many meetings you want wherever you want. You don't have to stay home and work on the farm. Really."

"Don't you get it, Feizhi? You have to make a commitment to him."

Lili sighed. He just didn't get it. But at least he was decent about my refusal. And perhaps just as important, Father didn't lose face and didn't beat me when I told him I said no! Lili couldn't help smiling as she remembered how she dreaded that father-daughter talk . . . But it was for the Kingdom, Lili told herself. That's why I couldn't do it. It wouldn't have been wise for me to marry Feizhi because he wasn't a believer.

But that's not the case now. The church elders have recommended three men who are very committed to Christ. I can't complain about that. And it would be an example to the other sisters. They need to get married. They need someone on the road with them. It would be good for them. Yes, she reiterated again as if to persuade her own self, it would be good for them. She let that thought linger for a while, eventually coming to the conclusion that the principle was good, but not completely convinced it was relevant for her. Yet what right have I to tell them to do something when I'm not willing to practice what I preach myself?

The house loomed ever nearer with her every step. "I don't see how it can work, God," she prayed, "but I will submit to the elders in obedience to your Word. I will take this leap of faith and I will trust you to make it work."

Lili reentered the house. The other four were already assembled, standing together by the table.

"Okay, Lil. We've made our decision," said Kuan stepping forward.

Lili closed her eyes and held her breath. She wasn't so sure after all that she was ready to leap.

"Since you can't make up your mind," Kuan continued, "you should draw lots."

"D-d-draw lots, did you say?" This was unexpected.

"Yeah. They did it in the Bible so why shouldn't you?"

"Oh . . . uh . . . okay . . . but . . . but then we should put in a blank one too. Like, what if I'm really not supposed to get married at this time? Then God will let me draw the blank one out, right?"

"Uh, okay." They all agreed.

Kuan wrote out the three names of the prospective husbands on pieces of paper and dropped them into a bag along with a blank slip. He shook the bag. "Okay. Here you are," he said as he pointed the opening towards her.

Lili closed her eyes again. She reached in and picked out a piece of paper.

"Who is it?" Sheng burst out, hardly able to contain her excitement. "Who is it?"

Lili glanced at the slip. She handed it to Kuan. "It's Brother Wu. Ruben Wu."

"Ruben Wu!" Sheng sighed in a dreamy voice. With starry eyes, she looked up, holding her bag up to her chest again, this time as if it were a bouquet of flowers. She looked as if she herself was to be the bride.

Wide, proud smiles of pleasure spread across the faces of Bai and Wan. "He's good!" Wan chirped as if he were the prospective father-in-law.

"No, no, no!" Lili broke into their reverie. "Once isn't enough! We have to draw again!"

The other four stared at her in disbelief.

"There are four pieces of paper, right?" Lili questioned, desperate to stave off what was all too quickly becoming inevitable. "So I should draw at least three times!"

Reluctantly they agreed. She was, after all, choosing her husband. Who were they to interfere with her process? Kuan replaced the slip and shook the bag again. "Okay. Here."

Lili reached into the bag again, the others holding their breath in anticipation.

"Well?" Kuan asked a little impatiently as she stood there momentarily without reading it. Lili looked down at the slip and passed it over to him. "Brother Wu again!"

"Okay! It's Brother Wu!" Wan cut in, waving his arms frantically. "That's enough!"

"What do you mean that's enough?" asked Lili perplexed. "I have another draw."

"No, no! Twice is enough!"

"What do you mean?" Sometimes Lili couldn't figure out how these older men thought.

"Look, three times you draw, right? Two times already it's Brother Wu." Wan smacked the back of his right hand against the palm of his left as he said this. "Even if you draw one more time and it's a different slip, it'll only be two to one. Brother Wu has outdrawn the other in either case. See?" he explained.

Lili was left momentarily speechless by his rationale. This wasn't a soccer match.

"So it's Brother Wu then!" a delighted Kuan concluded.

"Brother Wu!" Sheng and Bai echoed.

The four of them turned to face Lili. What could she say? "Brother Wu."

MINGYEN CHEN

2002. Mingyen and Winnie arrived at the house. It was another one of those "rare" visits to a cadre's home that Mingyen seemed more and more often to get invited to. It never ceased to amaze Winnie how highly regarded Pastor Chen was everywhere they went. This time it was Comrade Kan's house in Yunnan province. The comrade and his wife were in their late fifties, about ten years younger than Mingyen.

Mrs. Kan greeted them at the door, much to the surprise of Mingyen. "Oh, my husband is the chef today! He absolutely insisted. 'I will cook for my friend.'" She lowered her chin and the tone of her voice on the last sentence in an attempt to impersonate her husband's baritone.

"Well, we are honored indeed," said Mingyen.

"He really holds you in high esteem, Pastor Chen," the wife continued. "He always talks about your kindness to the village people and your wisdom."

Mingyen smiled warmly.

Winnie handed Mrs. Kan a basket of fruit as they entered the house. "Oh, you shouldn't have. But thank you." The lady of the house escorted her guests down the hall and into the living room. It was furnished simply with an Italian-styled imitation leather sofa, plus two matching armchairs, glass topped coffee and end tables anchored in black metal frames. There was a television, portable stereo and a book shelf. Mingyen and Winnie seated themselves on the sofa as their hostess set aside the basket. She poured her guests some cups of tea, which had been prepared beforehand, and laid them out on the coffee table. The centerpiece featured a sectioned, red imitation lacquer platter with an assortment of melon seeds and brightly wrapped candies. Winnie grabbed a small handful of seeds as the older folk engaged in some chitchat.

"That's quite an interesting piece of calligraphy you have," said Mingyen, referring to the framed artwork on the wall behind him. He was sitting on the edge of the sofa with his back half turned towards the picture. "The cursive styling is exquisite."

"Success comes after the sweat and tears," read Mrs. Kan. "It's one of my husband's favorite sayings."

"Well," said Mingyen with a smile on his face, "there's certainly some merit in it."

"And Jin certainly has been sweating over your Bible lately, Pastor!" said Mrs. Kan, referring to her husband by his given name. "I see him with it at least once or twice a week. He's really considering what you've told him."

"That's great to hear," Mingyen enthused. "And what about you? Have you thought about Jesus?"

"Oh, I've looked at the book a couple of times too, but perhaps not quite as often or as diligently as my husband."

"Well, let me encourage you not to wait for him, Mrs. Kan," said Mingyen. "You need to make a decision for yourself, regardless of where he stands. Everyone needs to know their God."

Comrade Kan emerged from the kitchen just then and invited them all to come to the dining table and seat themselves. The large round table was laden with a scrumptious array of dishes including chicken, seafood, vegetables and more. It appeared to Winnie that there was enough food to feed an army!

During the meal Comrade Kan turned to Mingyen. "You know what, Chen? When I retire you shall baptize me yourself. What do you say to that?"

Mingyen and the others around the table laughed warmly.

"Do you know how long your pastor has been talking to me about Jesus?" he said, waving his half-peeled prawn at Winnie. "Since as long as I've known him!" He chuckled with delight.

"Why don't you just get baptized now?" asked Winnie innocently. "Why wait until you're retired?"

"Oh, young lady, it's not that easy here, you know," replied Kan as he finished peeling his prawn, "I have to wait until I retire. That's the rule. You can't have any faith while you're a member of the party." He popped the shrimp into his mouth.

Winnie didn't agree with him but she kept it to herself.

"Pastor," said the host turning again to his guest of honor, "we missed you last month at the award ceremony."

Mingyen smiled, acknowledging his absence. "It was unfortunate I couldn't come." Mingyen had been honored as the "Good Overseas Chinese" by the Yunnan authorities for his work in the province. "I had a previous engagement."

"It was a splendid time!" Kan went on. "The banquet was exquisite!"

Mingyen could very well imagine it. As the honored guest, he would have been seated and served in the most exclusive private room with the twenty or so highest provincial authorities, the Communist party chairman himself included. The low to middle ranking cadres and guests would have been relegated to the "common" banquet hall and less expensive dishes. Mingyen never understood the way official party banquets were conducted. To him the segregation into private banqueting rooms according to rank seemed to defy the very essence of what the party stood for—equality and a classless state. Even the phrase "communist party rank" seemed to be an oxymoron. He smiled at this thought. "Well," he replied to his host, "like I said, it couldn't be helped. My commitment had been set a year in advance."

"Pastor Chen," Mrs. Kan broke in, "my husband informs me that you've been honored in Anhui and Hubei as well. Is that true?"

Mingyen smiled modestly in acknowledgement as he put a shiitake mushroom into his mouth.

"They were Most Honorary Citizen awards," Winnie chipped in proudly.

"That's so wonderful. We are truly honored to have such a distinguished person in our home."

"*Pleease* don't say another word," said Mingyen waving his left hand as if to shoo the compliment away. "I'm just an ordinary person like everyone else. God is the one who has allowed these things to happen." He picked up the piece of abalone on his plate with his chopsticks and took a bite. The chef had laid it on his plate while he was talking.

"If God is so good," said Mrs. Kan, "then why would he allow bad things to happen to people? Look at you, for instance. You had to endure the labor camp."

Mingyen swallowed the last of his abalone. "The ways of God are not the ways of man," he began to explain patiently. "Sometimes when we think terrible things happen, we don't necessarily understand the big picture. I tell you, being the cesspool man was one of the most extraordinary periods of my life. It was the time I felt God's closeness to me the most often and the strongest. It doesn't seem possible or sound rational to the human mind but that's why I said his ways are not our ways."

"You almost make it sound like an enjoyable time," replied Mrs. Kan as she selected a piece of chicken.

"Enjoy or not enjoy. So many people these days—that's all they think about. Does it feel good? Don't worry, be happy, they say . . . This is not what life is about. It doesn't matter how much you try—there will always be something about life that isn't pleasant or good to you."

"True," said Kan, nodding his head in agreement and piling more food on his guest's plate, "even in these prosperous times of China."

"But it's good to enjoy life," said the wife, thinking with pleasure of the new skirt she had purchased earlier that day.

"Yes," replied Mingyen, "and I'm not saying it's wrong. It's just not the main purpose of life. Tell me, when things aren't going well for you, Mrs. Kan, how do you get through it?" Mingyen put his hand up in "stop" mode to signal the chef that he had enough food on his plate for the moment. "If the joy of my life is determined by what or how much I possess, then I've missed the point. All the goods and knowledge in the world would not have sustained me through the years in the cesspool." Here the guest paused to look at his hostess.

She bent her eyes down to her bowl of half eaten rice, chopsticks still in hand on the edge of the table, as she envisaged in her mind what Mingyen must have endured. She was half ashamed at the shallowness of her perspective.

"It was the mercy of God," continued Mingyen. "Sure, it was a filthy and disgusting job. It was meant to be demeaning. But it was also the time I felt the richness and reality of God like I've never felt it since. I don't think I could have experienced that if my situation hadn't been so dire."

"But why does it take such a bad thing? God is loving, isn't he?" asked the bewildered hostess. "He doesn't like to see people suffer, does he?"

"No, he doesn't," replied Mingyen. "But he gave us a free will. The Bible says we live or die as a consequence of the choices we make in our lives. God won't interfere with what we decide if we don't want him too. He does offer us a way out through Jesus though. We can take him and everything he stands for, or leave him." He gathered some steamed fish with his chopsticks and popped it into his mouth.

"But you chose him and you had to suffer," said Mrs. Kan.

"God never said there would be no suffering if you choose Him," answered Mingyen kindly. "I don't know why, but that's the way it is with God. It's not pleasant to hear, I know. I suppose," he began rather lightheartedly, "if we didn't encounter some ugliness in the world, we wouldn't know what beauty is, eh? Besides, where would the success have been if I hadn't sweated or shed tears?" He smiled as he picked up another bit of fish from his plate.

"True again!" said the chef enthusiastically, instantly recognizing the framed words and waving his chopsticks full of spinach as if he were toasting someone with a drink.

"So, you see," concluded Mingyen, "good things can be found in seemingly bad circumstances."

"Well," said Mrs. Kan, shaking her head to signify she still couldn't comprehend, "I'm not so sure I could ever have so much faith in God as you."

"It takes time, dear," her husband interjected. "Faith like that doesn't just happen with the snap of a finger. Jesus says you only need as little as a mustard seed. Try that first!"

"There you go, Mrs. Kan!" chuckled Mingyen. "Listen to your husband!"

Everyone around the table laughed heartily with delight.

"Now tell me, Pastor," said Kan warmly, turning once again to his guest, "when do *you* plan to retire?"

"Oh, I have no plans to retire," said Mingyen.

"What?!" exclaimed the Kans in unison.

"People like us," Mingyen indicated Winnie and himself, "we don't retire. How can we? There's still so many people to help."

"But you can't go on forever," said Kan. "You told me yourself your arthritis bothers you in the knees when you climb the mountains."

Mingyen chuckled as he saw the look of concern on the faces of both his hosts. "If I stopped climbing the mountains tomorrow it wouldn't mean I can't still work for God. I could still help to organize projects from my living room with the help of a telephone and fax machine. Or, I could give advice or teach the younger workers who take over from me," he looked over at Winnie as he said this, "I could also pray . . ."

"But don't you ever get tired?" asked Kan. "I'm ten years younger than you but I sure feel tired!"

"Of course I do. If I wasn't talking to you right now, I'd probably be falling asleep!" Mingyen replied with laughter. Winnie and Mrs. Kan joined in too.

"I don't get it," said Kan, picking up a piece of chicken that had fallen from his chopsticks.

"You see, Comrade, with God, it's not about how much you produce or how efficient your operation is. And it's not about how much money you make either."

"It's not?" asked the confused comrade, who, since

China's opening up, had become accustomed to enjoying the profitability of his various business ventures. "Then what does he expect from his workers?"

"All he wants is willingness and integrity," answered Mingyen simply.

"That's it?"

"That's it." Mingyen turned his attention now to his bowl of soup which had been sitting there, ignored throughout the conversation.

Kan sat there, the piece of chicken still in his chopsticks, bewildered. He couldn't imagine making no profit. What would be the point in working then? "But you work so hard . . . " he said. His voice trailed off as his mind continued to mull over the thought.

"You must really believe in your God," said Mrs. Kan in awe, "You must really love him to keep going like you do."

"I do."

Mingyen was back in his hotel room. The news was on TV as he crawled into bed later that night. He felt his bones creak. The seasons must be changing, he thought to himself as he felt his right knee strain in particular. He spotted the teapot on the desk, beside the TV. Oh, she forgot to take it back, he thought, referring to Winnie. His protégé had been so excited at the "treasure of a deal" she had found on the street earlier that afternoon, she just had to show him the first chance she got back.

"Guess how much it was," she said to her mentor in an animated manner.

Almost immediately Mingyen spotted it was an imitation Yixing. He only hoped the poor girl hadn't been tricked into thinking it was the real thing and ripped off, like in times past. He made a show of picking up the little clay teapot and eyeing it from various angles. He lifted its top to look inside. Finally he tapped the body to hear the quality of sound. Inwardly shaking his head, his guess was that she had probably been tricked out of a little more than a hundred *renminbi*. He decided to be diplomatic. "Oh, it's hard to say."

"Come on," Winnie egged, "Make a guess."

Still the old man hesitated.

"I know it's a fake," she said, as if to reassure him. "I just want you to guess how much it was."

Thank goodness, he thought. He turned the pot again, pretending to garner a closer look at the flowers decorating the side, all the while deciding the nicest way he could put it (for he knew he himself wouldn't have paid anything for the thing). "Well," he began gently, "for myself, I wouldn't pay more than 30 *renminbi*."

Winnie beamed. "That's how much I paid!"

Mingyen smiled to himself as he recalled her pleasure at his answer. And it appeared, at long last, she *is* getting more streetwise. He had to give her that . . . But then he began to wonder if he was sometimes too hard on her, expected too much from her. After all, he himself hadn't always been very smart in the past. He blushed as he thought of the time he didn't know how to get off the bus when he moved back to Hong Kong in 1982. How could he have not figured it out or read the signs? It wasn't as if he couldn't read! How foolish he had felt then!

Mingyen's knee creaked again as he adjusted his position in the bed. It caused his mind to return to the dinner conversation earlier that night. I *am* old, he thought. He sighed as he lay there realizing it was all too true. He took up the remote from the bedside table and clicked the

TV off. Then he removed his glasses, folded them, and placed them beside the remote which was back on the table. Who am I trying to fool? He pulled the covers up to his chest and turned out the lamp. But then, what *would* I do? Certainly not watch TV all day!

In the blackness of his hotel room, he wondered how Joshua did it. *He* was old, Mingyen told himself as he thought of the Israelites' leader in the Old Testament, but he kept on going. He turned over on his left side in the bed, trying to settle into a more comfortable position. My body feels like it's ready to quit! Yet how can I? He rolled back onto his back, deciding that, for the moment, it was easier on his body as a whole. There is still much land to be taken, he reminded himself. Much.

He readjusted the blankets. And what of the younger generation? he asked himself. Are Kathy and Winnie truly able to take up the torch and run? Admittedly they were getting more adept at operating in China, but was it enough? Could they really do it? He decided to try his right side and rolled over. They're just little girls, he thought. They're like daughters to me, and he remembered lovingly and fondly the first time he accompanied each one on a mission into the country. Nope, he said to himself, definitely the back. He straightened the covers after repositioning himself again. I'm not indispensable. No one is. He rested the back of his hand on his forehead as he thought this. They'll never learn fully unless they do it themselves. Besides, he thought with a sigh, I won't be able to protect them forever. And even if I could, it wouldn't be healthy for them. They've got to develop dependence on God. But they're just little girls . . . He let out another deep breath. To pass the torch or not. That is the question.

LILI TANG

1996. The night air was frigid. If you didn't keep moving while outside, the bitter chill would get into your bones. Lili was glad to be inside tonight. Originally intending to accompany Mother Wu to a meeting, the older woman had insisted the younger stay home. Mother Wu could be quite insistent when she wanted. But Lili had to admit this time her mother-in-law was probably right. On the mend from the flu, Lili snuggled up in bed with Leisha, her eight month old daughter who slept peacefully under the quilted covers. Ruben was on night shift at the factory and wouldn't be home until the next morning.

Amazing! she thought as she gazed down on her baby. Such a teeny tiny life, breathing beside her, able to see and follow the motions of her hand with her bright, clear eyes (when they were open). Was it really possible that this little doll would one day grow up to be as big as me?

But how baby can wear mother out too! It seems like every time Leisha gets sick, I get sick too, Lili thought. Or vice versa. It could be extremely frustrating at times. It's true, she sighed, I am worn out. I feel like I haven't been 100% once this winter. Mother felt a sneeze coming on, so she got up from the bed and turned her head away to make sure daughter wasn't exposed. *Achoo!* She grabbed for her handkerchief and blew her nose. As she sat there on the edge of the bed, she couldn't help thinking that sometimes dealing with sickness at home was a lot harder than dealing with it out on the road. When she was traveling from village to village, she never seemed to get this sick nor for so long. Even when she was freezing in her first winter in prison, she didn't get a fever, sore throat or anything! But by the stripes of Jesus we are healed, she recited to herself. By those painful, bloody stripes. She knew she would be all right.

Lili settled back down on the bed beside Leisha, looking down lovingly on her sleeping daughter, an adult finger gently caressing her beautiful forehead, cheeks and nose. My baby. She leaned back against the wall, her head propped on her right hand, reflecting on the changes in her life over the past two years. To her wonder, Ruben was turning out to be pretty special too. He really is very good about everything, she thought. He takes care of everything—his mother, sister, the house, his work and, of course, Leisha and me. My work with the church has hardly been affected at all. If anything, it's somewhat more reassuring and pleasant now, knowing I have a "permanent" base of sorts, a place to call home, a place to stay a few nights every now and then. I haven't had that for at least fifteen years. Lili didn't realize how much she had missed that kind of stability until now. It really is so very nice to have your own home and family.

And then, he's so cool in a crisis. Twice now, since we've been married, he's contrived to help me get away when I was sure I was cornered by the PSB. But then I guess he's had lots of practice already with his mother. (How many times has he had to get her out of a difficult situation?) But still . . . He is great in an emergency, so calm and collected. There's no denying that.

Lili smiled to herself. She thought of the last time Ruben had come to her rescue, and of many other Christians simultaneously. The PSB had raided their meeting and the believers had scattered off every which way and that, trying to get away. Someone had managed to call Ruben (who had just finished his shift at the factory) and told him what was happening. He promptly went out, hired a truck and drove it slowly through the streets in the district of the meeting, managing to pick up a large number of the escapees and whisk them off to safety in several forays.

Lili glanced at her watch. Eleven thirty. Mother Wu isn't home yet. This is not like her. Something must have happened.

Carefully, so as not to wake Leisha, Lili got out of bed and went to have a look out the window in the front room. Nothing unusual. She walked over to the table and poured herself a cup of tea from the thermos. Seating herself on the sofa with her cup, she wondered if she should change her clothes. If Mother Wu had been arrested, someone would need to go down to the PSB office and handle the paper work for her, and Ruben was at work. Of course she, Lili, couldn't go if that were the case (being a fugitive herself), but she thought she might as well be ready, in case Ruben needed anything. Lili decided to get a few things together for Mother Wu which he could take to her later if need be. Then she heard the knock.

Instinctively, Lili quickly changed her clothes and opened the door. An imposing PSB officer filled the frame while another stood behind.

"Ah! Mrs. Wu Tang Lili! Long time no see!"

"Officer Huei."

"We had to break up one of your church meetings tonight. Unfortunately your mother-in-law was one of those arrested," Huei grinned in an ugly manner as he spoke. It made his angular face even more pronounced than usual, with his cheek bones and overbite jutting out in an unnatural way. "I was surprised, I must admit, to find that you weren't there. That's not like you."

"Well, you know, I have a baby to take care of now."

"Well, you'll still need to come with us for questioning. After all, you are the ring leader of the church . . . And we've also come tonight to search for illegal and subversive materials."

Lili stood aside to let them in. She knew the routine. The pair of officers rummaged through the house and "illegal" and "subversive materials" proved to be anything that caught their fancy, including Leisha's doll. The heist made Lili burn inside with a mother's anger at her child's being unjustly treated.

"My husband is on night shift," said Lili innocently. "He's not here to sign the papers. You won't be able to take these things away without the head of the household's signature."

Crap! Huei knew she was right. He stood there grimfaced.

"Would you like me to go get him for you, so you won't have to come back tomorrow?" asked Lili, her eyes wide and honest.

Huei bristled at the idea. He hated the thought of having to take a suggestion from one of these Christians. You never knew what they had up their sleeve. And with Lili . . . She was the most cunning of them all. Last time she ran off (and it took them months to track her back down again) when she was supposed to be picking up medicine for her "sick" mother-in-law. But that couldn't possibly happen this time. We've already got the old hag.

"Well?" asked Lili. "You could watch my baby for me. And you wouldn't have to slow down in your search."

That was true . . . It seems all right . . . And what mother would just run off and leave her child? "Well . . . okay. But be quick about it."

Lili ran out of the house. She took out her concealed cell phone and called her husband. "Mother Wu's been arrested. The police are at the house. You'll have to get back for Leisha." And with that Lili was off again.

"How can I ever say thanks enough, Mrs. Ao? You too, Chailing," said a grateful Lili, as she held her baby in her arms once again.

"It's nothing you wouldn't have done for us," replied Mrs. Ao.

Lili's silence confirmed her assent. "Was Ruben at the house, Chailing?" she asked Mrs. Ao's daughter. "Did you see him?"

"No. It was your neighbor, Mrs. Zhang. Mr. Wu was called in to do the day shift unexpectedly. Mrs. Zhang left the house first with a big hump on her back, you know, making it look like the baby was underneath the covering. I waited about forty minutes, then left with Leisha."

Lili let go a deep breath. "Well, thanks again, Chailing. You were very brave . . . Your daughter is very good, Mrs. Ao. You should be proud of her."

Mrs. Ao's pleasure in the compliment was evident in her ear-to-ear smile.

"Here, Ma. I brought the stuff you asked for."

"Thank you, Ruben."

"Are you all right? Is there anything else I can do for you?"

"No thanks, son. I think I'm okay for now."

Mother and son sat across from each other in the

county jail's visitor room, a table in between, speaking in hushed voices. A couple of guards stood on opposite ends of the room on the far wall.

"Any word when the trial'll be?" the son asked.

"No, but I think it should be soon. It's been a couple of months now."

"What do you make of it?"

"Oh, probably just the usual—three years for speaking at an illegal meeting and then a trip to the reeducation camp . . . How are you doing?"

"Surviving."

Mama Wu lowered her voice even further. "Have you heard from Lili?"

"Yeah. She's fine."

"And Leisha?"

"They're both fine."

"Do you know where they are?"

"They're moving from place to place every day. The PSB still have a man outside our house. I told her not to come home for anything at any time."

Mother Wu had a look of consternation on her face. "Such a terrible situation for a new mother and baby."

"Lili's been in tough situations before. She'll make it."

"But she hasn't been that healthy since giving birth. She's still weak. That's not good for her or the baby. I wish I wasn't stuck in here, then I could make her some special mother's soup."

"And how would you get it to her while she's on the run?" Ruben was chagrined at her suggestion. "Anyway, there's nothing we can do at the moment. Just pray."

Mother and son were momentarily lost in their own thoughts.

"I'm sorry, son."

"What are you sorry for?"

"I'm sorry that I'm so much trouble to you."

"You're not, Ma. This is just life. Lots of believers face similar situations. You know that. Anyway, it's been like this for the last ten years. Why start to worry about it now?" Ruben asked with a wry smile.

"It's just . . . It's just, you know, I feel bad because now you have your own family, you know, a wife, your own child . . . and, and here I am, just an ignorant old woman . . ."

"Hey, don't start talking like that. You are a servant of the Most High. You are doing his work and I am too. You and Lili take care of the church and I take care of you. We're all just doing our part."

Mother Wu sat there silent.

"Hey, did you hear me? C'mon now." Ruben reached over the table to grab a hold of his mother's hand. "This is no time to get down on yourself. You have to be strong. Your trial's coming up—you've got to be strong, so you can be a good representative of Christ there! Okay?"

"You're right, Ruben. You're absolutely right." And mother gave son a warm smile to show him he was.

His mother greatly encouraged, Ruben left the county jail. He walked towards the cement factory for his day shift, wrapping his scarf tighter around his neck to keep the biting wind out. What am I working for? he asked himself. I wear myself out and come back to an empty house. I cook food for myself and eat it by myself. I sleep in bed by myself. Then I get up and go back to the factory. What kind of family life is this? My wife's a fugitive, wanted by the PSB. I haven't seen my daughter in two months—she's not even a

year old yet and she's forced to run with Lili! Is this any way
to raise a child? But there's no one else to look after her . . .
And Ma's in jail again. Why bother keeping a home? Why
shouldn't I just quit my job and go and preach the Gospel
too?

"Hey Ruben! Ruben! Wait up!"

"Wait for us!"

Ruben looked over his shoulder and saw Guan and
Chao. Oh great. Just what I need, a pair of jokers.

Ruben's factory co-workers trotted up alongside him.

"Hey. How's it going?" asked Guan. "Haven't seen you
in a while. Must've been on night rotation."

"Yes," replied Ruben patiently.

"Hey, you doing okay? You looked pretty deep in
thought back there."

"Oh, I'm okay."

"I mean, we'd hate to see the Jesus boy down now,
wouldn't we, Chao?" The two co-workers chortled as they
elbowed each other. Guan continued, "So how's your
mother? Let's see now . . . I've lost count how many times
she's been arrested . . . Can you remember Chao?"

Chao snorted. "Too many times to count!"

"Seriously Ruben, how is she?" Guan asked, plopping
his arm around Ruben's shoulder, barely able to contain his
snickering.

"She's fine."

"And your wife? Heard from her lately?"

"She's fine too."

"Great family! All the women are convicts! Even your
daughter's on the run!" Guan howled. "Oh you're a great
man, Ruben! Such great control you've got over your
household!"

"Is it really worth it, Ruben," Chao scoffed, "believing in

that Jesus stuff?"

Ruben was resolute. "It's worth it, Chao. It's worth it." And he could hardly remember the last time he was so glad to arrive at work.

"You don't sound very good."

"It's just a cold. I'll get over it."

"Another one?"

"Caught it from Leisha."

"Maybe you should rest tonight. I'll preach for you."

Lili was flabbergasted. "Since when did you ever worry about my health, Kuan?" she asked, grinning.

"Since your mother-in-law gave it to me for not stopping you from working while you were pregnant!" Kuan chuckled. "Seriously. Why don't you rest tonight?"

"No. I'm fine. It's just a few sniffles."

"Who'll watch Leisha?"

"Sister Lai said she would."

"Mm. You sure you don't want a rest?"

"I'm sure."

"Okay, but don't go telling Mother Wu I'm a slave driver!"

The two co-workers laughed.

"Heard from Ruben lately?"

"Just spoke to him on the phone this afternoon. Mother Wu was sentenced yesterday. Another three years. He notices the PSB watch on our house is over for now. Hopefully I'll be able to go home soon for a while. Ruben misses Leisha terribly."

"I'm sure he does. It's awful being away from your kids for so long." Kuan thought grimly of the times he himself had been in the same situation. "When's the last time you were home?"

"About four months ago," said Lili. "Actually we miss each other a lot."

"Mm." Someone came to inform them the meeting was about to start. "You're sure you want to preach tonight."

"I'm sure." Lili nodded affirmatively.

"Then let's go."

SAIMEN LIANG

2003. The army stood at attention. It was ready for battle, waiting, it seemed, for the command to advance. The soldiers, numbering about 6,000, covered an area roughly the size of half a football field. Saimen looked down on the famed terracotta warriors of China's first dynasty, the Qin. He thought of the logistics of mobilizing all those troops, training them and maintaining order, and smiled in spite of himself. Of course he, Saimen, was no emperor but he could appreciate the challenges Qin Shihuangdi must have faced. He was, after all, on his own quest to launch an army.

Saimen climbed on to the bus for the drive back to Xian, the ancient capital. Seated by a window, he noticed the large mound of earth the vehicle passed as it exited the premises of the popular tourist attraction—the alleged tomb of the first emperor himself. The expansiveness of this burial site was such that archaeologists had not yet been able to excavate the whole thing; they weren't even sure they had found it all. But they do what they can with what they have found, thought Saimen to himself, as he noticed still more tourists arriving to see the famous grave. We certainly don't have it all yet either, but we've got to do what we can. He was thinking of his church.

It was a warm, spring day, and Saimen rather enjoyed the leisurely drive. The sun was out, although one would hardly notice, for there was a perpetual layer of smog that pervaded the historic city and its surrounding area. Saimen thought, with mild irony, how like the battle we face too—

we've got to keep the pollution out of the believers. And then there were the questions the filthy air itself represented—the new technology in conflict with the old, to preserve or to advance, tradition versus modernity. Within his own church, the evangelist recognized the similar debates and influences that were pressing on his members and, in particular, on his team of workers.

"There's too much work already! Where can we find time to learn about that?"

"The younger generation are not as motivated for the church. They just want to make money."

"We're barely managing at home—why look outside?"

He heard the arguments over and over in his head. And yet the team leader knew they *must*. They must advance. They must embrace the new times, the new opportunities. Otherwise, how could they, as a church, give an account to God in terms of doing their part to fulfill the Great Commission? Despite the difficulties, they must not cease. The plan to reach all of China was well and truly under way to being completed, progressing still at a rapid pace, and they must begin to look beyond. They must endeavor to make disciples of all nations.

Saimen considered what he knew from the Bible and what he had heard of mission efforts around the globe. The Gospel, the telling of which was originally placed in the hands of the twelve apostles, was first preached in Jerusalem. From there it rolled out and, over the centuries, revivals sprang up in Europe and North America, which spawned missionaries who were instrumental in triggering rebirth in Africa, South America, then Asia. The Good News had circumnavigated the whole earth, as far as Saimen could see, bringing renewal to every continent, every region, every zone . . . every zone, that is, except that encompassing the lands between China and Israel. The circle was not quite complete.

As he sat there with eyes gazing out the window and chin resting on one hand, mindlessly fidgeting with his cellular phone in the other, he thought about the lessons his church could learn from the missionaries who had come to China from the West. Even though the Bamboo Curtain had been pulled shut, the missionaries had camped themselves on the doorstep of the nation in anticipation of the day that it would be lifted again. Basing themselves for years in Hong Kong and Taiwan, they had immersed themselves in the Chinese culture and language, and, once they could enter the Mainland, they were ready . . . We must establish mission schools and training centers. We must do language studies. We must prepare ourselves as best we can in anticipation of our open door, he concluded.

By now the bus had entered the city limits. It turned down a street and Saimen found they were passing through part of the Muslim Quarter. They drove by narrow lanes filled with street vendors hawking tacky tourist souvenirs and cooked food. The aroma of fried mutton dumplings and fresh handmade noodles wafted in the air. Saimen's stomach growled in response.

On the streets a few elderly men wore traditional *jalabiyyas* and *kufis*, the odd woman a *hijab*. But just as many people were in western-styled clothes too. The Muslim apparel rules, quite obviously, were not as stringent in this neighborhood as in some Middle Eastern countries. Saimen pondered the disciplines required to follow the faith in that region. It wasn't unlike what he and his fellow Christians regularly experienced here in China, in terms of a harsh penal code and an alternative interpretation of "presumed innocent until proven guilty". The only difference, as far as he could tell, was one could be punished for *not* closely observing his faith there; whereas here, it was the opposite. In this he felt his church members would be adequately prepared. Still, it wasn't an easy mission his team was undertaking.

It would require the very best people they had. People who were tried and true. People who were stalwarts in the faith. It wasn't enough merely to want to go. The candidates had to have proven themselves over *years* in ministry, through testing and persecution, even in prison. These were not easy places they were going to live and work in. They would need help. So they would go as family units—husband, wife and, whether blessed here or abroad, with child. If necessary, these families would die in the land of their mission.

Saimen was grim as he thought of this. But that's the cost. We all have to be willing to pay it wherever we are, he thought, as he remembered the many times in his own life he had been spared. And precious in the sight of the Lord is the death of his saints.

"So, that's what we want to do," Saimen concluded. "We want to take the Gospel back to Jerusalem." He stood there, hands clasped in front of him, as he looked out at his audience. It was the next day. A dozen businessmen from the West were assembled in a hotel room in Xian. They sat in a scattered array, using the room's two double beds as seats and filling its few chairs. One chose to remain standing, leaning against a wall for support, while another sat on the edge of the desk. Shu and a translator were also there, the former having come to provide moral support to his friend. Saimen had just finished making his proposal, hoping to find some spiritual and practical support for his church's proposed mission training centers.

"That's quite an ambitious plan you have there," said a voice with a southern American drawl. The origin of the voice was in the cluster of men sitting around the edge of the first bed.

Several others nodded their heads in agreement as the translator interpreted the comment back to Saimen.

"Can you explain again how you're going to get there?" the same voice asked.

"Well," began Saimen again, "we won't fly there. Our intention is to walk. Every step of the way." He paused to take a breath and to let the translator do his work. "We intend to plant churches in every country along the way. This could take years, of course, but this is a long term project for us. It isn't something that will be done in two or three years, or even five or six." He paused again, this time to sip some hot water which was sitting in a glass on a small coffee table. "Even as I speak, we have begun our walk. We currently have missionaries in Myanmar and Thailand. They are learning how to work within another system, how to relate to another people."

"And these training centers," piped up the man standing against the wall, "what exactly will you be doing there?"

"Our intention is to provide a facility to learn a second language, preferably Arabic, but it could also be English, depending on the teachers we can find in China. It's definitely easier to find more English teachers. And we'll do some study on Arabic and Muslim culture." As the interpreter translated his words, Saimen looked out at the visitors, wondering if he was making any kind of impact on them. "Then," he continued, "we'd also like to provide some vocational training to make sure our missionaries have some useful trade or skills to earn a living and support their family in the country they go to."

Shu, who was standing against the window, to the left of Saimen, quietly and discreetly reminded his friend of something here.

"Yes," replied Saimen in response. He turned back to his audience. "Our philosophy of building up family teams is to take the 'ordinary person' approach. We don't rely on just one or two people. We don't rely on any superstar. It's a whole team effort and all these different families will just be ordinary citizens in the land, working for a living like regular people."

Again there were nods by several of the businessmen.

"And, with your generous help, we might get some valuable tips on how to be better missionaries, since your churches have sent out so many already. Your experience could help us know what to expect, what to better prepare for and so much more."

Beams of pride and approval appeared on the faces of several of the foreigners, as the translation of these words was completed.

"Long term within China," Saimen went on, "we are looking to support completely the training of these missionaries ourselves. We believe that, with our nation modernizing and increasing in wealth, and the fact that there are so many believers, we should eventually be able to raise the funds to do this." He paused here again for the interpreter. "We are also actively working to build unity within the different house church movements in China, to encourage them to be involved in missions too."

The first visitor spoke again. "But why the Middle East? Why not, say, Canada? The Koreans are sending missionaries to Canada."

"There are lots of reasons. First of all, the Koreans are already there." Saimen had a smile on his face as he said this.

There were a few chuckles around the room as his answer was translated.

"Seriously though," the leader of the house church continued, "we are not, in our assembly, as well educated as you Westerners. Nor are we accustomed to handling the temptations in the technology, luxuries and openness that are available in your home countries. It would be difficult for us to adjust to such a society. Our people, quite honestly, would die if they were sent there." He paused to let the thought sink in. "We are used to a less refined lifestyle, to hardship and suffering. It is how we were raised in the faith. There's no better Bible school than prison, our church members like to say!"

This drew out a few more chortles around the room.

"Our spiritual upbringing," continued Saimen, "is ideal for the places we are focusing on. India, Nepal and the Middle East—they all have strict laws because of their religions—but our people are used to living in severe, restrictive conditions. In these places, there is always the threat of imprisonment or execution because of extreme intolerance towards Christianity, but that has always been the case for us here." He said this in a matter of fact tone, opening both his hands simply, in a gesture that seemed to mirror his people's willingness to lay their lives out before God in this way. "Our people are not afraid to bleed in their mission fields; they would consider it an honor, for they know Jesus himself did the same for them. And if they have to, they will perish abroad too."

There was a noticeable quiet in the room after this was interpreted. A few of the visitors shifted uneasily in their seats. One of them scratched his head, unsure of what else to do with himself. Still another pulled out his cell phone to check if he had any text messages. This guy was serious. He wasn't playing around.

The man with the southern American drawl cleared his throat in an attempt to gather himself. "Well," he began, "I am greatly moved by your mission and by the commitment of your people, Saimen." He cleared his throat again. "I believe my church would be honored to help yours." He stood up, walked over to the leader of the house church, and warmly extended a hand of partnership.

"So what do you make of it?"

The question was asked by Shu. He and Saimen had left the hotel room, the meeting having been concluded a little over twenty minutes ago. They were walking beside part of the base of the Xian City Wall. This version of the defensive structure, as opposed to the Tang dynasty's original construction, was primarily built in the early Ming era and featured a moat, four corner watchtowers and numerous platforms in between for soldiers, to ensure invaders weren't making headway up their fortress. It was a rare historical site in the world, for it was still virtually intact; it was possible to walk the almost fourteen kilometer circumference of the wall along the top, just like the soldiers of old. It made Saimen wonder if they, their church, had enough defenses of their own against enemy infiltration.

"Saimen?"

"Huh?"

"Didn't you hear me?"

"Sorry. No. I was thinking of something else."

"I said, what do you make of it? The meeting?"

"Oh." Saimen took a second to redivert his thoughts. The two hour meeting had taken a lot out of him and he was glad to have something else to think of at that moment. "Well, it's hard to say. Wouldn't you agree?"

Shu nodded his head in the affirmative, glad to have his friend's attention again.

"Things aren't always what they seem in the physical."

"True."

"I mean, it's encouraging that they all expressed interest in helping us, but even they say they still have to get final approval from their boards."

"True." How else could Shu reply? He knew himself how it was.

"But, no matter what happens, God will provide for us."

"True again."

The two friends walked on in silence for a while, enjoying being outdoors after the stuffiness of the crowded hotel room.

"It's amazing, really."

Shu paused to look up at his friend in expectation of what he was going to say. "What is?"

"This city. This is where it all began." Saimen patted the old wall beside him as they continued their stroll. "Two thousand years ago, China began exporting products westward out of this place, along the Silk Road. At the same time, 2,000 years ago, the Gospel left Jerusalem and began its revival journey westwards around the globe." The philosophical evangelist stopped to look up and check the height of the rampart they were at. "It was a perilous journey either way. A traveler could easily lose his life along the way. But then defenses were built as time went on." Again Saimen gave the wall a pat, as if it were a good old friend. "Do you think we're ready? Do you think our defenses are solid enough?"

Shu knew Saimen was talking about their church looking beyond China's borders. "Who is ever 'ready' or has 'enough'?" The older man resumed walking, clasping his hands behind his back. "Did we have enough Bible teaching to become preachers? Were we ever ready to go to prison for the first time? Were we ready for the explosion in growth of our church in the '80s and then the '90s?" He had the air somewhat of a sage as he asked these questions, his eyes focused straight ahead. "Our people will survive," he concluded. "God will help them."

Saimen nodded his head in agreement. It was true. God would hold everything together. He'd been doing it all along. Why would he stop now? He wouldn't. It wasn't in his nature. "Well, Shu, it's 2,000 years later. China will again be exporting treasure westwards, and the Gospel will return to its starting point. God is bringing things full circle." He gave the wall a final pat.

LILI TANG

1997.

"Ha! Ha! Ha!" laughed Lili. "And remember the way we used to tell the Noah story?"

"How?" asked a giggling Sheng.

"We used to say Noah was righteous because of the oil he bought from the angel," Yangzi butted in.

The three women had just finished speaking on the first day of a two-day all-women conference and were relaxing after dinner at the Dong farm in Tongren county, Hunan. They were still seated around the dinner table, which was littered with empty dishes, the remnants of the meal they had just eaten.

"Oil?" asked a bewildered Sheng. "Where did that come from?" The older lady was originally from a different part of the province than the other two. She didn't share the same experiences the other two had in their teens.

"We didn't have a Bible," said Lili still full of mirth, "and that's what old Grandma Zhong told us!"

"But, but how—? What does an angel have to do with the story?"

"The angel sold the oil that Noah bought," Yangzi began to explain quite matter of factly. "God sent the angel to sell the oil as a test to find a righteous person in the earth."

"The angel had two deals," Lili jumped in here. "Buy one cup of oil for two *yuan* or two cups for three *yuan*. Which one's the best deal?"

"Two cups for three," answered Sheng.

"Ah!" said Lili, "That's the bargain everyone chose."

"Everyone except Noah," interjected Yangzi. "He couldn't bear the thought of the angel not making as much money as possible, so he chose to pay the one cup price for two cups."

"And because he was thinking of the best for God's servant, Noah was deemed righteous and chosen to build the ark," Lili concluded.

The three women burst into another round of cackling and giggling.

"You know," said Lili as their laughter died down, "ridiculous as those stories sound now, they really convicted us."

Yangzi nodded in agreement. "And then Deng Xiaoping came to power and opened the markets up. So many people became so greedy for money after that. But that Noah story really spoke to us about watching our motives."

"Imagine our surprise then," said Lili, "when we finally got a Bible and tried to find that story. We couldn't find it anywhere!"

The three women exploded in another round of laughter.

"It just goes to show," continued Lili, "how far a little bit of faith can go—because we sure didn't have much of anything else then!"

"Those sure were the good ol' days," said Yangzi.

"They sure were," replied Lili. She looked at her watch as she said this and noticed the time. "It's getting pretty late. What time do we start tomorrow?" she asked the other two, referring to the resumption of the conference.

"Eight," answered Sheng.

"We should probably get some sleep then," said Lili.

The other two agreed.

The sound of cicadas singing was all that could be heard on the Dong Farm that night. Yangzi and Sheng were already fast asleep. Lili lay awake in bed thinking of her family. She had had to leave a feverish Leisha. She hated leaving her daughter when she was sick. She hated leaving her *any time*, but it was definitely worse when she was sick. As a mother she often struggled—even tortured herself—when she examined her own feelings in regards to her daughter: Do I love Leisha more than Jesus because I don't want to leave her? She sighed as she gently turned over in bed—she didn't want to wake the other two. Yet it's not like I could stop preaching. This is what he's told me to do. There's no other way around it. The argument in her mind came full circle: I'd go crazy if I wasn't preaching.

Suddenly she became aware of a sound: Farmer Dong's dogs at the front gate had begun to bark with growing volume and intensity. At first it was just one dog, but now they had all joined in the noise. She instantly became alert. "Wake up!" she whispered in the dark to the other two, poking them with a finger at the same time.

Startled out of their sleep, the other two immediately became aware of the dogs too.

"What do you see?" hissed Sheng, her senses all heightened.

"Shh," replied Lili, who by now had crept out of bed and tiptoed over for a glance out of the window. She peered carefully around the curtain into the blackness of the courtyard, the moonlight having slipped behind some clouds.

"Well?" whispered Yangzi impatiently.

"Wait!" said Lili, holding out her hand to stop the other two from making a sudden noise by coming out of bed. "I think there's something."

"What is it?" Yangzi pressed.

"Not sure . . ." Lili drew the drape as gently and as far back as she dared for a clearer view, but she didn't want to make any noticeable movement in case there were unfriendly intruders. "There are some sticks—batons."

"PSB!" whispered Sheng tensely.

"Quick girls—we've got to get out of here!" said Lili moving away from the window. But there was nowhere to go. The only way in and out of this room led to the courtyard, which was now filling up with PSB officers. They were trapped.

The three women were each sent back to their respective home counties in Shanxi. Lili, subsequently, found herself in the Jinsha county PSB office once again.

"Mrs. Wu Tang Lili," said Officer Huei with a sneer in his voice, "we meet yet again."

Lili remained silent. Outwardly she was a picture of calm and indifference to the situation.

"You're awfully quiet today," said Huei, who had fully expected Lili to lay on the charm as usual. "What's the matter with you?"

What would be the point in answering? thought Lili to herself. I'm already sitting in the PSB office and there's no way out of this windowless room except the door you've just come through.

"I suppose you know the drill," continued Huei. "The investigator will arrive shortly, and I guess you'll need some things from home. Should I call your husband?"

Lili nodded once, remaining quiet. Huei stared at her momentarily before going away to make the call to Ruben.

He had never seen her like this before.

Alone in the room, except for the officer guarding the door, Lili was left to her thoughts. Inside she was mortified. She realized her arrest this time could result in her being apart from Leisha for at least three years. That was the minimum sentence that would be passed in a case like this. She began to prepare herself mentally for the separation from her daughter.

Who will take care of my little girl? she pondered. Who will teach her how to love God? Guard her? Protect her? Ruben has to work. Mother Wu is still in prison. Maybe Ruben can call his sister. She mentally sorted through the options, wishing all the while there was some other way. Never before had she had to face the consequences of her work in relation to her child. In the back of her mind, she knew prison would always be a possibility but the reality was what hit her in this moment. And now she began to appreciate more fully the price that Sheng, Kuan and the others in the church had had to pay.

The door swung open. Ruben walked in. In one hand he carried a bag of clothes and supplies for Lili, while in the other, Leisha trailed in tow. Leisha was nearly two and a half years old.

Lili rose quickly from her chair and scooped up her daughter, smothering her in hugs and kisses. She swung her child around in a circle, holding her high in the air, evoking squeals of delight from the toddler. She pulled her close to her and smothered her again with affection. Then she put Leisha down and turned to exchange a few quiet words with her husband.

Leisha, meanwhile, wandered around the room. The

little girl sidled up to the guard at the door.

"Hello, Uncle," said the friendly little girl. "How are you?"

The guard was stunned. No one ever greeted the guards. He determinedly kept his gaze straight ahead.

The child continued to smile at him sweetly. Then, seeing the uncle was on the shy side, "Would you like some of my candy?" Leisha persisted in trying to gain a new friend, holding out her full little hand to the man.

She was such a cute thing. The guard had to suppress a smile.

Just then the door opened. In walked Officer Huei again.

Immediately Leisha turned her attention to the newcomer, heading in his direction as she warmly greeted him. "Hello, Uncle!"

Huei stared at the little girl. His eyebrows were raised in utter astonishment, distorting the gauntness of his face. Combined with his mouth which seemed to say Oh!, although no sound emitted, one was left with the impression of a goldfish.

"Would you like to share my candy?" She stood in front of Huei and held her goodies out to him now.

Huei floundered for a second, unsure of what to do. He couldn't just bark orders at the husband and wife when there was a child in the room, especially such an adorable one. She even offered him candy. How sweet. "Ha! Ha! Ha!" he broke into a somewhat shaky laugh. "You are a good girl!" He patted Leisha on the head with his veiny hand as he said this. "Why don't you share your candy with the uncle at the door?" He pointed to the first guard Leisha had approached and signaled to him to take her out of the room. Instinctively Ruben moved to accompany them.

The little girl, however, seemed to have an innate awareness of what was going on. She looked to Huei, then to the guard, to her father and mother, then back again to Huei. She seemed to sense it was about to become a very grave situation. She reached up and placed her hand on Huei's leg, as if to make an appeal. "Uncle, you be nice to Mommy?"

Huei laughed again in the same shaky manner. "Ha! Ha! Little girl, you are so good. I'm a bad uncle. I have to take your mommy away. I'm so sorry, I'm a bad uncle." He lifted Leisha's hand from his leg and motioned to the guard to get the child out of the room pronto.

"Look at you!" yelled Huei to Lili, as soon as the door had closed. "What kind of a mother are you?"

Lili closed her eyes in reply.

"She's such a good kid and you—you're such a bad mother, making so much trouble for everyone! She even knows what's going on!"

Lili continued to keep her eyes closed. Inside her strength and peace of mind were being revitalized. It was a profound scene she had just witnessed. It filled her with tremendous relief and deepened her security in her God. Even at the tender age of two and a half, she saw that Leisha was somehow able to discern what was going on. She knew her daughter was going to be alright. She would grow up and be okay. The thought of an arduous investigation period couldn't bring her down now. Let them come!

AFTERWORD
by David Wang

Lili was imprisoned for three months and then released. She is now focused on training missionaries in her house church movement. While continuing his efforts to mobilize and promote unity and cross-cultural missions among the various underground churches in the country, Saimen was rearrested and is currently serving another prison term. Mingyen, meanwhile, is still trekking in the hinterland of China's ethnic minorities and mentoring those who will supersede him one day.

Extraordinary or fantastic as some of the events in their lives may be, all three of them, if asked, would say that their experiences are not unlike those of other Christians in China. The kinds of pressures and stresses they deal with, live with on a daily basis are "normal" for the many believers. After all, doesn't the Bible say there will be suffering and difficulties? Aren't those what Paul the apostle had to face? Peter? John? And the others? For every Lili, Saimen and Mingyen detained or put in prison, there are literally thousands of others ready to step up and fill their places. This is the way things are: The work of the church continues regardless.

Moreover, a Christian in China never sees being incarcerated as a setback. It is a time for "higher education", an opportunity to learn supplemental lessons in Life. The penal institution itself merely becomes another place to establish a church and encourage other believers. As one who has been involved in missions for forty years, it has truly been my honor and privilege to meet and fellowship with these modern day apostles.

The advances and progresses of the West are readily seen throughout the world. Information and media outlets herald them in a loud, clear voice that can be heard in all corners of the earth, and in China the reception is particularly good. A visitor from the industrialized world traveling in Shanghai, for example, can just about as easily find McDonald's or KFC for lunch as he can at home, or watch MTV on his hotel TV. The language may be different but the colors, packaging and styling are very familiar, and the visitor has in plain view the impact of his pop culture on society both at home and abroad.

In spiritual matters too, the West has been heard in China. Many of the current rural house church leaders gratefully acknowledge that their growth as Christians was enhanced as a result of the work and prayers of the early missionaries from Europe and North America. There were many pioneers—Robert Morrison, Hudson Taylor and Jonathan Goforth, to name just a few—who left their native lands in the late-eighteenth and early-nineteenth centuries to come and help build foundations for the Church in the Far East.

The present-day older generation in China either heard Bible stories or received volumes of the book itself from these early missionaries. Eventually, many years later, they passed them on to the new young believers, such as Lili, when such materials or information could not be obtained elsewhere. And older believers like Mingyen, for instance, were instrumental in making foreign language materials accessible to locals by taking the initiative to obtain from overseas, translate and publish Christian books and studies into Chinese. Who would have thought that some from the next crop of believers, like Saimen, would benefit from them secretly in the labor camps?

My vocation regularly brings me into contact with two different worlds: As the president of an international ministry, I am a frequent traveler to the West and, as a Shanghai native, virtually a weekly visitor to China. After four decades traversing cultures, I have watched with keen interest a generation born and raised in both societies. In each place the generation has struggled to find its place and identity in our world. As well, they continue to work to overcome their weaknesses and learn how to best maximize their strengths.

While the picture from the Mainland has not always been so easily discernible, slowly, gradually it is becoming clearer. The evidence that global pop culture is increasingly being tinged with an Asian flavor, including Chinese, is mounting. *Dim sum*, for example, was previously an alien phrase to anyone who was not oriental; yet it is becoming ever more accessible to eat in the West. And, on the big screen, movies that star Jackie Chan and Ziyi Zhang are scoring as "box office hits" and being distributed more eagerly and widely than they have in the past. Clearly there is an appetite for things Chinese in the industrialized world today.

But what is there of spiritual value that we can adopt from the People's Republic? More than food and cinema, here the impact of China on Western civilization can be of far greater substance and significance. For half a century, since the 1950s, concerted efforts were made to render Christianity in China obsolete or "confined to the history section of the museum", as Jiang Qing, Mao's last wife, is purported to have said. At the height of the most determined policies; when bleak became dire, which then became hopeless, gatherings of the faithful were illegal; untold numbers of believers were falsely accused, tortured, imprisoned and killed; and Bibles were prohibited and burned. Despite all this, however, the death of the church in China could not be achieved. On the contrary, the complete opposite appears to have happened. Against all odds, the church in China has become the most populous on earth.

How was it achieved? What values do the Chinese believers espouse, that they are able to experience consistently such growth and dynamism with God? There are, in fact, a number of indispensable insights that Christians in the industrialized world can gain from the rural house church. On the surface they appear to be straightforward, maybe even too simple. But consider a little, for there is a wisdom and knowledge here that few in the West perceive, and still fewer live. They include:

1. Every believer is a part of the priesthood.

Almost without fail, when someone becomes a Christian in rural China, it is automatically assumed that he or she will go home and tell the entire family about the saving grace of Jesus Christ. The new believers do not wait to complete a special course on how to introduce people to the faith. They do not wait for a church leader to come and lead the decisive prayer. Regardless of their knowledge of the Bible, or lack of it, as is most often the case, they are not hindered, worried or intimidated as they speak out—they literally "Just Do It". Even in the urban areas today, believers as young as two years in the Lord are leading congregations of a hundred or more! It is simply a fact of life that all have to be engaged.

New believers in China are especially taught to pray through their obstacles and problems. Because of the dangers and difficulties in meeting with other Christians, they are urged to do this regularly and fervently from day one. It is their key survival method, and they will pray alone and, when possible, with others. Now, as belonging to the Body of Christ, every individual has a part, a role, and therefore every individual affects the health of the Church as a whole. So, the individual will consider, how am I holding up my part? Or am I not?

New believers are also encouraged to remove all idols and ancestor plaques from their homes. Very often they do not wait for bishops or pastors to come and do this; they take care of the job primarily by themselves. They know their own relationship with God is real and that He knows them and hears them.

2. Prayer is the key lifeline.

Fifty years of persecution in China, by necessity, saw the removal of what traditionally are perceived to be important elements in Christendom—church buildings, seminaries and Bibles. How can a church possibly exist without these crucial elements? Yet, for a time, the land was without any of these. Despite the severe lack of resources, however, one thing did remain. The one thing that was not taken away from the church in China—and could not be taken away—was prayer.

Somehow over the years these Christians have mastered the art and science of knocking on the door of heaven and storming the gates of hell. They see what, in the West, are remarkable answers to prayer but what, to them, are ordinary, common responses from their God. What do they do that generates such supernatural results?

For anyone who has ever had the privilege of experiencing them firsthand, the prayers of these believers are impressive. They possess an indescribably deep intensity; a stirring yet powerful flow; and their length leaves an indelible mark. People in China are fully engaged physically, emotionally and spiritually when they pray. To the individual believer, prayer is not a matter of standing up or kneeling in the right position; rather, it is something that involves their entire body, mind and soul. The function of prayer is considered to be so fundamental that children as young as six or seven years can be found fasting and praying. There are some who may say that's too small, yet every believer is a part of the priesthood and every believer must learn survival techniques.

In the rural house church in China there is an ever present knowledge and awareness that Christians are in a spiritual war. Spiritual battles can only be fought and won with spiritual weapons.

3. Brokenness, contrition and repentance are not one-off affairs.

Over the years I have observed an interesting phenomenon in the church in China: When the believers come together, including the top level leaders, their meetings always go through a wailing and crying mode. Time after time I would come into meetings like this and I couldn't understand it. These people are saved by the Blood of Jesus! They are full-on in their service and devotion to Him. Who could fault them for that? What is more, they have impressive results and an impeccable track record to prove it! What many pastors, leaders and ministers around the world would give to be able to claim the same achievements for their church as these simple rural folks.

So why are they always so sad? I decided to ask them one day, eschewing my natural Chinese tendency to give them "elder brother respect" and "face", for my more straight-forward, "let's have it out" American attitude. How can you cry so much, especially since there is less and less persecution these days? Their answer is astonishing.

First of all, they say, they are not praying against persecution. They never do. Even in the most difficult times they do not pray for less hardship or for the end of such.

What they are doing actually, is repenting. Repenting!—they, of the church of hundreds, thousands and, yes, even millions; they, who have seen visions and experienced miracles! Remarkably they yield themselves to God over and over again. They allow themselves to be broken before Him as they see in themselves their own lack of growth, their own lack of maturity. They see the old habits and tendencies that still dominate parts of their lives and they want the Almighty to overcome them, change them, heal them.

4. The Word of God is a treasure.

Bible teachers beware! These believers *know* their Bible. From the most senior leaders to the younger aspiring ones, there is an extraordinary ability to quote passages left, right and center. Suggest a phrase—for example, "treasure in earthen vessels" or "fivefold ministry"—and the leaders of the rural underground church in China will recite entire chapters which contain them.

But they are not just great memorizers. They have much understanding too. As a Bible teacher to the most senior leaders in the house church movement, I have been regularly challenged and tested from my "students" as to the correct use of Greek words, the quality of translation of Greek words into Chinese, and other very in-depth questions. The discussions that ensue demonstrate an exceptional skill in handling the Sword of the Spirit, as well as an incredible love and insatiable appetite for the Word among these believers. It is truly a prize and treasure to them.

5. It is an honor to represent Christ.

In the West the difference between believers and gentiles has been blurred. Generally speaking, our attitudes, behavior and habits are similar. As a result, it can be quite a challenge to distinguish a Godly example or find Christ in a crowd.

In China, however, Christians very often expect themselves to be of a different standard, a different quality. They know they are Christ's representatives and wear the honor proudly. They do not live Christianity as a Sunday event or a "church activity"; rather, it is an every-minute-of-everyday existence. In short, Christians are transformed beings and, therefore, behave as such.

This attitude was made vividly clear to me on a visit to my family in the country once. While my kin and I were lining up in an orderly fashion at a bus stop, waiting to board the vehicle, people all around were shoving us aside. This made me quite angry and I couldn't help but glare at the pushy offenders. My elder sister gently patted me on the back and said, "David, please, you are a Christian. These are gentiles. Don't be cross with them."

For many believers inside China, Christianity is not a matter of having faith; it is about being Christ-like. His power lives in you; therefore, you possess the desire and the capacity to be like Him.

6. There must be willingness to sacrifice and undergo suffering.

Ultimately I believe this is the most important lesson we can learn from the church in China. In all my travels in the West, I have not heard this taught or preached about in a real or practical way. *If* it is mentioned, it is only done so in passing or as theory. In the rural underground church, however, particularly among the most senior leaders, suffering is viewed as identifying with Christ. We identify with both His resurrection *and* His suffering. Interestingly though, the Chinese believers, in general, do not emphasize or focus on the fact of it in their own lives.

Once, when I hosted several top Christian leaders from the West in Wenzhou, the visitors wanted to know, above all, every harrowing detail of the prison terms of a particular Chinese pastor. How many times were you tortured? How many days were you starved? What was the worst thing that happened to you in the labor camp? On and on they persisted in pressing for minutiae. Steadfastly, smiling, the pastor would respond with accounts of God's presence, comfort and strength in those dark times. This cycle of question-and-answer continued until finally, the Westerners became impatient and asked if the pastor had actually even suffered? The pastor again smiled and said, "Please read the story of Jesus' crucifixion. No one could have suffered more than Him. But did He talk about it?" I personally know this pastor and that he suffered like "hell on earth" in prison. But his kind of identifying and suffering with Christ is

389

commonly counted an honor and a pleasure among the believers in China. It is something we in the West have no concept of.

Furthermore the word 'sacrifice' in China is transported to an entirely different dimension from the understanding in the West. To Christians in the house church, sacrifice is not fasting from chocolate or coffee for a day or two. It is not foregoing the pleasure of purchasing the trendiest fashion or latest gadget either. For the underground church, to sacrifice is to give until it hurts—*really* hurts—even to the point of never seeing that which is given up again.

In the case of one Chinese lady of 23 years, she has sacrificed family relations. She said to her mother, "You won't see me again until I have been to Africa, until the lost there have been won for Jesus." She means it. She absolutely will not return to her village until she has fulfilled the calling of God in her life to be a missionary in the northern part of the continent. She has counted the cost. She is paying the price.

Throughout the entire house church movement in China, from the most senior leaders to the grassroot workers, whether poor or illiterate, it has been my greatest privilege to be associated with these Christians, to join hands with them. Their commitment to Jesus is total. It's wholehearted, wholesome, child-like. It's so uncomplicated, you don't know sometimes whether to call them simple, naïve or just pure-hearted. As Jesus Himself says, "Blessed are the pure in heart for they will see God." And they do. They see God intrinsically in every aspect of who they are and what they do. His Kingdom is in them, the life-force of their whole being. He is not a doctrine to them. He is not a set of lessons, rules or good ideas to try. He is just normal everyday life, like the air they breathe—without regular intakes they couldn't go on.

They've seen numerous miracles. They've experienced them firsthand. But for all the signs and wonders, they remain very much ordinary people. The habit of checking for alternative exits upon entering a meeting place is still practiced, as is the state of constant alertness to a possible police raid. Like anyone else too, there are areas in their personal lives in which they continue to struggle. Not every physical ailment in their bodies, for example, is healed yet and some memories have left emotional scars. The tragedies and tears have been plentiful, but there has also been much joy and laughter.

At the end of the day they know their faith is not about supernatural manifestations. It's about the Truth. They know it's inside them and that nothing can separate them from it. For them the challenge is to continue to let the Truth penetrate within, even deeper than it's ever been before. They know it's about cultivating and maturing their relationship with the *living* Word, the Word made flesh. *This* is progress.

Despite its paucity even now, the Bible has been and continues to be *the* manual on how to be a Christian for the believers in China. In the simplicity of their faith and relative unsophistication of their ways, "they overcame . . . by the blood of the Lamb and by the word of their testimony; they did not love their lives so much as to shrink from death."[16] They didn't and still don't have much, if anything at all. But they could talk about what God meant to them. So that's what they did and continue to do. By so doing they are defying all the logic of higher education models,

---

[16] Revelation 12:11.

corporate organizational structures and advancements in technology, and have become the largest church on earth and the fastest growing. Government sources acknowledge unofficially that there are now 75 to 100 million Christians in China—that's more than the population of the United Kingdom and more than double that of the state of California!

In a day and age dominated by the modernization, comforts and conveniences of global internet-connectiveness, it is no longer an easy task for citizens of the twenty-first century industrialized world to identify with the lives of the New Testament believers. Yet, existing as it does in a developing nation, the Church in China shows the world it *can* be done. It shows the world the Word is still alive. It's still true. It's still trustworthy. After all, it is in Him that we live and move and have our being.

Indeed, the Blood was not shed in vain. It may have been spilled 2,000 years ago, but its power to protect and to triumph remains as strong as ever. The Church in China understands this. That's why they're still red.

ACKNOWLEGEMENTS

Thank you to the Asian Outreach teams in Hong Kong, for your patient help in all the unseen details. And a very special thank you to Mooi, in particular, for your tireless translation skills.

Thank you, too, to those who read and in some cases re-read the manuscript in its various stages, and for their ever insightful comments: Andrew Higgins, Usha Casewell, Tom Benyon, Stewart Stemple, Francis Tsui, Boaz Wong, Catriona Woodrow, and Bruce and Diane Taylor.